MW00780665

THE
BABY
RESOURCE
GUIDE

I'm Expecting is a division of Hazen Publishing Inc.

Publisher: Kari E. Hazen
Editor-in-Chief: Troy M. Smith
Layout Production: Troy M. Smith and Jude Lowell
Cover and Illustrations: Karen Olson
Proofreader: Carol J. Hazen
Baby Pages Representative: Kari E. Hazen
Local Editors: Boston: Allison Aley, Felice Lopez, Kelly O'Toole
              Los Angeles contributors: Anne Dullaghan, Connie Hurston,
                Juliana Rose Meyers
              Portland: Deanna Nihill
              Sacramento: Kari MacDonald, Mary J. Patt
              Seattle: Andrea Rowe, Karen Wilkinson

Disclaimer: The authors have made every reasonable effort to provide the most accurate and updated information at the time Portland Baby Resource Guide went to print. The authors have not solicited or accepted payments or consideration of any kind from any person as an inducement to exclude or include material in this book, or to influence its content. However, the reader should bear in mind that the very nature of this book required that the authors receive their information from sources who may have had a bias or who may have been mistaken and that much of the material in this book is based entirely on the personal opinions of the authors and their sources and thus may be inaccurate. Therefore, the readers should make their independent evaluations of any product, service, or course of conduct mentioned herein prior to buying, using or engaging in the same and should not rely on this book as being authoritative in any respect. The authors strongly recommend that the reader discuss all health related issues, services and products with their medical professional and not rely on any health related "advice," suggestions, or information contained in this book. This book is simply intended to provide its readers with a starting point in their quest for information and, hopefully, a certain degree of entertainment.

Published by Hazen Publishing Inc. dba I'm Expecting, Auburn, CA. Phone: (530) 823-3659; E-mail address: Karihzn@aol.com. For information regarding custom editions or for information on reproducing The Baby Resource Guide in another city or for The Baby Pages contact Kari Hazen at (530) 823-3659. To be listed in the next Baby Resource Guide, phone (530) 823-3659.

Visit our web site at www.thebabyguide.com

Baby Resource Guides are published in Boston, Los Angeles, Portland, Sacramento, and Seattle.

Manufactured in the United States of America.

HEAR WHAT PEOPLE ARE SAYING ABOUT THE BABY RESOURCE GUIDE . . .

"The Baby Resource Guide was by far the most helpful item I bought during my entire pregnancy. The product reviews and hospital comparisons were used when I was buying my merchandise and in selecting a hospital. The 'Where to Shop' section was a lifesaver for making purchases. This is a book that is used, cover to cover, and I'm sure it will be a big help when my baby is born."

—Vickie Blocker

"When I became pregnant, we didn't know where to start to prepare for our baby. The Baby Resource Guide gave us valuable insight into baby products, provided information on my maternity leave rights, and helped us save money with all the coupons in the back of the book. Preparing for a baby can be complicated but by the time Grant was born, with the help of The Baby Resource Guide, we were ready for everything, except the lack of sleep!"

—Christy, Rob and Grant Solorio

"The Baby Resource Guide really saved me during my pregnancy! Since this was my first baby, I didn't know where to shop for maternity clothing or baby products. And I knew nothing about the many classes available in town. I keep the guide with me in my car at all times for quick and concise information!"

—Lori Sacco

"The Baby Resource Guide was a godsend. I became pregnant shortly after moving to the area and was not familiar with local resources. Your guide covered every area where I had questions and needed product information. I carry it around with me in my purse whenever I am out. The guide is complete, clear, and accurate. I can't say enough about how wonderful and essential your guide is. Thanks!"

—Lori Bainton

"The Baby Resource Guide has been an invaluable source of information. We are new to Seattle and it really helped me to familiarize myself with the area as well as find the answers to some important questions. I have two of the guides: one for the house, highlighted with notes in the margins, and one in the car, so if I need an address or phone number, or have questions I can call from the cell phone, plus the coupons are on hand. It is so comprehensive and I love learning about other families from their testimonials. I don't feel alone with the obstacles that we have come to. This guide is the perfect gift for baby showers and expectant parents. Thanks for saving my sanity. This book is really a life saver!"

—Stefanie Leigh Grife

ACKNOWLEDGMENTS

The Baby Resource Guide is a collaborative effort of many people who believed in the need for such a book for new and expectant parents. We are thankful to the more than 100 people who made suggestions, contributed ideas, researched, wrote articles, shared their Life Experiences, reviewed articles, checked chapters, double-checked resources, proofread, and helped guide the project all along the way.

We are especially grateful to the medical and marketing staffs at the following health systems who helped us shape the book you have before you now:

- Glendale Memorial Hospital, Glendale, California
- Mercy Healthcare, Sacramento, California
- Northwest Hospital, Seattle, Washington
- Providence Health System, Portland, Oregon
- UC Davis Medical Group, Sacramento, California

Special thanks go to these dedicated health care professionals who gave freely of their time to review the book prior to publication: Kenneth Frank, M.D.; Nanci Newell, R.N.C.; Phillip Patton, M.D.; Carmen Rezak, R.N.P., and Carl Warsowe, M.D. Thanks to our other reviewers: Robin Song of the Placer County Office of Education Child Care Services, Cathy Morris of the Placer County (CA) Buckle Up Baby Car Seat Project, Sherri Martin and Janis Grusz of Safety for Toddlers of Kirkland (WA), Adrienne Disbrow, Linda Fraguglia, Dawn Malicoat, R.N., Kerry Breeler, Anthony Urquiza, Ph.D., Adrianne Westlake and Lisa Yount.

Contributing articles new to this edition are Ignacio Valdes, M.D.; Carmen Rezak, R.N.P.; Dawn Frankwick, M.D.; Adrienne Disbrow, ICCE, CMT; Sally Ellsworth, R.N., ICCE; Donna Hudson-Bryant, R.N.; Joseph Antognini, M.D.; Kari MacDonald; Dianne Neilson, R.N.; John Kuhn, M.D.; Charles F. Simmons, Jr., M.D.; Sharon D. Simmons, R.N., B.S.N.; Michael Lucien, M.D.

Thanks to those organizations allowing us to reprint articles: the American Sudden Infant Death Syndrome Institute, Child Care Resources of Seattle (WA), Fairview Press, the North American Registry of Midwives, the Pregnancy and Infant Loss Center, Providence Health System of Portland (OR), Northwest Hospital of Seattle (WA), and Washington State's Safety and Health Assessment and Research Program.

Special thanks go to the local editors and researchers who enthusiastically embraced this project and made each city's book special. Thank you, Allison Aley, Felice Lopez, Kelly O'Toole, Lindy Forrester, Sandy Lima, Juliana Rose Meyers, Deanna Nihill, Kari MacDonald, Mary J. Patt, Andrea Rowe and Karen Wilkinson. Thank you to Cheryl Deamas of Work at Home Moms (www.WAHM.com) and the moms who helped pull the Los Angeles book together.

We are grateful to all of the parents who shared their life experiences. Thanks to those who helped complete the guide and make it comprehensive and accurate.

To the business community, book stores, and childbirth organizations—your support shows the need for this guide. We salute you!

TABLE OF CONTENTS

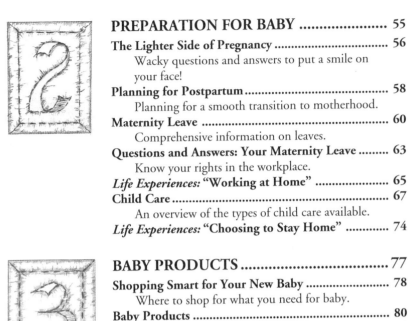

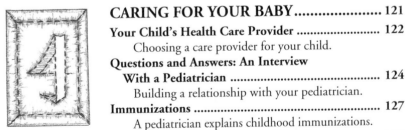

INTRODUCTION

Every day is a miracle. Nothing is more true than when you think about the birth of a child.

Think about it. It all starts with two people coming together, creating two cells that offer the blueprint of a human being. These cells multiply to create a heart, a mind and a soul. Every day a fetus is in its mother's womb, it gains strength to face this miracle... life.

As a parent, there are times when you will sit back and look with amazement at your child, overcome with awe that you created this special human being. It is frightening to think of the new responsibilities given to you, all with no instructions and no exam by which to validate your proficiency as a parent.

There are so many questions that come with the birth of a new baby. In today's complex society it may be difficult to find the answers you need. We may find ourselves living thousands of miles away from our families with no support network and possibly working through pregnancy and beyond, while at the same time wanting to be an involved and educated parent.

Because of this, a company named *I'm Expecting* was born. Its mission was to compile a resource guide for area parents. It started as a simple idea, yet grew as many area parents and experts contributed their thoughts and experiences to our endeavor, all with the hope of helping you in your new parenting role. And now, through the support of the baby business community and parents, The Baby Resource Guide is in print.

The Baby Resource Guide is meant to be many things, none of which is to replace medical advice or treatment, or to take the place of Consumer Reports. Please take care of yourself and your baby. Cherish these special days. As a soon-to-be parent, you are experiencing our greatest miracle... life!

❧

In today's complex society it may be difficult to find the answers you need.

❧

HOW TO USE THIS BOOK

The Baby Resource Guide has been providing vital information for new parents for six years. The book has grown from a 200 page local guide to the 400+ page compendium before you now. Beginning with this issue, all resources and articles specific to your local area are located in the back of the book. Check both the national and local sections to find all relevant information on any topic. Convenient tabs help you find both the national and local listings within the book's six chapters. In the front section, you'll find national resources following most articles, plus the guide's irreplaceable slice-of-life stories we call "Life Experiences." Chapter topics include:

- **So You're Having a Baby!** From choosing the right practitioner and information about preconception counseling to ways to help you through your baby's delivery, this chapter prepares you for what you need to know about staying healthy through pregnancy, finding a childbirth educator, and both avoiding and preparing for a possible Cesarean birth.

- **Preparation for Baby.** Planning for postpartum should begin well before your baby's birth. Included is information about maternity leave, with the latest on the Family Medical Leave Act and the Pregnancy Discrimination Act. You'll also learn about child care options.

- **Baby Products.** Confused about available baby products? We've done the homework; just read our reviews to make the best choices on everything from car seats and cribs to swings, baby carriers, high chairs and breastfeeding accessories. Then go to stores to try out equipment and make your own decision. The local section of this chapter has reviews of stores in your area. Make sure you call ahead to verify locations. Businesses do occasionally change and we know your time is valuable.

- **Caring for Your Baby.** The nitty-gritty of caring for that new little one is here. A pediatrician answers parents' questions about doctor visits, and another pediatrician fills you in on immunizations. There's a great introduction to breastfeeding and a section on child safety.

- **Special Concerns.** Life doesn't always run smoothly. We present information for parents of children with special needs and articles on infertility, premature infants, and multiple births. There is an important article on coping with grief.

- **Taking Care of Yourself and Your Family.** Your family life is changed forever once your baby is born. Here's help for you to cope with the stress a new baby brings. Support groups are a way for new moms to connect with others. You'll find a primer on postpartum depression, then ideas for everyday life with baby. The local section includes a great many ideas for family activities in your area.

This isn't a book you read in one sitting. But dip into it here and there, use the index, which combines both the national and local sections, and you're on your way to learning more and more about having a baby—your special baby. And if you have a Life Experience you'd like to share, or know of a helpful resource we should add, drop us a line—we know that parents are the greatest resource of all.

SO,
YOU'RE
HAVING
A
BABY!

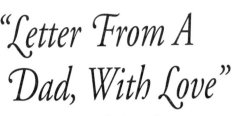

"Letter From A Dad, With Love"

A Life Experience by Bruce Patt

A few weeks before our baby's due date . . .
Dear baby girl,

You're ready now, and waiting, and this might be the first of very many times of patience in your life. Nothing I've read suggests that you're actually thinking yet, but something in you must sense, innately, that it's time to move on. But prevailing conditions can conspire against our instincts, and that's when we have to just do our best, have faith in the process, and be patient. I'm writing this to you, but I mean it for me as well; I probably need the advice even more.

Today, you live in the most exquisite harmony, awash in love and sustenance within your mother's womb. You don't have an idea of you, yet, and you haven't met any of the rest of us. There's no balance to seek, no conflict, no worry. But once you're born, harmony will be something which you will probably be striving for. At least that's been true for me. While I wasn't looking for it here, through my letters to you I have begun to find that sense of balance within my own life. Although you are an entirely separate human being, you, my little girl, are irreversibly a part of who I am. Whenever I introduce myself to people, if I simply say I am Bruce Patt I will be omitting the most important part: I am your father.

It's hard to be patient, even when you're feeling pretty well balanced. You know it's time to get on with it. But other people have their say, too; this time, it's your mother, whose body has not received your signal to begin opening your gateway to life. I could imagine you in there, bags packed, ready to travel, but the bus hasn't arrived. Although this isn't an issue for you now, by the time you read this letter you will have already experienced many times how waiting can be an opportunity. One time several years ago I was traveling to a

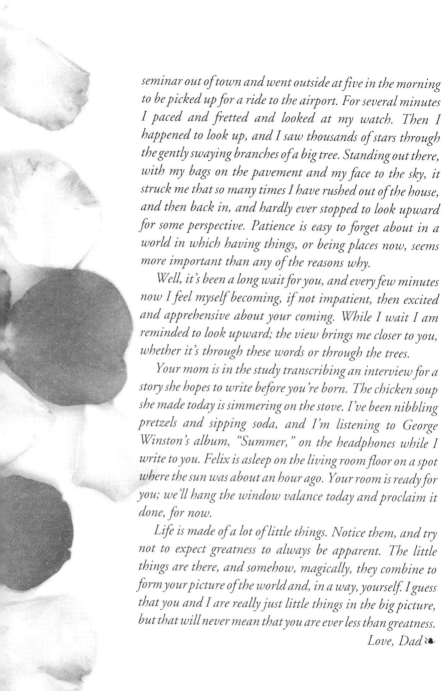

seminar out of town and went outside at five in the morning to be picked up for a ride to the airport. For several minutes I paced and fretted and looked at my watch. Then I happened to look up, and I saw thousands of stars through the gently swaying branches of a big tree. Standing out there, with my bags on the pavement and my face to the sky, it struck me that so many times I have rushed out of the house, and then back in, and hardly ever stopped to look upward for some perspective. Patience is easy to forget about in a world in which having things, or being places now, seems more important than any of the reasons why.

Well, it's been a long wait for you, and every few minutes now I feel myself becoming, if not impatient, then excited and apprehensive about your coming. While I wait I am reminded to look upward; the view brings me closer to you, whether it's through these words or through the trees.

Your mom is in the study transcribing an interview for a story she hopes to write before you're born. The chicken soup she made today is simmering on the stove. I've been nibbling pretzels and sipping soda, and I'm listening to George Winston's album, "Summer," on the headphones while I write to you. Felix is asleep on the living room floor on a spot where the sun was about an hour ago. Your room is ready for you; we'll hang the window valance today and proclaim it done, for now.

Life is made of a lot of little things. Notice them, and try not to expect greatness to always be apparent. The little things are there, and somehow, magically, they combine to form your picture of the world and, in a way, yourself. I guess that you and I are really just little things in the big picture, but that will never mean that you are ever less than greatness.

Love, Dad

PRECONCEPTIONAL HEALTH ASSESSMENT

By Ignacio Valdes, M.D., and Carmen Rezak, R.N.P.

Seeking counseling with a physician and other health care practitioners prior to pregnancy is vital and can decrease maternal anxiety, risks of congenital birth defects and maternal and fetal complications in pregnancy and delivery. During this preconception visit a complete history and physical examination will take place, in addition to certain laboratory tests. Any anxieties and concerns may be expressed and questions answered during this visit. The following areas are of particular importance:

MEDICAL HISTORY

Certain health problems need to be identified and treated prior to becoming pregnant. Diabetes significantly increases the risks of birth defects if not treated prior to pregnancy. Hypertension, epilepsy, asthma, thyroid disorder and lupus erythematosis should be well controlled before pregnancy, labor and delivery. Other pertinent information to identify is a history of deep vein thrombosis, kidney disease or heart disease. Your health care provider will also ask you about your menstrual history, contraceptive methods used, previous sexually transmitted infections, allergies, surgical history, and rubella (German measles) status. Screening for rubella and receiving the appropriate vaccination will prevent congenital rubella syndrome. It is recommended to wait three months prior to getting pregnant after being vaccinated.

FAMILY AND GENETIC HISTORY

Emphasis is placed on the mother's health because it is crucial to give the baby a healthy environment in which to develop. But the health of the father is important, too. The provider will ask questions about family members (both mother's and father's) with any history of birth defects, mental retardation, Down syndrome, diabetes, anemia, twins or any possibly inheritable disease. Testing for inheritable diseases such as Tay-Sachs, sickle cell anemia, cystic fibrosis or thalas-

❧

Emphasis is placed on the mother's health . . . but the health of the father is important, too.

❧

semia may be needed as well. On rare occasions substances in the environment or workplace may be harmful to a pregnant woman or fetus. It is important to offer information on exposure to toxic chemicals, radiation, lead, insecticides or other substances.

Depending on the history obtained, the provider will counsel the patient on its significance, or in some cases, refer the patient to a geneticist or genetic counselor. The goal of preconception counseling, relative to family and genetic history, is to provide the prospective parents sufficient information to make informed decisions.

MATERNAL AGE

Today more women are investing time in their careers and opting to delay starting a family. Most women in their 30s and early 40s have uncomplicated pregnancies. If a woman is in good health, there is no reason why she cannot have a healthy baby. The risks for miscarriage, diabetes, hypertension and chromosomal abnormalities—such as Down syndrome —increase with advancing maternal age. After the age of 35, the risks of chromosomal abnormalities are significant and many women elect to undergo amniocentesis after receiving counseling.

It is important to be informed about potential problems and discuss plans with the provider to ensure a woman gets the proper medical attention.

OBSTETRICAL HISTORY

Although it is uncommon for most complications of pregnancies to recur, it is nevertheless important to go over the significant details of all previous pregnancies. Questions regarding previous miscarriages, tubal pregnancies, abortions, stillbirths, neonatal deaths, preterm labor, vaginal bleeding and high blood pressure (hypertension or preeclampsia) are asked.

Specific information regarding labor and delivery may also be important. This would include: length of labor, complications of labor such as bleeding or fetal distress, mode of delivery (Cesarean section or vaginal), infant's weight and any post-delivery complications.

Preconception counseling can relieve a couple's anxiety by discussing any previous complications and exploring beliefs about previous losses. Counseling is a good time to encourage a couple to express fears, show support and to prepare for future pregnancies with optimism.

NUTRITIONAL NEEDS

It is important to follow a well-balanced diet, not only during pregnancy, but also during the time of preconception. A good prepregnancy diet is the best way to ensure that a woman and future baby get a healthy start.

Dietary habits are discussed and may be altered to optimize the development of the fetus. Vegetarians may need to make certain changes to increase protein consumption. Eating disorders and obesity may impact pregnancy and should be investigated prior to conception, as well.

Folic acid has been shown to significantly decrease the incidence of neural tube defects in infants, when taken at the time of conception. Although significant quantities of folic acid can be found in several foods (broccoli, beets, orange juice, green peas, avocado, romaine lettuce, spinach, various types of beans, wheat germ, fortified cereals), it is recommended that all women of childbearing age take a multivitamin containing at least 0.4 mg of folic acid.

GENERAL HEALTH AND LIFESTYLE

Good general health before pregnancy can help a woman cope with the stress of pregnancy, labor and delivery. It can also ensure that neither mom nor baby is exposed to things that can be harmful.

Only a few medications are known to cause birth defects; however, all medications (prescription and nonprescription) should be reported to the provider and certain changes may be necessary prior to conception. Oral contraceptives are not known to cause birth defects, but it is generally recommended to discontinue the pill approximately three months prior to conception.

Alcohol, tobacco and mood-altering drugs pose certain risks to the fetus and should be avoided. Low birth weight, placental irregularities and infant mortality, as well as long-term effects on the physical, emotional and intellectual development of children born to women who use these substances during pregnancy, have been reported. Testing for HIV and hepatitis B may be appropriate. These viruses can be passed to the fetus during pregnancy.

The importance of preconception counseling cannot be overemphasized. Seeking education and guidance, as well as a physical examination and review of the medical history, from a physician and other health care practitioners, can assist a woman and her partner in making informed decisions about future reproduction. Planning for a healthy baby should begin prior to conception.

PREGNANCY NUTRITION

By Dawn Frankwick, M.D.

While your body is busy preparing and nurturing your new child, you may tend to overestimate your nutritional needs. In reality, you should only add an additional 300 calories a day (equivalent to a glass of whole milk) while pregnant. You do not need to eat for two! By understanding what your body needs on a daily basis, you can be sure to choose those foods that provide the most benefit to you and your growing baby.

DIETARY RECOMMENDATIONS

The United States Department of Agriculture's food pyramid recommends lots of fruits and vegetables, breads and whole grains, and limiting the amount of fat, oil, and sugar. Specific recommendations include:

- **Grains: 6-11 servings a day.** Some sample servings are a slice of whole-grain bread, 1/2 cup of hot cereal, a pancake or waffle, 1/2 cup rice or noodles, a muffin, biscuit, or two tortillas. Emphasize whole grains to increase your fiber intake. Limit white flour and processed grains due to limited nutritional content.

- **Vegetables: 3-5 servings per day, and fruit: 3-5 servings per day.** Vegetables and fruits are important for their abundance of vitamins and minerals. Fresh is best, followed by frozen, then canned. To keep the vitamin content high, don't overcook vegetables. Consider buying organic produce.

- **Dairy products: 4 servings per day.** These foods can be very high in fat content so you may wish to choose low-fat versions of these items. Sample servings include one cup of milk, cheese (2"x1"x1" cube), or a cup each of yogurt, cottage cheese or frozen yogurt. These dairy products are high in calcium, which helps calcify baby's bones and minimize your risk of future osteoporosis.

- **Proteins: 2-3 servings per day.** Protein foods are important to build strong muscles and blood. Cut back on red meat, and emphasize skinless poultry as a good low fat choice for protein consumption. Don't forget about other protein sources—fresh fish, eggs, beans, tofu, peanut butter, and nuts. Cut back on processed meats such as hot dogs, sausage and bacon.

🍃

You should only add an additional 300 calories a day while pregnant. You do not need to eat for two!

🍃

Discuss weight gain goals with your provider. The American College of Obstetrics and Gynecology (ACOG) currently recommends a weight gain of 30-35 pounds for women of normal prepregnancy weight. Special attention should be paid to the needs of vegetarian women, those carrying twins, or those with allergies or medical needs that may affect nutrition. If you take any prescribed or over-the-counter medications, vitamin supplements, laxatives or diet aids, tell your provider.

Taking a good multivitamin, with your provider's approval, can be a good way to ensure adequate vitamin intake. Extra supplementation of iron is frequently necessary since the average diet doesn't meet minimum nutritional needs. ACOG recommends taking iron supplements between meals or at bedtime with water to maximize absorption. Iron may cause your stool to turn darker in color, or cause constipation. You can minimize these effects by drinking lots of fluids and eating high fiber foods. Beware: with vitamin supplementation, more is not better. Too much vitamin A can lead to bone, urinary tract, and central nervous system defects.

Don't forget water! Drinking two quarts of water each day can lessen your hunger and reduce constipation. Consider keeping a sports bottle with you and setting a goal of drinking two or three bottles of fluids each day.

HEALTHY SNACK OPTIONS

- Cheese, whole grain crackers, and grapes
- Frozen yogurt, fruit, and nuts
- Pita bread with cheese, tomato, and avocado
- Unbuttered air-popped popcorn
- Whole grain muffin with raisins
- Baked potato topped with low-fat cheese and broccoli
- Sliced vegetables or fruit with a yogurt dip
- Brown rice cakes with cottage cheese, scallions and tomato

KICK THE JUNK FOOD HABIT

- Switch to low-salt variety of pretzels, snack chips or crackers.
- Bake your own treats and reduce the amount of sugar and fats.
- Save candy for special occasions rather than an everyday indulgence.
- Choose unbuttered popcorn instead of potato chips for a quick snack.
- Avoid deep-fried foods such as French fries, potato chips and fried fish.
- Mix 1/2 cup fruit juice with 1/2 cup plain carbonated water or seltzer instead of soda pop.
- Choose low fat frozen yogurt or a frozen fruit juice popsicle for dessert.
- Have vegetable pizza and eliminate high-fat, high-salt meat toppings.

Nutrition hints courtesy of Northwest Hospital in Seattle, Washington.

CHOOSING YOUR PRACTITIONER

If you're thinking about becoming pregnant, or are pregnant, your very first step should be to get prenatal care; it is important for you and the unborn life that depends on you. It is equally crucial that you not wait for your initial prenatal visit to begin preparing your body for the birth of your child. If possible, meet with your practitioner before you are pregnant to discuss any issues you may have.

Your health care practitioner is the expert on prenatal care; listen to his or her instructions and establish an open and honest relationship. Your practitioner's goal, as well as yours, is to bring a new, healthy life into this world.

You may have questions about finding a practitioner. Many expectant mothers may already be completely satisfied with their present obstetrician, midwife or general practitioner. Others may choose to "shop around" or simply do not have a provider at all.

There are a variety of providers and referral agencies that can help you locate prenatal care. A good place to start is with your medical insurance or the state medical program to find out if you can select a provider of your choice, or if you must use a plan's specific provider. Ask friends or relatives for their recommendations. Keep in mind the personality, needs, and communication style of the person referring you. Her provider may have met her needs, but may not be right for you.

What you will probably find is that practitioners vary considerably in their philosophy, training, experience and expertise. The following information on providers' qualifications may help you make your choice.

❧

Your practitioner's goal, as well as yours, is to bring a new, healthy life into this world.

❧

FAMILY PHYSICIANS

A family physician has been trained to care for a broad variety of patients—from pediatrics to obstetrics to geriatrics. This allows you to have one physician overseeing not only your medical treatment, but also your family members'. Check to see if your family physician delivers babies. Family physicians have completed their undergraduate degree, four years of medical training, followed by three years of specialty training in family medicine that includes obstetrics and pediatrics. Family physicians who have successfully passed an oral and written examination given by the American Board of Family Practice are known as "Board Certified." The initials ABFP will follow their name and title. In case of a pregnancy complication, a family physician will have an obstetrician as a backup.

NURSE PRACTITIONERS/ PHYSICIAN'S ASSISTANTS

Some physicians' offices have either a nurse practitioner or physician's assistant. Depending on your physician, they may do some or most of your prenatal office visit. They are not licensed to deliver babies. A nurse practitioner has a bachelor's degree in nursing and then attends graduate school and completes an internship before practicing. In most states, a master's degree in nursing is also required. Registered nurse practitioners may be primary care providers and work in close collaboration with medical doctors. A physician's assistant has graduated from a rigorous specialized medical program, although it may not necessarily be in obstetrics, and cannot practice independently.

OBSTETRICIANS

An obstetrician has completed college, four years of medical school, and four years of specialty training in obstetrics and gynecology. Obstetricians are trained specifically in pregnancy and are acknowledged experts in their field. Obstetricians are able to identify pregnancy risks and perform surgical procedures as needed. Obstetricians who have success-

fully passed an oral and written examination given by the American Board of Obstetrics are known as "Board Certified." The initials FACOG verify that they have completed this training and joined the American College of Obstetrics and Gynecology.

PERINATOLOGISTS

A perinatologist is a doctor who specializes in the care of high-risk problems of pregnancy. These include conditions such as diabetes, heart disease, and preterm birth. Perinatologists' training is the same as an obstetrician's, plus an additional two to three years of subspecialty training.

MIDWIVES

For women who have a normal, low-risk pregnancy, a midwife can offer everything from prenatal care to the baby's delivery. Midwives tend to view birth as a normal, healthy event which, in most cases, works best with as little medical intervention as possible. Midwives are trained to watch for and identify potential or actual complications and, if necessary, can provide emergency treatment until additional medical assistance is available. Licensed midwives work with a physician backup. Although regulated individually by states, the following categories of midwives are recognized in the United States:

Certified Nurse Midwives. Certified nurse midwives practice most often in hospitals and birth centers. They are registered nurses who have a graduate degree in midwifery, and must attend an educational program and pass a follow-up examination to become accredited by the American College of Nurse-Midwives Certification Council. They can be licensed in the individual states in which they practice.

Certified Professional Midwives. These midwives are certified through the North American Registry of Midwives (NARM), and have passed a written examination and skills assessment test. Certified Professional Midwives' credentials are not accepted in every state.

Direct-Entry Midwives. "Direct-entry" midwives are licensed in some states. They are not required to become nurses before training to be midwives, and most often practice in birth centers and homes.

Midwife definitions courtesy of the North American Registry of Midwives.

NATUROPATHIC PHYSICIANS

In Arizona, Arkansas, Connecticut, Hawaii, Maine, Montana, New Hampshire, Oregon, Utah and Washington, naturopathic physicians may be licensed to provide maternal care and attend births, generally in home or birthing center deliveries. The naturopathic physician, a graduate of one of the U.S.'s three four-year postgraduate naturopathic medical schools, practices holistic health care, treating patients with homeopathy, clinical nutrition and botanical medicine. High-risk deliveries are referred to an obstetrician.

INTERVIEWING A HEALTH CARE PROVIDER

The determining factor in choosing a practitioner is often your medical insurance. Your insurer will likely give you names of providers for you to choose from. Once you have a number of possibilities, call their offices to see if they are accepting new patients, verify that they accept your insurance carrier, and ask if an interview is available. Some providers provide a free, short consultation in person or by telephone, but others charge for an interview and many are too busy with patients. In the latter case, the only way to know if the provider is right for you is during or after your first prenatal visit. Some practices have an informational session open to prospective clients.

After the interview or first visit, ask yourself if you and your partner will feel comfortable with the qualifications and communication style of the practitioner. Also, consider how comfortable you feel with your provider's office staff. You probably will have more encounters with the office staff during your pregnancy than with the actual provider. Therefore, a friendly, open and available office staff may make a difference about how you feel about your provider.

Only your own circumstances and criteria can determine your provider-patient relationship. Use your judgment and trust your intuition when making your decision. Finding a provider that you can work with and trust completely will make for a happier, less stressful pregnancy, labor and birth.

֍ RESOURCES ֍

■ **AMERICAN COLLEGE OF NURSE MIDWIVES**
888-MIDWIFE
818 Connecticut Ave. N.W. #900
Washington, DC 20006
Web site: www.midwife.org
E-mail: info@acnm.org
The American College of Nurse Midwives offers information about nurse midwifery services and accredited university affiliated nurse-midwifery education programs. They will provide a list of midwives affiliated with their organization.

■ **HEALTHY MOTHERS, HEALTHY BABIES (HMHB)**
(202) 863-2458
409 21th St., S.W., Ste. 309
Washington, DC 20024
Backed by more than 100 national member organizations, Healthy Mothers, Healthy Babies coordinates services that foster healthy families. State coalitions work in their communities to promote maternal and infant health. Individuals can write for resource lists on topics such as pregnancy, breastfeeding and nutrition, adolescent pregnancy, and immunization, and to find out more about their local HMHB programs.

■ **INFORMED HOMEBIRTH/ INFORMED BIRTH AND PARENTING (IH/IBP)**
(313) 662-6857
P.O. Box 3675
Ann Arbor, MI 48106
Minimal intervention at birth is the focus of this organization, founded in 1977. Originally focusing on home birth,

IH/IBP has since expanded to provide information on alternatives in birth and parenting, and referrals to childbirth educators, birth assistants, and midwives. A 14-page pamphlet, priced at $1.50 (plus 50 cents postage), introduces advantages and disadvantages of home birth, information about safety, and state midwifery organizations. Several books and videos are offered through IH/IBP, and each spring the group hosts a conference in Michigan for parents and early childhood educators, emphasizing Waldorf education from birth through the early grades.

■ **INTERNATIONAL ASSOCIATION OF PARENTS AND PROFESSIONALS FOR SAFE ALTERNATIVES IN CHILDBIRTH (NAPSAC)**
(573) 238-2010
Rt. 1, Box 646
Marble Hill, MO 63764
If you're interested in family-centered maternity care and childbirth alternatives, NAPSAC is a great place to find information. The organization offers a wide variety of pregnancy and parenting books and pamphlets, including the NAPSAC *Directory of Alternative Birth Services* for $7.95. A $20 yearly membership will pay for their quarterly newsletter, discounts on publications, and information on becoming a local NAPSAC leader to promote safe alternatives in childbirth.

■ MIDWIFERY TODAY

(541) 344-7438
P.O. Box 2672-708
Eugene, OR 97402
Web site: members.aol.com/midwifery/
index.html
E-mail: midwifery@aol.com
Midwifery Today will provide pamphlets on topics such as home births and questions to ask your midwife. They make referrals to midwifery organizations. For an annual membership fee of $67, members receive a quarterly magazine subscription and "The Birth Kit," a quarterly newsletter, and the opportunity to attend the group's conventions. "The Birth Kit" subscription alone is $20.

■ MIDWIVES ALLIANCE OF NORTH AMERICA (MANA)

(316) 283-4543
P.O. Box 175
Newton, KS 67114
E-mail: MANAinfo@aol.com
MANA works with the North American Registry of Midwives and the Midwifery Education and Accreditation Council to establish independent midwifery as a viable health care option for women. They support a woman's right to choose her care provider and place of birth—home, birth center, or hospital. MANA promotes the "midwifery model of care" which is based on the fact that pregnancy and birth are normal life events. For referrals to local midwives, you must request information by mail. You can also request the brochures "What is a Midwife?," "Expecting a Baby? Consider a Midwife," and further information about the positive aspects of midwifery from this organization or from Carol Nelson, 107 The Farm, Summertown, TN 38483.

■ NATIONAL ASSOCIATION OF CHILDBEARING CENTERS (NACC)

(215) 234-8068
3123 Gottschall Rd.
Perkiomenville, PA 18074
E-mail: birthctr@midwives.org
A not-for-profit membership organization, NACC is the nation's most comprehensive resource on birth centers. NACC is dedicated to developing quality, holistic services for families that promote self-reliance and confidence in birth and parenting. NACC sets national standards for birth center operation, promotes state regulations for licensure, and national accreditation by the Commission for the Accreditation of Birth Centers. If you are interested in finding out more about birthing centers, write to NACC, including a $1 donation, and the organization will send you information about birth centers in your area and information on how to select a birth center.

■ NATIONAL MATERNAL AND CHILD HEALTH CLEARINGHOUSE

(703) 356-1964
2070 Chain Bridge Rd., Ste. 450
Vienna, VA 22182
E-mail: nmchc@circsol.com
A sister organization to the National Center for Education in Maternal and Child Health, the Clearinghouse provides consumer education materials on maternal and child health topics such as prenatal care, nutrition, infant care, breastfeeding, child health and dental care. You may request a free publication catalog by mail.

USING A LABOR DOULA

🐚

A doula

understands

the natural

process of

pregnancy,

labor and

birth, and

the

emotional

needs of

expecting

families.

🐚

By Adrienne Disbrow, CIMI, Doula, CMT, ICCE

A doula is a professional experienced in childbirth who provides continuous physical, emotional, and informational support to the mother and expecting family before, during and just after childbirth. She understands the natural process of pregnancy, labor and birth, and the emotional needs of expecting families. A doula recognizes childbirth as a life-changing experience and understands her role as a member of the family's perinatal team during this experience.

Doulas come in all shapes and sizes with different philosophies, personalities, and experiences. Most importantly, you must be comfortable with and confident in your doula. Following are some general characteristics to look for in a doula.

- She should be flexible and in general good health, with good communication skills—and be an especially good listener.
- Because she is going to support you during your baby's birth, she should be able to put aside her personal beliefs and support you in your informed decisions.
- She should be professional, responsible, warm, compassionate, and enthusiastic.

CHOOSING A DOULA

Feel free to ask questions to help you determine if the doula is right for you and your family. Some good questions to ask when interviewing doulas:

- What is your training and experience?
- What services do you provide (i.e. in-home prenatal visits, in-home labor support, postpartum visits, etc.), and when do your services start?
- Are you available prenatally by phone?
- Do you have a backup doula?
- What are your fees?
- What do you consider the most important elements of care when working as a doula?

WHAT CAN A DOULA DO FOR YOU?

- **During pregnancy:** A doula can help your family prepare your birth plan and clarify your goals and perceptions of birth. She can also answer general childbirth questions. Your doula may also have videos and a lending library available for your use. You will probably meet with a doula several times before the birth to go over your birth plan and to discuss and practice comfort measures.

  If you are placed on bedrest, a doula may offer services to help with day-to-day needs. Examples would be light housekeeping, running errands, grocery shopping, etc. (There may be an extra charge for these services.)

- **During labor:** Depending on your desires, your doula may be present during early labor in your home or may meet you at your chosen birth location. She provides emotional and physical support to the laboring mother and her husband or support person. She will suggest comfort measures and can provide information and support if medical intervention becomes necessary. She does not make decisions for you, but can aid the family in decision making. She is also a constant companion during an unfamiliar experience and in unfamiliar surroundings. Doctors and nurses cannot be with the laboring woman continuously. Having a doula professional is a reassuring factor.

  Recent studies indicate that the presence of a doula during the birth decreases the need for forceps by 40%, reduces the need for epidurals by 60%, reduces oxytocin use 40%, shortens first time labor by an average of two hours, and decreases the chance of Cesarean section by 50%.

  A doula does not replace the partner or other support person during labor. Rather, she enhances the experience for both laboring mom and her support person by instilling confidence in both. A doula can be particularly valuable for moms without a labor companion.

- **During the early postpartum period:** Your doula can help your family make the adjustment to a new member. She may offer breastfeeding help and referrals if necessary. She makes at least one follow-up visit to check on and talk with mom and admire baby, of course. She may offer additional services of in-home help for an added fee.

Doula fees are not generally covered by insurance. Although fees nationwide average around $250, costs for doula services, including birth support and both a prenatal and postpartum appointment, may range from no-cost to $500, depending on special skills offered by individual doulas.

&a RESOURCES &a

■ ASSOCIATION OF LABOR ASSISTANTS AND CHILDBIRTH EDUCATORS (ALACE)

(617) 441-2500
P.O. Box 382724
Cambridge, MA 02238
E-mail: alacehq@aol.com
Web site: www.alace.org

ALACE is a national nonprofit organization dedicated to supporting women's choices in childbirth, and provides training and certification for childbirth educators and labor assistants/doulas. ALACE can refer parents to labor assistants across North America. "Professional Labor Support—Your Newest Option in Childbirth" is an ALACE brochure which articulates the benefits of using a labor doula. A quarterly magazine, *Special Delivery*, covers pregnancy, birth, midwifery, and labor assisting topics, and is available with ALACE membership ($20/year).

■ DOULAS OF NORTH AMERICA (DONA)

(206) 324-5440
1100 23rd Ave. East
Seattle, WA 98112
Web site: www.dona.com/
E-mail: AskDONA@aol.com

Doulas certified through DONA have passed a certification process that ensures their competence and adherence to the organization's code of ethics and standards of practice. Most of their members assist women and couples through labor and childbirth, although they do have postpartum doulas, who specialize in providing care and support to families with newborn babies. DONA publishes a referral directory, free for the asking, which lists their members nationwide.

■ INTERNATIONAL CHILDBIRTH EDUCATION ASSOCIATION (ICEA)

(612) 854-8660
P.O. Box 20048
Minneapolis, MN 55420-0048
Web site: www.icea.org

This international organization certifies birth doulas, postpartum doulas, childbirth educators, and postnatal educators. They offer references, referrals and resources for parents, as well as an extensive mail order catalog, called "Bookmarks," of books and materials related to childbirth and parenting.

■ NATIONAL ASSOCIATION OF CHILDBIRTH ASSISTANTS

(707) 939-0543
P.O. Box 1537
Boyes Hot Springs, CA 95416

The oldest national certifying organization of childbirth assistants, NACA trains doulas through a variety of courses, workshops and publications nationwide, and will refer expectant parents to a local NACA-trained doula. NACA doulas focus on facilitating an expectant woman's understanding of pregnancy, birth and postpartum, and reports shorter, more relaxed labors with less fear and tension before, during and after labor. Their doulas encourage active participation in decision-making by parents before and during childbirth.

ENSURING YOUR BABY'S HEALTH

❧

In real life,

pregnancy is

often a

delightful

surprise that

necessitates

some quick

changes in a

pregnant

woman's

lifestyle.

❧

Ideally, a woman would plan to become pregnant in six months time, stop all oral contraceptives, quit smoking and drinking, avoid x-rays, aspirin, and antacids. She would begin taking folic acid to reduce the risk of neural tube birth defects. She would reach her ideal not-too-heavy, not-too-thin weight, and exercise regularly.

In real life, however, pregnancy is often a delightful surprise that necessitates some quick changes in a pregnant woman's lifestyle. The first and foremost consideration is to do all you can to ensure your baby's health.

First, disclose to your health care provider any information about previous pregnancies, especially those ending in miscarriage or termination. Also, let your practitioner know if you've experienced any past sexually transmitted disease (STD).

Most providers recommend that pregnant women consume no alcohol. There is no known "safe" amount to drink, so it is in your baby's best interests to abstain during your pregnancy. Fetal alcohol syndrome (FAS) is often present in the children of heavy drinkers, with symptoms ranging from low birth weight to heart defects and mental retardation. Even women who drink moderately may give birth to children with hyperactivity and learning disabilities.

Another way you can improve your baby's chances of good health, and your own, is to quit smoking. Babies of smokers are smaller and shorter, and more likely to die of Sudden Infant Death Syndrome (SIDS) than children of nonsmokers. According to the American College of Obstetrics and Gynecology, other effects linked to maternal smoking are an increased risk for ectopic pregnancy, miscarriage and stillbirth, premature birth and vaginal bleeding. Many women quit smoking for good when they are pregnant. It is a time of change and reprioritization; quitting smoking can be a positive way to welcome your baby.

Illegal drugs are harmful to the fetus. Drugs cross the placenta, and their toxic effects can affect the baby's development. It just isn't worth the risk to your baby to use drugs. If you have any trouble quitting, ask your physician for a referral

CHEMICALS WHICH MAY AFFECT THE FETUS

Chemicals can enter your body through the air you breathe, through contact with your skin or through your digestive system if you accidentally swallow them. The fetus is exposed if the chemical passes from the mother's blood through the placenta to the fetus. These are among those chemicals harmful to the fetus:

- anesthetic gases
- benzene, tuolene
- cancer chemotherapy drugs
- carbon disulfide
- carbon monoxide
- ethanol (alcohol)
- ethylene oxide
- glycol ethers
- lead
- mercury

Strong irritants react with the first tissue they contact—usually the eyes, nose, throat or skin. Common irritants are ammonia, chlorine, bleach, and acids—hydrochloric, nitric and sulfuric. Very little of these chemicals enters the bloodstream, so they are unlikely to affect the fetus.

You can ask your employer for the Material Safety Data Sheets (MSDA) for products you use. Forms include information on hazards to childbearing. Further questions can be answered by your state's Department of Labor or your practitioner.

Information from the Washington State Safety and Health Assessment and Research Program.

to a treatment facility or rehabilitation program.

Medications prescribed before your pregnancy, and some over-the-counter drugs, can be harmful to your fetus. Even antacids, with their high concentration of sodium, can affect your pregnancy. Tell your health care practitioner what medications you take; call before starting a new over-the-counter medication to make sure it is safe for you and your baby.

Research is unclear as to whether caffeine intake is harmful. Caffeine enters the fetal bloodstream, and some believe it may increase the risk of miscarriage. Caffeine intake can also increase heartburn, which some women experience during pregnancy. To be safe, it's best to cut back to a minimal amount.

That means to curb coffee, tea and cola consumption, and (unfortunately) avoid too much chocolate.

There is no hard and fast evidence that aspartame (NutraSweet), taken in reasonable amounts, is harmful to the fetus, although the phenylalanine in aspartame is transmitted to the fetus through the placenta.

If relaxing at the end of the day means some time in a hot tub or sauna, that's another habit you'll have to stop for the duration of your pregnancy. Very warm water can raise the fetus' temperature to dangerous levels within just a short time, increasing the risk of neural tube defects.

While home improvement is hardly a bad habit, it's wise to avoid paints, paint thinner, insecticides and fertilizers during pregnancy. If you are in contact with these materials or other teratogens (harmful agents which can cause birth defects) at your workplace, discuss with your employer the possibility of switching jobs for the duration of your pregnancy. A good place to find current information on teratogen dangers is online with Genetic Drift's Teratogen Update, published semiannually by the Mountain States Regional Genetic Services Network, found at http://www.MSRGSNet /Genetic Drift/Teratogen Update.

Toxoplasmosis is a mild disease caused by a parasite found in raw meat and cat feces. If you are infected during pregnancy, your child may have mental retardation or vision problems. To avoid the disease, wash thoroughly with antibacterial soap after handling raw meat or vegetables, and have someone else change your cat's litter box. Keep the cat off your bedding.

Most physicians recommend a vitamin supplement rich in folic acid for women planning to become pregnant, to be continued for the duration of pregnancy and while breastfeeding. When taken daily before conception and during the first three months of pregnancy, 0.4 mg of folic acid reduces the risk of neural tube defects such as spina bifida, caused by incomplete fusion of the spinal cord, and anencephaly, an incompletely developed brain. Foods rich in folic acid include leafy vegetables, beans, citrus fruits and cereals. Follow your practitioner's guidelines for vitamin supplements carefully, as overly large doses of some vitamins can cause problems for your baby.

On a more positive and proactive note, eating a healthy diet and drinking plenty of fluids is a good way to give your baby a good start in life. Find an exercise program you can stick with, and make it part of your daily routine. Get adequate rest. Check with your provider if you are over- or underweight for specific recommendations. All women, especially those on vegetarian diets, should consult with their health care provider to ensure adequate protein intake.

As a pregnant mother-to-be, you have a great responsibility to your child. This is the time to break bad habits and make a clean start for your family.

HOW MUCH CAFFEINE IS IN . . .?

Coffee	7 oz.	80-175 mg.
Espresso	1 oz.	100 mg.
Tea	7 oz.	40 mg.
Iced tea	12 oz.	70 mg.
Cola drinks	12 oz.	35-45 mg.
Citrus drinks, i.e. Mountain Dew	12 oz.	55 mg.
Milk chocolate	1 oz.	15 mg.
Unsweetened baking chocolate	1 oz.	25 mg.
Chocolate chips	1/4 cup	13 mg.

QUESTIONS AND ANSWERS
Your Insurance Provider

Medical insurance coverage during pregnancy is a financial necessity today. If you do have coverage when you become pregnant, don't do anything that may risk the loss of that coverage. If you don't have, or can't acquire, insurance that covers a pregnancy, at least make sure that you have medical coverage that will guarantee to cover your newborn. The major financial risk parents face at the time of birth is the cost of care for medical problems of a newborn infant.

But what if you are already pregnant and don't have insurance? You can always negotiate with the hospital for a special uninsured early release delivery. This will reduce the hospital expense significantly and minimize your obligation. The other option if you are uninsured is a public assistance program. Qualifications vary from state to state for coverage associated with pregnancy.

Whatever you do, with or without insurance, at least opt for a prenatal program. Don't be tempted to cut corners by skipping this important care.

To help you understand the ins and outs of maternity insurance coverage, a private insurance broker discusses different aspects of insurance coverage.

Q. *If I do not have insurance and plan to become pregnant, what options are available to me?*

A. There are two options that you should consider. First are individual health insurance programs, such as Blue Cross/Blue Shield and any local HMO plan sponsors that offer individual coverage in your area. A woman under 30 applying for medical coverage can usually find coverage for about $100 per month. Consult with a qualified health insurance broker in your area (look in the Yellow Pages under Insurance) for the options available to you.

The second option is an employer-sponsored health insurance program. Check to see what benefits are available to you, and consider health insurance benefits as important as salary when looking for employment.

Q. *What questions should I ask my insurance company about maternity coverage?*

A. Here are a few to consider:
- What is the cost per provider visit?
- Does the insurance offer a co-payment plan or pay a percentage of each visit?
- What is the calendar year deductible that you must fulfill before coverage begins?
- Is the maternity deductible separate from a general services one?
- Will my newborn baby incur a separate deductible for its share of hospital charges following a healthy birth?

- What hospitals accept your insurance plan?
- What coverage is provided if complications arise?
- Is there a difference in coverage for a Cesarean or vaginal birth?
- How are laboratory charges handled and which labs may you go to and still receive coverage?
- Are twins or other multiple births handled any differently?
- Is the newborn child covered for the first 72 hours automatically or do you need to immediately enroll the child as a dependent?
- Do you have to pay provider and hospital bills up front and then be reimbursed by your insurance company? Are claim forms necessary?
- Who should you contact if you have questions about your policy?

Q. *What questions should I ask my insurance provider regarding well-baby care for my new baby?*

A. Well-baby care is defined as general checkups, immunizations, and other preventive care office visits when your infant is not ill. The checklist below provides questions to ask your insurance provider.
  - Is well-baby care covered?
  - What specifically is included?
  - What amount will insurance pay toward each office visit?
  - When the baby is born, does well-baby care cover any hospital visits?
  - Are immunizations included?
  - Is there a yearly dollar limit on well-baby coverage?

Q. *How soon should I add my new child to my insurance plan?*

A. The standard time is 30 days. This ensures that your new baby will be covered under the plan without any gap in coverage.

NEW FEDERAL HEALTH CARE REGULATIONS

Health coverage is more flexible than ever under the federal Health Insurance Portability and Accountability Act of 1996 (HIPPA). Now an individual leaving an employer's group coverage—even with a preexisting condition—cannot be denied coverage, as long as he or she was covered for the previous 18 months. The Act applies to those who meet the 18-month coverage test and are not eligible for most other coverages, including COBRA, Medicare and Medicaid, but not conversion policies. This provision of the law is due to take effect July 1, 1998.

As each state sets its own HIPPA guidelines, check carefully before switching insurers to make sure you won't end up with a gap in coverage.

For more detailed information on HIPPA or COBRA rights, consult a health insurance lawyer or research the Acts at your local library.

HOSPITAL CHOICES

❧

Because mothers may spend such a short time in the hospital, educational and postpartum programs may be more of a consideration factor.

❧

During your pregnancy you are faced with many choices. Deciding where to have your baby is probably one of your biggest decisions. Often, though, your insurance coverage dictates which hospital you must use to deliver. Delivery at your hospital of choice, if not covered by your insurance, may mean you'll be paying in cash for your hospital stay. Happily, almost all hospitals today offer expectant parents a wide array of services that make your stay comfortable and more "home-like" than ever before. Because mothers may spend a limited time in the hospital, the educational and postpartum programs may be more of a consideration factor. Here are some things you may want to consider when choosing your hospital:

- Where your health care provider delivers
- Hospital location
- The nursery facilities
- The number and type of labor and delivery rooms
- The hospital and nursing staff
- The quality of care
- Whether your insurance covers care at that hospital
- The types of educational programs offered
- Hospital policies on issues important to you, such as: electronic fetal monitoring, number of people allowed in the delivery room, eating and drinking during labor, rooming in with your baby, whether accommodations are made for partners to stay overnight, whether postpartum rooms have private showers
- Postpartum care
- Your overall feelings about the hospital

Before making your choice, try to obtain as much objective information as possible. Tour the local hospitals; ask friends, relatives, and coworkers for referrals; and ask questions to ensure the hospital meets your needs.

When talking to others about their birth experiences, you'll find patients who have received exceptional care at one hospital and others who were not completely satisfied at the same facility. The nurses and hospital staff make the personal difference and depending upon who cares for you, experiences may vary.

TYPES OF HOSPITALS

Some expectant parents are more comfortable with the smaller atmosphere of a community hospital while others prefer the comprehensive services a larger facility offers. Large hospitals often include nurseries equipped to handle most newborn emergencies, and may be more apt to offer extensive educational programs for expectant and new parents. Some large metropolitan areas may have a hospital which is a teaching facility affiliated with a medical school. Teaching hospitals generally have state-of-the-art equipment, and you may be seen by residents and interns as well as fully licensed physicians or midwives.

Some people are more comfortable surrounded by all the latest technology "just in case," while others feel that the presence of that technology makes it more likely that it gets used whether it's needed or not. It's important to think about these issues ahead of time.

CONSIDERATIONS

- **Cesarean delivery rates.** Nationwide, Cesareans account for over one-fifth of hospital births. The rate varies for many reasons, including the number of high-risk maternity patients and the patients' individual or medical needs. Expectant parents should discuss the possibility of a Cesarean delivery with their health care provider and find out under what circumstances the procedure would be done.

  Know that Cesarean delivery rates at hospitals are a sensitive issue. Also, realize the hospital does not perform the Cesarean; the physician does. Ask your provider about his or her personal Cesarean rate. Cesarean statistics are broken down by primary (number of first-time Cesarean deliveries) and secondary (repeat Cesarean deliveries).

- **Nursery levels.** The majority of newborn babies only need Level I care. Level II nurseries are equipped to handle most newborn emergencies. Most can care for premature infants who are at least 30-32 weeks gestation. Level III, the most sophisticated type of nurseries, are equipped with high-technology equipment and specialists who are capable of handling the most serious types of newborn emergencies. Level III nurses are trained in advanced life support. Each Level III nursery is equipped for long-term care of premature infants.

- **Fetal monitoring.** Nearly all U.S. hospitals require patients to receive an initial 20-minute fetal monitoring reading in accordance with the American College of Obstetrics and Gynecology (ACOG) guidelines. How long you will be monitored depends on your medical condition and the hospital's or your provider's policy. It is a good idea to explore the monitoring policy of your health care provider before labor begins.

- **Rooms.** Hospital rooms vary from the traditional to specially furnished private "homestyle" suites. The latter style of room is becoming increasingly common. Called Labor/Delivery/Recovery/Postpartum (LDRP) rooms, this concept was implemented nearly 20 years ago. The single-room suite offers the comfort and convenience of not being moved from room to room, as well as allowing more privacy and involvement by partners and other family members.

Labor/Delivery/Recovery (LDR) rooms offer patients the advantage of remaining in one room during labor, delivery, and recovery. Following recovery, mothers are moved to a "postpartum" room.

Most LDR and LDRP rooms offer the comforts of home with the sophistication of advanced medical technology. These rooms are equipped with all the necessary medical equipment, often stored out of sight, but readily available if needed. They also may offer such amenities as custom decor, whirlpool baths, televisions, VCRs and a hide-a-bed for your partner or guest.

- **Rooming-In.** The option to keep your baby in your room day and night, called "rooming-in," is generally encouraged. With short hospital stays as the norm, rooming-in gives mothers a better chance to observe and bond with their babies.

- **Lactation specialists.** While most hospitals support breastfeeding mothers with nursing information and assistance, many go one step further, with a lactation specialist on staff. Some hospitals charge for this service, while consultations are free at others. A lactation specialist

BIRTH CENTERS

Birth centers offer a viable option for low-risk maternity clients. Most women who give birth in a birth center find it to be a positive, empowering experience.

Moms and babies are seen by their birth center's midwives or physicians for their entire maternity care, including prenatal care, labor and delivery, postpartum, and early newborn care. Emergency medications and equipment are available at each birth center, including oxygen, resuscitative equipment, IV material, and certain medicines. Midwives perform deliveries with no anesthesia or instruments, such as forceps. Mothers who deliver at a birth center need to plan an unmedicated birth. If pain medication or pitocin become neces-

sary, the mother will be transferred to a hospital, but the transfer rate of most birth centers is very low.

The setting for birth centers is similar to a bed and breakfast (without the breakfast), though families may bring foods of their choice, and design the atmosphere to include music, lighting, friends and loved ones. Because nonmedicated births generally result in quicker recoveries, the length of stay for a normal delivery in a birth center is a minimum of two to four hours after the birth, with a maximum stay of 24 hours.

Most major insurance companies cover birth center deliveries. Many insurance companies recognize the safety and cost effectiveness of this setting for birth.

is trained to give expert advice on breastfeeding techniques to new mothers.

- **Overnight guests.** Your primary support person stays with you during labor, delivery, and recovery. Support persons are generally allowed to stay overnight in postpartum rooms, except when you're sharing the room with another patient. Siblings are not usually allowed to stay overnight.

- **Visitors and visiting hours.** Most hospitals allow visitors, including non-immediate family members, during labor and delivery. Most also allow siblings to be present during a vaginal delivery with the supervision of an adult (other than the primary support person). Choose a supportive adult to supervise the child's experience.

  Most hospitals have open visiting hours and even those with structured hours do not restrict the support person or significant other. Given the relatively short postpartum stay for many mothers, hospitals usually advise that you limit the number of hospital visitors (other than support people and immediate family), so that you can focus on rest and recovery. Let your visitors know in advance what you would enjoy and ask all who plan to visit to be free of any illness. New moms and babies don't need to be exposed to colds or flu.

- **Safety precautions.** Extreme care and safety precautions are taken to secure your baby while in the hospital. Security personnel, video camera surveillance of all entries, staff identification, alarm systems, and

patient education are the most common security measures. It is typical for hospitals to use the Identaband systems in which babies and parents/partners are banded at birth using the same numbers and names. Some hospitals have begun using a new computer chip identity tag system to ensure the safety of their patients. Most hospitals will not reveal details of their security programs until you are admitted into the hospital to protect you and your infant. The more informed you are about the hospital's security program, the more knowledgeable you will be in the rare case that a security issue arises.

- **Classes.** Childbirth and parenting classes are available through most hospitals. Many also offer exercise classes, support groups, and lending and resource libraries. In most cases, classes are available to the general public, whether or not you plan to deliver at that hospital. Nominal class fees are charged to participants.

- **Postpartum care.** Sometimes the time between the discharge from the hospital to the first visit with the pediatrician can be filled with questions and concerns, especially for first-time parents. Most hospitals have addressed this need by providing different options for postpartum follow-up soon after discharge, including a home health visit or free telephone consultation. Also, hospitals have lactation consultants and consulting nurses available by phone, and can refer you to a public health nurse or private lactation consultant if needed.

"Souvenir Pregnancy"

A Life Experience by Leanne Jordan

My husband and I had just returned from a glorious second honeymoon, happy that our 4- and 6-year-old daughters were old enough to spend a week being pampered by Grandma and Grandpa. I was hoping that the renewed passion we'd experienced would continue when we resumed our daily routines. Was I ever wrong.

The day after our return, the girls and I all came down with pneumonia. A week later we were all on the way to recovery, when I was struck by a severe cold, followed by a sinus infection. I was miserable. Gone were the feelings of carefree abandon, physical fitness and the tan I'd acquired on our vacation. I hardly noticed that my period hadn't begun. It must just be all the illness hitting, I thought. But once the sinus infection cleared up I was still tired all the time.

It should have been obvious. That wonderful honeymoon we took without the kids had given us an unexpected souvenir: I was pregnant. (Those high school family life teachers are right: you can get pregnant when you aren't mid-cycle!)

Although my husband was joyful, I couldn't bring myself to feel excited. Our daughters were finally out of babyhood and all the exhausting mom-work that entailed. The elder was in first grade, and her sister was due to start preschool. I was looking forward to going back to work part-time. Now my plans were in complete disarray.

I even dreaded telling my parents. One of two daughters, I knew my parents felt our family was already the perfect size. Avid population growth types, they had always let us know two children was plenty. Once I finally informed them, they were more bemused than upset. They checked our side of the family tree—in the past century, only one other family had more than two children.

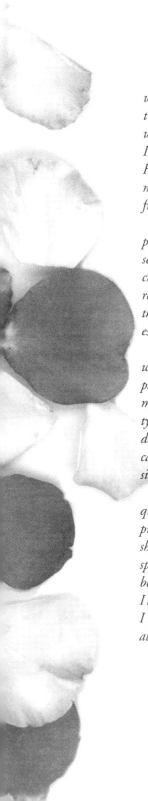

Medically, the pregnancy was as easy as the other two. I was more tired due to the fact that there was more to do with two active girls already at home. "Three!" other people would say. "How are you going to manage it?" What could I tell them: "I'm not exactly thrilled about it myself"? Hardly. I felt ashamed of my own thoughts. How selfish of me to want the freedom from diapers, from sleepless nights, from the constant worry that babies bring.

Yet there were some positive aspects of this unexpected pregnancy. Maternity clothes were a lot cuter than they were several years ago! And I met some wonderful friends at our childbirth education refresher class. My mother instinctively realized my reluctance and comforted and reassured me throughout those difficult months. Our daughters were especially thrilled at the prospect of a new baby in the house.

As the delivery date grew closer, I began to come to grips with my own feelings. We hauled out the crib that had been packed away for our future grandchildren. I sorted through my remaining baby clothes (none, except for a few heirloom-type dresses) and baby blankets (three, currently used in the doll crib). I reread my dog-eared breastfeeding and infant care books, and agonized over the right kind of diapers to buy since there were even more bewildering choices than before.

And then, suddenly, I was in labor. A call to my folks, a quick trip to the hospital, one contraction that hurt, one push, and Ethan was born. My husband and I were so shocked to have given birth to a boy that we could hardly speak. He was blue as a blueberry and needed a pat on the behind and some good suctioning. Once I got to hold him, I looked into his deep blue eyes, and then, and only then, did I know without a single doubt that I would love him with all my heart. ❧

YOUR HOSPITAL STAY: ONE DAY OR MORE?

By Nanci J. Newell, B.S.N.

With recent and continuing changes in state and federal laws about maternity lengths of stay, this is no longer an easy question for anyone. Expectant parents may hear conflicting answers depending on who they ask and what they read. It is essential that parents are informed and ask the right questions to avoid unpleasant financial surprises late in pregnancy, or worse, when they get their bills following birth.

THE LAWS SAY:

Legislation in many states takes precedence over any federal legislation, but what it usually boils down to is that the decision regarding the length of stay following birth is up to the provider and you, based on your medical needs at the time. Medical need is the key phrase and does not necessarily mean the same thing to mothers as it does to providers. In general, medical necessity means blood loss, infection, or any other medical condition which would require continuing care in the hospital. The amount of rest needed or the number of other children or responsibility waiting for a new mother at home does not constitute medical necessity. Federal legislation is far from clear and defers to any state legislation at this time. Since the whole question of length of stay has became such a hot political topic, it is expected that several federal versions may be debated repeatedly during upcoming sessions of Congress before anything is finally passed at the national level. In the meantime, there are more questions to be asked.

INSURANCE COMPANIES SAY:

Most insurance companies have no incentive to limit a mother's length of stay in the hospital or birth center. They simply will not pay either the hospital or the doctor or midwife. Many contracts are negotiated with hospitals so that no matter what services are used by patients, a flat fee is paid per delivery. The same thing applies to many doctors, midwives and other providers. There are hundreds of insurance companies and

It is essential that parents are informed and ask the right questions to avoid unpleasant financial surprises.

many variations of individual plans. Managed care is here to stay.

In areas without a state-mandated maternity length of stay regulation, nurses and case managers are reporting from many hospitals that many expectant parents are being told by their insurance companies that they can stay for two days following a normal vaginal delivery and three days following an uncomplicated Cesarean birth. What insurance companies are not telling expectant parents is that they can stay two days or three days providing there is medical necessity. So, when parents come to the hospital to have their baby, and are planning to stay two days, they are surprised to hear that they need to leave after 24 hours because it is not medically necessary for them to stay longer. This results in the provider giving the family the "bad news" that they must leave earlier than expected, and no one wants to be the bearer of that message.

The pediatrician or family practitioner is also responsible for determining whether or not a baby is medically stable and can be discharged from the hospital. The baby may be ready for discharge sooner or later than the mother is, and that potential difference may also create unexpected changes in plans for new parents. No new parent wants to feel rushed to leave the safety and comfort of the birth suite.

Clarify the following inquiries with your insurance company well in advance of your expected date of delivery:

- Exactly what is covered
- What "medical necessity" means
- How long a stay for new mothers and babies is covered following birth if there is no medical necessity

- Ask if there is anything not normally covered, such as circumcision
- Ask if hospital follow-up services such as support groups, classes, clinics, lactation services, and/or home visits are covered
- Ask if and how many provider follow-up office visits are covered
- Document the name of the person with whom you speak and ask for written confirmation

HOSPITALS SAY:

Make an appointment to see the admissions person or financial advisor at your hospital's birth center or obstetrical unit early in your pregnancy. Take all your insurance documents with you and have the hospital representative call your insurance company and verify with you what is covered.

Again, clarify what constitutes medical necessity. Ask how long most new mothers and babies stay following birth. Ask what normal charges can be expected and what your insurance company normally pays so that you can plan ahead for any deposits or differences in coverage. Ask if there are hours of the day or night by which discharge must take place in order to avoid further hourly or daily room rate charges. Some hospitals have specified checkout times; some do not.

Where public assistance is needed, an application can be made at this time with your financial advisor's help. Payment plans can be arranged so that when you come to the hospital there are no unpleasant surprises in either the charges or the length of stay. Ask for written confirmation of all arrangements made.

Ask what services are in place following discharge from the hospital for follow-up care. Some hospitals have extensive care services and support available for new parents and some do not. These services may include telephone hotlines or calls from a nurse, in-hospital clinic visits with a nurse, lactation services, doula services, home follow-up nursing visits, classes, and support groups. If available, ask what is included in the customary charges and what is not included in the charges.

PROVIDERS SAY:

Doctors and midwives do not want you to feel rushed in leaving the hospital or birth center. Neither do they want you to stay longer than is medically necessary. Ask how long most new mothers stay if they have an uncomplicated vaginal delivery and how long they stay if they have an uncomplicated Cesarean birth. Ask what constitutes a complication for either. Ask what follow-up arrangements are made for return visits to office or clinic following discharge from the hospital. Develop a "Plan A" with your provider for discharge based on your expected medical needs, in the event that all goes as you expect. Develop a "Plan B" in case it does not. Following birth, your doctor or midwife will be visiting you, following your post-delivery progress, and determine with you when you are stable and medically ready to be discharged.

THE PRENATAL PLAN

What can be done now to be prepared for a short length of stay in the hospital so that new parents can assume the care of themselves and their infants without feeling totally overwhelmed and exhausted? Actually, a great deal can be done in advance to make the transition to parenthood far more enjoyable.

- Determine what insurance coverage is available for pregnancy, birth and care of the newborn.
- Ask about home care coverage.
- Ask if lactation services are covered.
- What are the length of stay limitations? Do they differ with complications?
- Ask your practitioner what the usual length of stay is for patients.
- Tour your hospital.
- Attend early discharge, breastfeeding, and infant care classes.
- Develop a preliminary plan for child care if you plan to return to work.
- Talk to a financial counselor (usually located in admissions).
- If you have any unusual circumstances or additional needs, talk to the case manager or social worker at the hospital.
- Read as much material on prenatal and baby care as you can.

It is nearly impossible to absorb all of the new information about care for yourself and your newborn during a short hospital stay. It helps a lot to have attended some classes in advance, even if you don't have a baby with whom to practice.

STAYING IN SHAPE

By Lisa Yount, MSPT

Many different approaches and educational opportunities are available to assist you in preparing for the exciting event of birth and newborn care. Today, not only is exercise during pregnancy accepted by most providers, it is highly recommended. Even if you do not routinely exercise you can safely perform exercises that will make your pregnancy more comfortable. Because every pregnancy is different, an exercise program should be designed for the individual with special attention to both the pregnancy and postpartum periods.

During pregnancy, your balance, coordination, endurance and strength can be altered. Structural and hormonal changes cause the stretching or tightening of muscles, relaxing of ligaments and the loosening of joints. The curve in the lower back becomes more pronounced as the baby grows and the center of gravity moves forward. If adequate muscular support is lacking, the stress to the pelvis and back is increased, resulting in poor posture, fatigue and backache. It is important to exercise and maintain control of the voluntary muscles to help support the backbone and pelvis, which are put under significant stress. To be at your best during the pregnancy and to prevent future problems, it is essential to improve your physical condition. The important key muscle groups are the abdominal muscles, the pelvic floor and the postural muscles.

Be sure to talk to your health care provider before beginning an exercise program, and follow his or her instructions. This is not the time to start a vigorous program. The goals of prenatal exercise should include preventing discomfort, backache and fatigue. This is done by toning the essential muscle groups, stretching, relaxing, and performing proper body mechanics. Prenatal exercises strengthen the body and decrease the discomforts of pregnancy. You will have greater endurance for a long labor, and recovery is thought to be quicker. Feeling good physically also helps you to feel good mentally. Participants in exercise programs report decreased fatigue, decreased moodiness, wonderful peer support and shorter recovery periods.

Difficulties with present or previous pregnancies or general health problems may be contraindications to exercise during pregnancy. These concerns should be discussed with the physician.

❧

The goals of prenatal exercise should include preventing discomfort, backache and fatigue.

❧

EXERCISE GUIDELINES

- Exercise regularly (three times a week).
- Avoid increasing the body core temperature; strenuous exercise should be limited to 15 minutes, and exercise should not be performed in hot, humid weather.
- Exercise heart rate should not exceed 140 beats per minute.
- Begin the exercise program with warm-ups and end with cool-downs.
- Repeat each exercise only a few times; change your body position to work the same muscle groups in different positions.
- Do not hold your breath during exercises. Avoid any exercise that causes you to do a Valsalva maneuver (bearing down).
- Exercises should be performed slowly; avoid bouncing motions.
- Avoid heavy resisted exercises overhead or with long leverage, for example, putting dishes in a high cupboard or lifting weights with straight arms.
- Avoid positions that increase the curve in your lower back.
- Drink plenty of fluids.
- Limit time spent exercising on your back, and stop if you feel any tingling or dizziness.

WARNING SIGNS

Although exercise during pregnancy is recommended, be aware of the signs indicating that exercise should cease or a physician be contacted:

- Bleeding
- Frequent uterine contractions during or after exercise
- Lower back or pubic pain
- Sciatic (lower back or leg) nerve numbness
- Pain, numbness or tingling in the wrist/hand
- A breathless, dizzy, light-headed feeling or fatigue
- Palpitations or rapid heart beat
- A noticeable decrease in the activity of the fetus

Inherent benefits to exercise can be appreciated during pregnancy and the postpartum period. The program should be individualized to provide the highest level of fitness without compromising the health or safety of the fetus or the pregnant mother.

PROPER POSTURE AND BODY MECHANICS

Proper posture and body mechanics are especially important during pregnancy and the postnatal period because of the structural (muscles, ligaments) and hormonal changes and increased possibility of injury.

- When walking for exercise, let your arms swing at your sides and don't put your hands in your pockets or hold them tight against your chest. Keeping your hands free helps to absorb shock as well as to keep your arms free to avoid loss of balance.
- When picking up objects (including children), bend at the hips and knees, not the lower back, putting one leg forward. Be sure the weight is held close to you and use your legs to return to a standing position.
- Avoid repetitive bending and twisting such as unloading the dishwasher or dryer. The proper unloading method for a dishwasher

would be to first unload everything to the counter, close the dishwasher, and then put the dishes away, a few items at a time. Use a laundry basket (only half full) to transfer clothes from the dryer to a table. Fold clothes at a dining table (or other furniture of similar height) to avoid bending to the dryer or floor.

- Push your vacuum cleaner like a lawn mower, walking behind it for long stretches, rather than using push-pull motions.
- For the care of newborns and infants, be sure to take advantage of high changing tables, and bathe the baby in a sink instead of a bathtub to avoid back strain.
- When nursing, bottle feeding, or cuddling with the baby, sit in a well-supported chair or rocker. Use pillows under your arms and under the baby to support and position the baby most comfortably.

SIMPLE EXERCISES

A complete prenatal exercise program includes stretching, strengthening, aerobics and relaxing. The following are a few basic exercises for all stages of pregnancy and the postnatal period. Perform a few repetitions several times daily:

- **Kegels.** Tighten the muscles of the pelvic floor (as if you were stopping the flow of urine). Hold five seconds; relax.
- **Pelvic tilts.** Tighten stomach and buttocks muscles to turn your pelvis as if to "put your tail between your legs"; relax.
- **Shoulder rolls.** Raise your shoulders to your ears, pull your shoulders back; relax.
- **Scapula pinches.** Squeeze your shoulder blades back together. Hold five seconds; relax.

STAYING COMFORTABLE AT WORK

If you sit for long periods of time at work, consider these guidelines for proper posture and comfort:

- Adjust the height of the chair to fit you to the desk. Be sure that you don't have to bend over to your desk (chair too high) or hold your shoulders up (chair too low).
- Adjust yourself to the chair. This may require bringing in a pillow for behind your back and a step stool or phone books for under your feet. Keep enough bend in your hips so that your knees are equal to or above your hips.
- Do not cross your legs or extend them straight out in front of you.
- Use a slant board or copy holder to avoid prolonged head-down positions.
- When using the phone, keep your head erect or neutral and avoid holding the phone between your ear and shoulder.
- It is very important to get out of your chair often. A good guideline is to get up every half hour, even just to fill up a water cup or to stretch.

CHILDBIRTH EDUCATION

By Sally Ellsworth, R.N., FACCE

Having a healthy baby is the goal of all expectant parents, and most expectant parents choose to take some form of childbirth preparation classes to help them toward reaching this goal. Since women carry vivid, powerful memories of their birth experiences for many years afterward, most childbirth preparation classes try to help women achieve not only a healthy outcome to their pregnancy but the most positive birth experience possible by providing information about labor, delivery, postpartum, birthing options and alternatives, and coping strategies. Classes also help the labor partner to learn many comfort measures and techniques to use to assist the laboring woman.

There are a number of factors to keep in mind when selecting a childbirth preparation course. Feel free to ask prospective class sources about any of the following:

🔊

Most childbirth preparation classes try to help women achieve . . . the most positive birth experience possible.

🔊

- **Qualifications of the instructor.** Although in most states there is no law requiring licensure of childbirth educators, most are certified by one of several national or regional childbirth education organizations. These organizations also encourage their instructors to recertify on a regular basis to keep up to date on skills and knowledge.
- **Location of classes.** Most couples will probably prefer to take classes that are located close to home, although this is not always possible. Classes are taught in a variety of settings—hospital classrooms, public health departments and clinics, private doctors' offices, private homes, churches and community centers.
- **Size of classes.** Class size varies depending on where and with whom classes are taken with some as small as three couples or as large as 30 couples. Some instructors will teach private classes (for one couple only) and may even be willing to come to your home. This would be helpful for women who are on bedrest due to a pregnancy complication.
- **Timing.** Most programs suggest starting your classes some time within the last eight to ten weeks of your pregnancy, but of course you should try to sign up for classes much earlier to ensure the best chance of getting

into the class series of your choice. Some programs, especially those offering instruction in the Bradley method, suggest starting your classes in the fifth month, so that nutrition, exercise and relaxation can be emphasized.

- **Length of class series.** Most childbirth education series are six classes in length although some are as short as three or as long as ten. Most classes are taught weekly with each class being two to three hours in length. In some locations, instructors offer a somewhat condensed weekend program, compacting as much as 15 hours of instruction into a Friday evening, Saturday, and Sunday format.
- **Price.** Again, this will vary according to location and instructor with some classes being free and others costing as much as $150. The average cost of most class series is $60-$75. The least expensive classes are offered at clinics, health departments and adult education programs. The most expensive classes are those taught one-on-one in a private setting.

- **Philosophy of instructor and program.** Bear in mind that some classes are designed to prepare couples for the health facility in which they plan to deliver and offer little information on choices and alternatives. Some classes are designed for couples planning a home birth and, as such, place much emphasis on birthing with few or no interventions; some classes place a great deal of emphasis on a nonmedicated birth. Some assume that all or most of the women in class will use medications or anesthesia. Yet other courses may be taught from a religious perspective.
- **Other classes offered.** Most instructors or organizations offering childbirth classes will also offer a variety of other classes and services that may include: early pregnancy classes, refresher classes (an abbreviated series for couples who have previously taken classes), breastfeeding classes, Cesarean preparation classes, VBAC classes, baby care classes, infant and child CPR classes, and labor support (doula) services.

As you can see, there are as many choices in childbirth classes as there are in hospitals, practitioners and insurance providers. Choose carefully to get the most out of your time and money and to optimize your chances of having a healthy, happy, fulfilling childbirth experience.

🎐 RESOURCES 🎐

■ ACADEMY OF CERTIFIED BIRTH EDUCATORS AND LABOR SUPPORT PROFESSIONALS

800-444-8223
2001 E. Prairie Cir., Ste. I
Olathe, KS 66062

The Academy of Certified Birth Educators trains and certifies both birth educators and labor support professionals. Their courses are approved by Doulas of North America. Birth educators pass a certification course and exam. The academy encourages women to incorporate breathing for pain relief during labor.

■ ACADEMY OF HUSBAND COACHED CHILDBIRTH (AAHCC)

800-4-A-BIRTH
P.O. Box 5224
Sherman Oaks, CA 91413
Web site: www.bradleybirth.com

This organization trains and certifies instructors in the Bradley method, the first method to emphasize the husband as labor coach. The Bradley method stresses proper nutrition, relaxation and slow abdominal breathing. There is also a strong emphasis on an unmedicated birth and breastfeeding as the optimal form of infant nutrition. Women are usually encouraged to start classes in the fifth or sixth month of pregnancy and Bradley class series are usually a bit longer than other methods. Contact AAHCC for a list of certified instructors.

■ AMERICAN SOCIETY OF PSYCHOPROPHYLAXIS IN OBSTETRICS/LAMAZE

800-368-4404
1200 19th St. NW, Ste. 300
Washington, DC 20036
Web site: www.lamaze-childbirth.com
E-mail: aspo@sba.com

ASPO promotes the Lamaze method of prepared childbirth and certifies and recertifies instructors (titled ACCEs or FACCEs) in this method, which emphasizes that birth is a natural and normal phenomenon and that most women can birth their babies with little or no medical interventions. Lamaze classes teach a variety of coping skills to the pregnant woman and her partner including relaxation, visualization, massage, and attention to breathing. ASPO/Lamaze has a mail order bookstore and will provide a list of local certified instructors.

■ ASSOCIATION OF LABOR ASSISTANTS AND CHILDBIRTH EDUCATORS (ALACE)

(617) 441-2500
P.O. Box 382724
Cambridge, MA 02238
E-mail: alacehq@aol.com
Web page: www.alace.org

ALACE is a national nonprofit organization dedicated to supporting women's choices in childbirth, and provides training and certification for childbirth educators and labor assistants/doulas. ALACE provides expectant parents with information to help them understand their options and make informed decisions. They can help expectant parents find a childbirth educator, labor assistant or midwife across North America. A quarterly magazine, *Special Delivery*, covers pregnancy, birth, midwifery, and teaching/labor assisting topics, and is available with ALACE membership ($20/year).

■ BIRTHWORKS

(609) 953-9380
P.O. Box 2045
Medford, NJ 08055
Web site: members.aol.com/birthwks CD/bw.html
E-mail: birthwksCD@aol.com
Birthworks defines itself as an innovative and experiential organization that believes every woman has the knowledge to give birth. Believing that birth is an instinctive process, no specific breathing patterns are taught in Birthworks classes, and instructors help each woman find the best way to breathe during labor. They offer a referral service for education classes.

■ CHILDBIRTH EDUCATION FOUNDATION

(717) 529-2561
P.O. Box 251
Oxford, PA 19363
E-mail: jperon@delphi.com
The Childbirth Education Foundation provides information to discourage unnecessary medical intervention. The group publishes and distributes a large selection of childbirth, newborn care, and parenting education literature. Call or write for a complete list. The majority of the organization's literature focuses on circumcision with several publications supporting the decision not to circumcise.

■ GLOBAL MATERNAL CHILD HEALTH ASSOCIATION

(503) 682-3600
P.O. Box 1400
Wilsonville, OR 97070
This nonprofit corporation promotes preserving, protecting and enhancing the well-being of women and children during pregnancy, birth, infancy and childhood. Their education workshops focus on natural childbirth and midwifery. Topics include "Gentle Birth Choices" and "Water Birth: Gimmick or Godsend?" They offer educational videos, a "Gentle Birth" information booklet, referrals and sources for birth tub rentals and sales. You might want to check out Barbara Harper's book, *Gentle Birth Choices*, promoting the Global Maternal Child Health Association's philosophy ($16.95, Healing Arts Press).

■ INTERNATIONAL CHILDBIRTH EDUCATION ASSOCIATION (ICEA)

(612) 854-8660
P.O. Box 20048
Minneapolis, MN 55420
Web site: www.icea.org
E-mail: info@icea.org
This organization does not promote any specific method of childbirth but instead stresses "freedom of choice based on knowledge of alternatives." ICEA trains and certifies instructors (titled ICCEs) in a method that incorporates both Bradley and Lamaze techniques. ICEA instructors are often also ASPO/Lamaze- or AAHCC-certified. This organization has an extensive mail order bookstore and will provide names of instructors in your area.

LABOR PAIN RELIEF

By Donna Hudson-Bryant, R.N., C.C.E., C.D. (DONA)

Labor hurts. Because of this, we focus much of our energy in preparing for birth. Why does it hurt? How much will it hurt? How long will the pain last? Will I be able to take it? Will there be any help for me? These are the questions we ask ourselves whenever we are in pain. Pain frightens us at a very primitive level, because of its unknowns. But we know a lot about the labor process and can learn from that.

Most women fear the pain of labor. Fear is very powerful. It creates a rush of adrenalin which makes the heart race and quickens breathing. Blood flow shifts to the vital organs and large muscles of the legs and arms. Since the uterus is not a vital organ, when in this "fight or flight" state in labor, the working uterine muscle does not get normal blood or oxygen flow. This causes a painful build-up of lactic acid in the muscle. Contractions become less coordinated so, though they still come and they still hurt, the cervix is slow to open and the baby slow to descend. In other words, you have a more painful labor, which proceeds very slowly. This in itself is frightening, and feeds back into the cycle.

Grantly Dick-Read first described this fear-tension-pain cycle in the 1930s. He felt if women were prepared and approached birth without fear, their pain would be relieved. This is the basis for current methods of nonmedical pain relief in childbirth. In the 1950s, Ferdinand Lamaze introduced the concept of painless childbirth through a kind of Pavlovian training in breathing techniques. Other methods of "prepared childbirth" followed, all involving education and practice for giving birth, promoting a state of relaxation and decreasing fear. While no amount of preparation really makes labor pain-free, there are many safe alternatives for making labor pain more manageable.

♨

Uterine contractions work to pull open the stretchy muscles of the cervix and the birth canal. This stretching hurts.

♨

UNMEDICATED BIRTH STRATEGIES

Pain is a signal, a protective mechanism. Labor pain and sensations are messages to us from our bodies. They show us how to help labor along. It is no coincidence that positions that reduce pain also help labor progress more quickly. Perhaps the pain is relieved by moving your body in a certain way. Maybe your stamina improves by drinking and eating. Every woman, every baby, and every labor is unique. Each woman must find what works for her in each labor. Here are some suggestions:

- **Feed your body for the work it must do.** If your provider permits, drink water or juice every hour or eat lightly if you feel hungry. Try popsicles, sweetened tea, cereals, rice, beans, soups, toast or crackers, peanut butter, and yogurt.

- **What goes in must come out.** Urinate every hour or two while you are awake. A full bladder can hold the baby back and make labor more painful.

- **Use natural forces to help your body do its work.** Use gravity, motion, heat, cold, and water to lessen pain and make the work easier for your body. Try standing, kneeling or sitting leaning forward onto something higher—your partner, a wall, or piece of furniture. Take walks, squat on a low stool, get on your hands and knees, or rock in a chair. Take relaxing showers or baths, or use hot or cold compresses

- **Your breathing can help you relax.** There is no one right way to breathe, as long as you do not hold your breath or hyperventilate. Slow, rhythmic breathing is relaxing and conserves energy. Making noise with your breath releases tension. Sighing, moaning, or groaning are helpful, as long as your jaw and throat are loose and open.

- **Set a mood in the labor room.** Certain sights, sounds, and smells can make it easier to relax. Dim the overhead lights. Music is soothing and can help shut out distracting or frightening sounds. Use music with a special meaning or that music which you used for relaxation during pregnancy. Certain aromas promote relaxation, decrease pain, and mask unpleasant odors. Clary sage and lavender may be helpful; consult an aromatherapist for instruction.

- **Set a mood for your mind.** Use visualization, meditation, and imagery to help maintain a sense of calm. Repeat a word, "open" or "baby," each time you breathe out, or try counting your breaths.

- **Being connected to other people can really help.** Get support from someone strong who will stay with you throughout the entire labor—your partner, mother, friend, doula, or midwife. This person shouldn't be afraid to see you in pain.

- **Touch can feel great in labor.** Whether you do it yourself or someone does it for you, massage can help labor pain a lot. Try massage that is firm and deep, smooth and light, or just as pressure. Massage your belly, shoulders and neck, breasts/nipples, hands, lower back, thighs, and feet. Hugs, kisses, and even holding hands can feel great.

- **Try to save your strength as you go.** Rest if you feel tired, because you do not want to burn yourself out. Find restful positions, such as sitting supported in bed or side-lying. Use lots of pillows. Try slow, deep breathing and relaxation exercises to get your body quieted down. A catnap between contractions can be very refreshing.

■ **Use moderation and balance.** Change what you are doing every hour while you are awake. If it is night, try to sleep, or simply rest. If you have been sitting, get up and walk. After you go to the bathroom, grab something to drink or eat, then go to a different place and try something new.

Women who remain alert, active participants in their labors often describe feeling more powerful after the experience, and draw on these feelings as a source of strength as they face the challenges of mothering a new baby.

Keep an open mind about the use of pain medications in labor. Pain medications and anesthesia can promote relaxation and rest. No remedy or medication will relieve pain for the entire labor.

Take the time to understand your options for medical pain relief, then wait to see how your labor unfolds. Pain in giving birth is inevitable. Sooner or later, each woman must come to terms with her feelings about that.

COPING WITH BACK LABOR

Some labors are more painful than others. This is particularly true of what is known as back labor. This means that pain is felt almost entirely in the woman's lower back. The pain may be constant, intensifying tremendously during contractions. Often this means the baby's head is in a posterior position, so that the back of her head presses against the lower spine with each contraction. Back labors are often longer, since the baby must turn herself around to face the other way. There are some additional tricks to ease the special pain of back labor. In addition to relieving back pain, these things also encourage your baby to turn:

■ Walk between contractions and stand during them.
■ Lean forward whenever possible. Never lie on your back.
■ Lie on your side where the baby's back is, opposite where you feel the most kicks.
■ Rock, tilt, or gently sway your pelvis while leaning forward.

■ Use heat on your lower back. After 20-30 minutes, switch to cold. Try a warm bath or shower.
■ Gently but firmly stroke your belly. Start where the baby's back is and stroke towards the middle.
■ Have your partner press hard on the painful spot with a fist or heel of a hand, or massage your lower spine with something hard, like a ball or rolling pin.
■ Stand facing forward, with one foot on a chair beside you. Lunge towards the chair during contractions. Lunge towards the side where the baby's back is, or whichever side feels best.
■ Have your partner stand behind you while you lean forward. Your partner places the heel of each hand on the middle of each buttock with fingers pointing toward the spine. As your partner presses down and in towards your spine (double hip squeeze), give feedback as to hand placement and how hard to press.

MEDICAL PAIN RELIEF IN CHILDBIRTH

By Joseph F. Antognini, M.D., University of California, Davis

With childbirth comes pain. Some women experience small amounts of pain. For others, the pain of labor detracts from a positive labor experience. Fortunately for women today there are numerous medical methods available to diminish labor pain. Nationwide about 70% of births are medicated, with variations depending on specific geographic areas. Medicated births include epidural analgesia, spinal analgesia, pudendal blocks and "walking epidurals." Also, labor pain may be relieved by traditional methods including intravenous and intramuscular opiates, such as morphine and Demerol.

Labor pain relief may be administrated through an anesthesiologist who attends four years of college, four years of medical school and an additional three to five years of specialty training. Hospitals may also have nurse anesthetists perform obstetrical anesthesia. These nurses have received two years of training on top of a nursing degree.

EPIDURALS

An epidural is a technique in which local anesthetic and/or opiates are injected into the epidural space and bathe the spinal nerve roots after they've left the spinal fluid and spinal cord. The goal is to relieve a significant amount of the pain of labor without disrupting the natural progress of labor and the mother's ability to move and push during the delivery.

The procedure for epidural placement is straightforward. After a discussion between the laboring mother and the anesthetist, the patient's lower back is cleansed and a small amount of local anesthetic is then injected into the skin, which permits placement of the needle through the ligaments of the back, and then into the epidural space. Once that space is reached, a small catheter—which looks very much like a fishing line—is inserted through the needle and the needle is then removed and the small flexible catheter left in place. Sometimes the catheter will touch one of the nerves in the lower part of the back which will cause a sensation of electricity in the leg or into the buttocks, very similar to the sensation of

❧

Numerous

medical

methods

have been

developed to

diminish

labor pain.

❧

hitting your funny bone. This is usually not long-lasting and is present for a split second.

Small test doses of the anesthetic are then given to insure proper placement and functioning of the catheter, followed by the full dose or continuous infusion as required for either epidural analgesia or epidural anesthesia. Urinary catheterization is often needed with both epidural and spinals. Common side effects include a decrease in blood pressure and itching. On very rare occasions reactions from an inadvertant injection into a blood vessel or the spinal fluid could result in seizures and heart irregularities or excessive numbness. However, these side effects, while very rare, are also easily recognized and treated so that the technique is quite safe. Backaches may occur after an epidural but appear to be no more common than those occurring after a general anesthetic. A spinal headache can occur if the epidural inadvertently goes into the spinal fluid.

One of the benefits of an epidural is that if the mother requires a Cesarean section, more anesthetic can be administered which will then numb the mother from the middle of the chest down. This allows the procedure to be performed with the mother awake but pain-free so she is then able to enjoy the experience of her child's birth.

SPINAL ANALGESIA

In some patients, instead of injecting in the epidural space, an injection of local anesthetic and/or opiate is made into the subarachnoid space which is closer to the nerves and therefore less anesthetic is required. This technique is called spinal analgesia. In some patients spinal opiates can be administered, either morphine or fentanyl which help relieve labor pain. These are often given with a local anesthetic and help to decrease the required amount of local anesthetic. A disadvantage is that only one injection can be made whereas with an epidural catheter injections can be made periodically or an infusion performed. Spinal analgesia also has the risks of developing a spinal headache, lowering the mother's blood pressure and causing mild itching.

"WALKING EPIDURALS"

Walking epidurals (or spinals) are so named because the patient is able to walk while receiving pain relief. This is because only an opiate—drugs such as morphine or fentanyl—is injected, not a local anesthetic which can weaken the muscles, therefore preventing walking or making it dangerous. In some patients opiates are sufficient to relieve pain and, because they do not affect the nerves to muscles, patients are able to walk around during labor (walking epidural).

PUDENDAL BLOCK

A pudendal block also can be used to relieve labor pain. This involves injecting a small amount of local anesthetic through the vaginal wall near the cervix.

GENERAL ANESTHESIA

In some patients the epidural catheter, which is otherwise apparently placed properly, does not relieve all of the mother's pain. This sometimes occurs because of some peculiarities of the patient's anatomy which prevents the local anesthetic from reaching all the nerves that carry the pain. Sometimes this requires additional anesthetics including intravenous medications or, in the situation of a Cesarean section, may require administration of a general anesthetic. Although general anesthesia is considered safe for the mother and baby, this is usually the last choice for a medicated birth and attempts are made to avoid general anesthesia. General anesthesia renders the mother unconscious and therefore makes her unable to experience the birth of her child.

Patients who require a general anesthetic will be brought to the operating room and placed on the table and appropriate monitors will be placed including a heart monitor, blood pressure monitor and oxygen monitor. After breathing oxygen, the patient receives intravenous medications to induce general anesthesia and is unconscious for the duration of the operation. After the patient is unconscious, a small plastic tube is placed into the windpipe through the mouth; this protects the mother's lungs and makes it easier for her to breathe during the surgery. The anesthetic is maintained with inhaled anesthetics like nitrous oxide (laughing gas) and isoflurane. Luckily, only a small amount of these anesthetics get to the baby.

REACTIONS TO ANESTHESIA

It is unusual to develop an allergic reaction to the medications that are administered to the mother, but it is possible to have a rare reaction to the local anesthetics or opiates. More commonly patients will develop side effects such as backaches or headaches which are not true allergic reactions. In general the more drugs the mother receives, the more possible effects on the mother and the infant. However this is probably most important for the newborn in the setting of a general anesthetic, and even then, if the baby is removed quickly, there is usually not a problem. Some patients also develop itching as a result of opiate administration.

Mothers may experience shaking with a spinal or epidural. It is thought to be due to the disruption of the body's temperature regulation. The spinal or epidural lowers the body's core temperature and you shiver in order to raise your temperature.

Consider talking to your health care provider about the risks and reactions of different types of anesthesia before laboring. Many hospitals and organizations offer an education session on anesthesia prior to birth or as a part of a childbirth education series.

INSURANCE CONSIDERATIONS

Epidurals, general anesthesia and all the medical services performed are usually covered by insurance programs. Check with your individual plan, talk with an insurance representative and make notes about who you spoke with and when, to ensure maximum financial benefits. If you are receiving federal or state assistance, talk with your case worker to see what type of medicated options are available. It is better to know ahead of time the costs involved, than to be hit with a large bill after the birth.

"My Cesarean Birth"

A Life Experience by Kelly O'Toole

I never thought I would have anything but a normal delivery with my first child. Why should I think differently? I had a perfect pregnancy. I was never sick, had no complications, no heartburn, no swelling even through the summer months. People told me I was glowing and I felt great.

I read lots of books on pregnancy and loved attending childbirth classes. My initial fear gave way to excitement as my due date approached. Cesarean birth never crossed my mind. I didn't read those chapters in the pregnancy books and frankly didn't pay close attention to the childbirth class on Cesareans. That is not going to happen to me, I thought.

During my eighth month my husband Michael kept insisting that the baby's head was up near my ribs, not low where it should be. I asked about the baby's position at every visit. Either my doctor didn't want to worry me or simply thought the baby would eventually turn. A few visits later, she finally ordered an ultrasound to check. A week later the ultrasound technician confirmed that the baby was breech, buttocks down. Less than four weeks to go and my whole plan for childbirth had been literally turned on its head.

My doctor recommended a version—she would attempt to turn the baby from the outside. It would require going to the hospital and being hooked up to an IV in case of fetal distress, which could mean an emergency Cesarean. We discussed the risks as well as the chance that the baby couldn't be turned. Even if successful, there was always the chance the baby would flip back to the original position. We decided to try the version and scheduled it for the following week. By this time I was 38 weeks, but everyone, including my doctor, told me not to worry about a Cesarean. At the visit before the version, I asked my doctor lots of questions about Cesarean births. She answered my questions but told me to wait and see how the version would go. I went home with some answers and lots of fear, nervousness and anxiety.

The next night, six days before the scheduled version and ten days before my due date, my water broke. We were going to the hospital to have our baby by Cesarean birth! I felt extremely nervous. I didn't know what to expect. I was also excited because our baby would be born within a few hours.

When I got to the hospital they hooked me up to a monitor. I was apparently having small contractions that I couldn't even feel. They took a sample of the fluid leaking from my cervix to confirm that my water had in fact broken. They wheeled me off to the operating room and my husband was whisked away to change into scrubs. He wasn't allowed to join me until I was prepped for surgery.

Finally, with an IV and monitors attached to my arms, a surgical screen placed in front of me and a room full of nurses, doctors, a pediatrician, an anesthesiologist, a med student and finally my husband—looking very funny in scrubs and a blue surgical hat—we were ready to begin. After a short time, my husband could see the doctor pull out first one foot and then the other, both shoulders and finally the head of our newborn baby Matthew. "It's a boy and he is poohing and peeing all over the place!" I heard the doctor say.

Matthew was carried to a table by the pediatrician where she suctioned out his breathing passages. Not having passed through the birth canal, he needed lots of fluid suctioned out of him. With Michael watching, she initially examined, washed and swaddled him. I couldn't see any of this as I was still flat on my back in the middle of surgery. Michael held Matthew and brought him over to show me. I saw a bright red face peering out of a bundle of blankets, his wide eyes looking at me. He was beautiful and I wanted to reach out, but I was in the middle of surgery and unable to hold him.

At this point the anesthesia was beginning to affect my stomach and the large meal I had eaten a few hours earlier. I was feeling incredibly nauseous and uncomfortable. I felt horrible and had to motion several times for that hospital blue vomit dish. In recovery, I shook uncontrollably from the anesthesia while Matthew was in the nursery. It was hours before I could hold and nurse him.

Despite the fact that the Cesarean experience was not pleasant, I was elated about my child. He was perfect and healthy and more beautiful than I could imagine. That was enough for me at the time. My recovery seemed fairly easy. I took very little pain medication and was taking walks the first day home from the hospital. Only later, after hearing my friends' birth stories, I began to feel disappointed. I prepared for nine months to give birth. I knew it would be a long and grueling process, but at the end of it I would have delivered my baby. Instead I went through a surgical procedure, where my baby was delivered for me, not by me. A Cesarean is far from the end of the world, but it is also far from what I expected.

When I became pregnant with our second child, I was surprised at the emotions that came up as I anticipated this baby's birth. I kept thinking my Cesarean might have been avoided had we known our son was breech earlier. I was excited to try a VBAC. I wanted to try to deliver this baby. I didn't want a Cesarean unless absolutely necessary. The reality is that you can't always control your birth experience. However, I do know that you can educate yourself and make choices that can impact your experience. I took a refresher childbirth class from an instructor who discussed positions during labor to help with pain management. I enrolled in an exercise class that included relaxation techniques. I had high hopes that this time I would be able to extend my arms and hold my baby immediately after giving birth. After 17 hours of labor, much-needed support from my husband, and the help of a fantastic practitioner, I did exactly that.

I am thankful that I was able to have a VBAC. It was everything I had hoped it would be. My Cesarean birth could have been easier if I had been prepared for it mentally. The outcome of both births was the same, however. I have two beautiful, healthy boys. I have had two very different births but at the end of the day I look at my sons and I give thanks. Being a mom, no matter how you get there, is the best experience of all. ❧

HINTS FOR AVOIDING A CESAREAN SECTION

While Cesarean sections are safer than they used to be, they are still major surgical procedures. For babies, the outcomes of C-sections are about the same as for vaginal deliveries, but for mothers, C-sections pose higher risks of complications. In addition, the recovery time is much longer after a Cesarean: ten days, as opposed to two or three for a vaginal delivery, and six weeks before you can pick up that heavy diaper bag.

Still, over a fifth of births are by Cesarean section. In 1995, 20.8% of U.S. births were by Cesarean, compared to 10.4% in 1975. Cesarean rates do vary considerably by individual hospitals and providers.

In order to reduce the possibility of a Cesarean delivery, there are some proactive steps women can take. "At least 40% of all C-sections could be avoided with proper management of pregnancy, labor and delivery," says Cristin Babcock, M.D., a Portland, Oregon, obstetrician.

The first thing you can do is to talk with your provider early in your pregnancy and stress that a vaginal delivery is a priority for you. After that, there are five key things you can do to help reduce the likelihood that you'll need a C-section.

- **Prepare for childbirth.** You'll be better able to handle the stress of labor if you take a thorough childbirth preparation course—six weeks, if possible. After the course, you'll be more confident about labor and delivery.

- **Stay active in labor.** During labor, remain upright and active as long as you can to help your body along. Physical activity, warm showers and baths will help gravity work to bring the baby's head down into the pelvis.

Taking an active role in your labor also means taking childbirth preparation classes and learning as much as possible about what to realistically expect during labor. "Many women expect a pain-free delivery, but that's not realistic," says Dr. Babcock. "Having an epidural too early, to stop the pain, may also stop your labor and make a C-section necessary. If you need pain relief, one of the most important things you can do is to hold out until your cervix is dilated at least five centimeters."

ટ

"One of the most important things you can do is to hold out until your cervix is dilated at least five centimeters."

ટ

- **Actively manage labor.** If labor is not progressing, talk with your provider about what can be done to stimulate labor so it doesn't go on too long or put unnecessary stress on the baby.
- **Don't induce labor unless medically necessary.** Although it may be tempting to "schedule" your baby's delivery by inducing labor, you may pay for that convenience with a C-section. Inducing labor often prevents the cervix from dilating enough or keeps the baby from moving into the correct position for delivery. Instead of taking that risk, be patient and work with your body.
- **If you've had a previous C-section, ask for a trial of labor.** Most women assume that if their first baby was born by Cesarean, the next one will be, too. That's not necessarily the way it has to be.

Many women can deliver their second child vaginally. If you'd like to try, let your physician know that you would like a "trial of labor"—trying labor first, before resorting to C-section.

Not every C-section can or should be avoided. In come circumstances, a physician may recommend inducing labor or performing a C-section as the best way to protect mother and child. In other cases, a mother may try all of the suggestions listed above and still end up delivering by C-section.

Every delivery is different, and if a Cesarean becomes necessary for you to delivery a healthy baby or to protect your own health, don't view it as any kind of failure—rather, be thankful that such options exist.

Reprinted with permission from Providence Health System's "Good Health" magazine, Summer/Fall 1997.

❧ RESOURCES ❧

■ **INTERNATIONAL CESAREAN AWARENESS NETWORK (ICAN)**
(310) 542-6400
1304 Kingsdale Ave.
Redondo Beach, CA 90278
E-mail: icaninc@aol.com
Web site: http://www.childbirth.org/section/ican.html
ICAN has a threefold purpose: to lower the rising Cesarean rate through education, to provide a forum where women and men can express their thoughts and concerns about birth, and to provide a support network for women who are

healing from past birth experiences and for those who are preparing for future births. ICAN has grown from one chapter in 1982 to the current 30 chapters nationwide. Contact the organization to receive the free brochures "Working for the Birth You Want" and "Things You Can Do to Avoid an Unnecessary Cesarean" and a free copy of "The Clarion," an informative newsletter which contains Cesarean news updates, book reviews, birth stories, and encouragement from families around the world. A one-year subscription is $25.

QUESTIONS AND ANSWERS
Cesarean Births

According to the American College of Obstetricians and Gynecologists, the percentage of Cesarean births have decreased from a high of 24.7% in 1988 to 20.8% in 1995. VBAC rates, just 12.6% in 1988, were 27.5% in 1995.

The following answers regarding Cesarean births were provided by Larry Veltman, M.D., who practices obstetrics and gynecology with Women's Healthcare Associates in Portland, Oregon, and is the Medical Director of the Women's and Children's Program for Providence Health Systems.

Q. *Under what circumstances might a Cesarean be necessary?*

A. The most common reasons for a Cesarean delivery are: the inability for the cervix to dilate or the baby to descend through the birth canal, some type of fetal distress, a problem with the presentation of the baby, the placenta covering the opening of the cervix (placenta previa), or when the placenta begins to separate from the uterus before the birth (placental abruption). These are not the only reasons that a Cesarean birth may result. In fact, sometimes a vaginal delivery can actually occur even with some of these conditions present. Good communication with your health care provider is essential to understand why a Cesarean delivery is necessary in your case.

Q. *What can be done to avoid a Cesarean birth?*

A. Some Cesarean births are mandatory. For example, if the placenta covers the cervix (placenta previa), vaginal birth is impossible without a possible fatal hemorrhage. On the other hand, when a baby is breech, sometimes it can be turned prior to labor (a procedure called version). It is also important during early labor to try to walk and to delay epidural anesthesia. The lack of walking in early labor and early epidural anesthesia have recently been associated with a higher chance of a Cesarean birth. Women who have experienced a Cesarean birth should thoroughly explore the option of a VBAC before deciding on a repeat Cesarean birth.

Q. *What kind of anesthesia is used for a Cesarean birth?*

A. A Cesarean delivery is usually performed using epidural or spinal anesthesia. This allows the mother to be awake during the operation and is usually safer for the mother and baby. On occasion, under emergency circumstances, a general anesthetic (putting the mother to sleep) might be required. In any instance the operation should not be painful to the woman undergoing the delivery.

Q. *If I have a Cesarean delivery, who will be in the delivery room?*

A. In addition to the surgical nurse, obstetrician, and anesthesiologist, there is usually a circulating nurse (who can get needed supplies), a surgical assistant who helps the obstetrician, and one or more individuals who are trained in newborn resuscitation. These individuals may be nurses, respiratory therapists, and/or physicians.

Pediatricians, or family physicians trained in newborn resuscitation, are usually present for most high-risk Cesarean deliveries but may not be present in the operating room at low-risk deliveries (such as repeat Cesarean deliveries). This will vary from hospital to hospital depending upon the training of support personnel. Most hospitals will also allow a support person into the operating room unless general anesthesia is required.

Q. *Can my partner be present during a Cesarean birth?*

A. In most instances, yes. It is very comforting to have a support person present during a Cesarean birth, but not essential. Usually a partner is allowed to be by the mother to give her moral support. The operative area is covered and it is not necessary to observe the actual procedure. The anesthesiologist will also be at the head of the operating table and gives a great deal of support. In the case of a general anesthetic, the woman's partner may be asked to leave during the delivery.

Q. *What type of recovery is expected from a Cesarean birth?*

A. With a Cesarean delivery you undergo both recovery from the pregnancy as well as recovery from a surgical operation. Therefore, there will be a longer hospital stay (usually two to four days), and more time needed for recovery once at home. There should be thorough instructions concerning when to call the doctor (fever of above 100.4, hemorrhaging, unusual pain, or any redness, swelling or opening of the incision). Driving, heavy lifting, and exercise is usually not recommended for two to four weeks. After about six weeks most women can return to normal activities.

Q. *If a woman has a Cesarean birth can she have a vaginal delivery with a subsequent pregnancy?*

A. In most cases, a woman will be encouraged to have a vaginal birth after a previous Cesarean. This is called a VBAC (pronounced vee-back). This issue should be discussed at the time of the Cesarean birth and again at your prenatal visits during the next pregnancy. There are certain indications for high success rates in achieving a VBAC. There are also a few reasons why a VBAC should not be attempted.

It is important to know about the type of uterine incision (not the skin incision, but the actual incision in the uterus). There is also a rare chance that the previous uterine incision could separate during a subsequent labor. A vertical uterine incision (which is quite rare today) as opposed to a horizontal uterine incision is usually a reason not to attempt a VBAC.

Overall, however, vaginal birth after a Cesarean holds less risk for the mother and the baby than just repeating the Cesarean because it was done before.

Q. What is important about a physician's or a hospital's Cesarean birth rate?

A. Cesarean rates vary from physician to physician, from hospital to hospital, and from community to community. It is important, however, that the rate itself is not the only factor considered in choosing a provider. For example, if a physician refers all high-risk pregnancies to other practices, that physician will have a lower Cesarean rate. Conversely, if a hospital or a provider cares for an unusual number of high-risk pregnancies, this will be reflected in a higher Cesarean rate (sometimes in the range of 30%). The important issue is to have confidence that all birthing options will be considered for both the mother and the baby. If the best outcome is achieved by a Cesarean, then the mother should proceed with that option.

STAGES OF LABOR

Unless your birth is a scheduled Cesarean section, you should experience some of the following stages of labor. Also, this chart may be helpful for subsequent VBAC (Vaginal Birth after Cesarean) births.

STAGE	DILATION	CONTRACTIONS	WHAT TO DO
FIRST STAGE			
Early Labor	0-4 cm	20-5 min. apart; 30-60 seconds duration	Take a walk; relax; bathe or shower
Active Labor	5-8 cm	3-4 min. apart; 45-60 seconds duration	Use relaxation and breathing methods; walk if possible
Transition	8-10 cm	2-3 min. apart; 60 seconds duration	Pant, don't push; suck on ice chips
SECOND STAGE	10 cm	2-5 min. apart; 60-90 seconds	Work with coach to push for baby's birth!
THIRD STAGE		Very mild	Push when instructed to expel placenta

PREPARATION FOR BABY

CHAPTER TWO

THE LIGHTER SIDE OF PREGNANCY

A dear friend, Claire Voyant, who has had experience dealing with over six pregnant couples, has graciously agreed to answer the most often asked questions about pregnancy, childbirth and babies, no matter how ridiculous they may be (the questions, not the babies).

By Joyce Armor

Q. *Is it true that I'm more likely to get pregnant if my husband wears boxer shorts rather than jockey shorts?*

A. Yes, but you'd be most likely to get pregnant if he were wearing no shorts.

Q. *How can I be sure I'm really pregnant?*

A. Time your contractions.

Q. *I wear a size 34C bra (when I wear one) and have never needed much support. Why should I start wearing a bra now that I'm pregnant?*

A. No reason if you don't mind switching in the future to a size 34 long.

Q. *Does pregnancy cause dandruff?*

A. Pregnancy causes anything you want to blame it for.

Q: *My wife is six months pregnant and so moody that she overreacts to the simplest problem. Sometimes she's borderline irrational.*

A: So? What's the question?

Q. *What's the most common pregnancy craving?*

A. For men to be the ones who get pregnant.

Q. *Now that I'm pregnant, my breasts and rear end are huge and even my feet have grown. Isn't there anything that gets smaller during pregnancy?*

A. Of course. Your bladder.

Q: *All the expectant women I know seem so sure of themselves. Am I the only pregnant woman who has ever had second thoughts about becoming a mother?*

A: Yes.

Q. *Is there anything that will alleviate the nausea I've been feeling during my pregnancy?*

A. Yes. Vomiting.

Q. *Both my husband and I are extremely good looking, and I know our baby will be too. I think he (or she) should be in commercials right away or even a TV series. Whom should I talk to about this?*

A. Your therapist.

Q. *The more pregnant I get, the more often complete strangers smile at me. Why?*

A. Because you're fatter than they are.

Q. *What position should the baby be in during my ninth month of pregnancy?*

A. Head down, pressing firmly on your bladder.

Q. *I hate baby showers. Is there any way to avoid them?*

A. Yes, change the baby's diapers very quickly.

Q: *My childbirth instructor says that it's not pain you feel during labor, but pressure. Is she right?*

A: Yes, in the same way that a tornado might be called an air current.

Q. *Who had the longest labor in recorded history?*

A. Whoever your most boring acquaintance is.

Q. *Can a sterilization operation be performed during a Cesarean?*

A. Only if it's on your wife. Schedule your vasectomy on your own time.

Q: *Please settle an argument I'm having with my sister. Can a mother get pregnant while nursing her baby?*

A: Yes, but it's much easier if she removes the baby from her breast and puts him down for a nap first.

Q: *Do newborns have a sense of taste?*

A: Apparently not, or why would so many of them wear those shapeless sacques and washed-out colors?

Q. *I'm pregnant for the first time, and I'm already worried about how far apart I should space my children. What do the experts say?*

A. Most experienced parents space their children at least six feet apart.

PLANNING FOR POSTPARTUM

Many women spend their pregnancies reading about their baby's prenatal development. They plan nurseries and consider names. They choose a layette and birth announcements. But often little thought goes toward their own postpartum planning. Nothing can fully prepare you for the emotions and physical elation and discomforts you'll feel, unless you've had a baby before. But just as each pregnancy is different, so is each postpartum period. Take a little time to mentally prepare for the days and weeks after your child's birth.

THE FIRST DAY

Plan to be euphoric, tired, anxious and extremely hungry! This is prime bonding time, so spend as much time as possible with your newborn. Ask your nurse to help you with nursing your baby, within the first hour postpartum if possible.

- Have a phone list ready so you or your partner can make calls from the hospital. Visitors may come to see you and the baby, but limit the visits so you don't get overly tired.
- If you have older children, consider giving a "big brother" or "big sister" gift when they meet their new sibling.
- Besides taking vital signs, a nurse will visit you often to massage your uterus until it firms up and to verify that the lochia (post-birth blood flow) is moderate.
- You may be given an ice pack, pain medication or anesthetic spray for your tender perineal area.

THE FIRST WEEK

Your lochia will still be flowing rather heavily, and there may be blood clots. Over the next couple weeks, it will turn pink, then whitish. It is recommended that you use sanitary pads rather than tampons. Have a box of heavy-flow pads on hand for your first week home.

- When you read about milk coming in, it may not prepare you for the actual event. Two to four days after delivery, your milk changes from the thick, yellowish colostrum to a thinner milk. Your breasts may become very full and sore, making it difficult for baby to latch on. This will

↝

Take a little time to mentally prepare for the days and weeks after your child's birth.

↝

subside when you get into a regular nursing pattern.

- If you plan to bottle feed, you must avoid stimulating milk production in order to dry up the milk supply. A firm support bra worn 24 hours a day will help, as will ice packs and cold compresses.

- Nursing your baby may stimulate afterbirth pains for a week or so. The pains are stronger with second and subsequent children, and are caused by your uterus working to return to its prepregnancy size.

- Urination and bowel movements may be difficult for a few days. Nervousness about tearing episiotomy stitches can inhibit urine flow. Plan to drink plenty of fluids. To make bowel movements less painful, a diet rich in fiber and a stool softener will ease discomfort.

- A few repetitions of Kegel exercises several times a day will help you regain perineal muscle tone. These should be worked into your daily routine to prevent stress incontinence when you get older.

- Hemorrhoids are a side effect of pregnancy, labor and delivery. Sprays, dry heat, or witch hazel compresses will be soothing.

- Watch for danger signs. ACOG recommends you call your practitioner if you experience any of these problems: fever over 100.4 degrees, heavy bleeding, nausea or vomiting, urinary difficulties or perineal pain, swelling or pain in legs, chest pain or cough, or hot or tender breasts.

THE FIRST MONTHS

- Depression after childbirth is common and can range from "the baby blues" to serious depression. Read about PPD in Chapter 6.

- Your menstrual periods will resume about six to eight weeks after childbirth if you are not breastfeeding. Nursing mothers may not have a period for several months or more.

- Check with your obstetrician about the best birth control method to use postpartum. If you wait until your period starts to resume using birth control, you may be too late!

- Your obstetrical checkup, generally four to six weeks postpartum, is often the go-ahead signal for resuming your sexual relations. Others may feel ready a few weeks earlier, but be sure to think "gentle." You may need a vaginal lubricant if you experience dryness. Some breastfeeding mothers experience menopausal-type changes vaginally due to hormone fluctuation that can increase discomfort. If lubricant isn't helping, ask your provider; treatment is available.

- When you find some time alone, you and your partner may want to reconnect with some snuggling and talking. New dads may feel left out. Make sure your partner knows he is loved and appreciated.

- Exercise can increase your strength and energy level, and help you get back into shape.

- Rest is essential but not often possible. Ask your partner to take over as much of the household duties as possible, so you are ensured as much sleep as you can.

MATERNITY LEAVE

For women who work, planning ahead for your maternity leave is the key to making a smooth transition from leaving your job to enjoying your time at home with your new baby. The more informed you are about your rights in the workplace, the better you can maximize your options.

This section of the resource guide focuses both on the laws that protect pregnant women and on the "gray" areas that surround maternity leave. This section is not intended to replace legal advice. It should also be noted that the laws change often in this area, so use the resources given to fully understand the most current information.

One resource we found very helpful is a book entitled *Everything A Working Mother Needs To Know* by Anne C. Weisberg and Carol A. Buckler. The book offers both a legal and logistical approach to maternity leave.

THE FAMILY AND MEDICAL LEAVE ACT

❧

The more informed you are about your rights in the workplace, the better you can maximize your options.

❧

In 1993, President Bill Clinton signed the Family and Medical Leave Act of 1993 (FMLA). If your state has its own family leave act, compare the state and federal regulations. You are generally allowed to use the more generous guidelines in planning your leave. The FMLA requires employers with 50 or more employees to permit most personnel to take up to three months of unpaid leave. This leave can be for the birth or adoption of a child, to care for a parent, spouse, or child, or personal leave if that individual has a serious health condition.

This Act prohibits employers with 50 or more employees from denying most employees' requests for a family care leave of absence. (The 50 employees is limited to worksites with 50 or more persons employed within 75 miles of the worksite.) The Act also requires employers to guarantee re-employment in the same or equivalent position to workers who return from family leave. Employers must also pay for employees' existing health benefits while they are on leave. However, an employer is not required to pay for health benefits if the woman is on pregnancy disability. If the employee does not return to work at the end of the leave, the employer may collect the cost of the premium.

WHO IS ELIGIBLE FOR FAMILY LEAVE?

All employees with more than a year of service and at least 1,250 hours worked in the last 12 months with the employer are covered by this Act. Both spouses may take the full amount of the leave, as long as they do not work for the same company. The employer may limit the family leave for birth or adoption, not to exceed a total of 12 weeks between both spouses working at the same company.

Another provision in eligibility for the FMLA is the "Key Employee Exception." This means if you are a salaried employee among the highest paid 10% in a company and if restoration or taking the leave would lead to substantial and grievous economic harm to the employer, you may be refused the leave. This places a heavy burden on the employer to justify exempting an employee. If your employer does refuse your leave based on the "Key Employee Exception" it would be to your benefit to contact the U.S. Department of Labor, Wage and Hour Division, to clarify this clause.

HOW ARE THE TWELVE WEEKS DEFINED?

In accordance with the Family Medical Leave Act, you may take 12 unpaid work weeks in a 12-month period. This 12-month period does not have to be in one calendar year.

Employers may require, or an employee may elect, to substitute paid vacation or any other accrued time off for a portion of an employee's available unpaid leave. An employee may only substitute accrued sick time for a portion of the unpaid family care leave if the reason for the leave would otherwise entitle the employee to use sick leave.

MATERNITY LEAVE

THE PREGNANCY DISCRIMINATION ACT

All women who work in companies with 15 or more employees are protected against discrimination under federal law by the Pregnancy Discrimination Act of 1978. In effect, this 20-year-old law equates pregnancy discrimination with sex discrimination.

It is generally agreed that a woman is disabled by pregnancy at least two to four weeks before her due date and four to six weeks after a vaginal birth. The period is a bit longer for recovery from a Cesarean birth. These disability periods are, however, up to each health care provider. You are only entitled to the full four-month leave under the Pregnancy Discrimination Act if your provider certifies you to be disabled for that length of time. If you are medically able to return to work, but choose not to, you are not covered by the Pregnancy Discrimination Act.

Check with your state's disability leave regulations; they may be more lenient than the national requirements.

To receive a free Equal Employment Opportunity Commission brochure titled "Facts About Pregnancy Discrimination," call 800-669-3362.

ARE YOU PAID DURING YOUR LEAVE?

The employer does not need to provide any salary unless the employee uses vacation time or other paid time off during the period of family leave.

During your leave, you can not be forced to sacrifice any seniority or benefits. When you return from the family care leave, you will have the same seniority and benefits as before your leave. Your employer also cannot consider your leave a break in service for purposes of a layoff, promotion, job assignment, employee benefits (including vacation) and for any seniority provision under a collective bargaining agreement. Your employer, however, does not need to pay into your pension or retirement plan during your leave. You must be allowed to make contributions to your retirement plan.

WHEN TO NOTIFY YOUR EMPLOYER

You should give your employer at least 30 days advance notice in writing or as soon as possible when taking your leave for birth or adoption. Longer notice is always appreciated. If your leave is an unanticipated emergency, you must verbally notify your employer within 24 hours and provide written notice within three days of taking your leave.

✒ RESOURCES ✒

■ **9 TO 5 NATIONAL ASSOCIATION OF WORKING WOMEN JOB SURVIVAL HOTLINE**
800-522-0925
Hours: M-F (EST) 10:00 a.m.-2:50 p.m.
This is a hotline devoted to answering questions about the National Family Medical Leave Act (FMLA), and all other employment-related topics. They can provide a fact sheet highlighting the legal language of the Act. The 9 to 5 staff can also help you if you have questions about maternity leave, health and safety on the job, or sexual harassment. The hotline operator will make referrals specific to your state's employment policies.

■ **U.S. DEPARTMENT OF LABOR EMPLOYMENT STANDARDS ADMINISTRATION, WAGE-HOUR DIVISION, FAMILY MEDICAL LEAVE ACT OFFICE**
(202) 219-8412
200 Constitution Ave., N.W.
Room S3502
Washington, DC 20210
This department's staff are the experts on the federal FMLA, and can send you a complete copy of the Act.

QUESTIONS AND ANSWERS
Your Maternity Leave

The following interview with the Microsoft Corporation Benefits Department answers commonly asked questions about maternity leave. The information below should not take the place of legal advice or information from your company's human resources professional.

Q: *When should I notify my employer about my pregnancy?*

A: At Microsoft, we encourage our employees to notify their manager regarding their estimated leave of absence dates as soon as possible. This enables the manager to arrange for contingent staffing and/or time to determine what duties will need to be temporarily reassigned.

Q: *Although the law provides guidelines for maternity leave, is there room for negotiating a flexible or longer leave than what the law or current company policy stipulates?*

A: It's important that the employee be familiar with her company's leave of absence policies. In some cases, employers may allow you to extend your leave by using your floating holidays or accrued vacation. Additionally, based on the type of work you do, in rare instances some employers may be open to allowing you to take your leave of absence on an intermittent basis.

Q: *What is the benefit of a short term disability plan?*

A. If your physician determines that you will not be able to work up until the time you deliver, short term disability plans allow the expectant mother time off prior to her delivery and maternity leave. Some short term disability plans provide benefits only after sick leave benefits are exhausted.

Q: *Once my employer knows of my pregnancy, should I expect to be treated any differently and will my responsibilities change?*

A: Based on the type of work that you do, your health care provider may indicate that some of your job duties may need to be modified until after you return from maternity leave. It is best to discuss this with your health care provider and your employer, so that your employer can determine the feasibility of your request for this temporary accommodation.

Q: *After I've had my baby, should I call my employer? And what should I say?*

A: Employers and co-workers are usually anxious to hear if you had a boy or girl, how you are feeling, and information about your new family. Additionally, if your employer has a health care plan that your newborn will be a part of, this is a good time to enroll your baby in the plan.

Q: *Can a man take advantage of a parental leave?*

A: New fathers are eligible for leave under the provisions and in accordance with the 1993 FMLA unless both spouses work at the same company. In this case, they may choose to share the allotted time allowed by the Act.

Q: *What if my maternity leave is up and I decide I really don't want to return to work?*

A: If, at the end of your leave, you decide not to return to work, it is best to inform your employer right away so that they can hire someone to replace you. Also, under the FMLA of 1993, the employer may require you to pay back the health benefits that were paid for during your family leave.

PLANNING YOUR LEAVE

Here is a checklist that may be helpful while planning your maternity leave.

- Consult your library and review the Family Medical Leave Act of 1993.
- Review your state's maternity leave laws.
- If your employer does not qualify for the FMLA, review the Pregnancy Disability Act.
- Write a letter to your employer regarding your pregnancy and anticipated leave.
- Discuss the following questions with your human resources department:
  - Will I receive any income during my leave?
  - Does the company provide short-term disability insurance?
  - Does the company allow the use of vacation and sick days during a maternity leave?
  - Will my current position, or a comparable one, be held open for me?
  - What expenses does the company medical plan cover, and what expenses should I expect to pay?
  - Is health plan coverage available for my new baby, and how soon must I enroll the baby?

"Working at Home"

A Life Experience by Mavis Heyward

How did my journey toward working from home begin? I've really made a round-trip visit and picked up some priceless treasures along the way. In June 1986 I left a $38,000 a year job at an aerospace company to start my own tax, accounting and auditing firm from home. Eleven years ago, clients and society alike believed that if you operated a business from home, you were more likely to be a fly-by-night company; my home-based business lasted only three months. I moved to a small office downtown, then a larger office, then once more to an even larger office.

As the years went on I dropped the employees, and gave birth to three lovely, adorable, talented and mischievous gifts from God (otherwise known as children). Just before the birth of our first child, my husband quit his job as a controller at an auto dealership and joined my firm to allow me more time with our baby. We briefly discussed operating out of the home, but at that time we lived in a two-bedroom condo, so the discussion was short and sweet. A few years later I again brought up the subject of operating out of the home. This time I had some fuel. We had two more children and had moved to a larger home. The time was right: a year ago we began operating out of our home and haven't looked back since then.

Now I have peace of mind that can't be matched by any corporate office. It may not be as plush, but I know that it is my domain and in it I am as relaxed as I could possibly be. I also get to watch my children grow and mature. The challenges of operating a business and mothering are multiplied, but the opportunities for learning are too. The children get real life lessons of business at an early age so they see the importance of ABCs and 123s.

From a business point of view, the main overhead expense-rent-has been cut. I could expect my office rent to increase at least 5% every three years. Now we are able to

maintain our clients' fees at a reasonable level. (That's the tax lady talking.) Also, I can now work at my peak hours: very early in the morning. My husband's peak hours are after noon and after 10 p.m. It works well for him also.

It's not all peaches and cream, though. Disadvantages include distractions, lots of them: I'll look out the window and see work that needs to be done; I'll walk to the bathroom and see that it needs to be touched up or the carpet needs to be vacuumed; I'll notice the laundry basket that is full or spot the magazine that I have been wanting to read. Scheduling is a major challenge even now. Interruptions in my schedule drive me crazy, but they cannot be avoided. While the two oldest children go to Grammy and Papa's house three days out of the week, the baby stays home everyday.

My personality tug-of-war is an issue that is not unique to home-based businesses as much as it is to a working mom. My personalities consist of being a Mom, a Wife and a Professional Woman. Sometimes I have to remind myself that I am a professional woman who has a "secular job" that needs to be done daily, especially when the distractions are bombarding me. Other times, I don't want to stop working even to feed myself, let alone the rest of the family.

Sometimes I feel I could easily transition into a non-working stay-at-home mom, but then I think of the skills I've acquired and the clients that I'd be leaving behind. I don't really want to stop working. This focused attitude is actually a form of selfishness that my husband has helped me to see. We are continually working on this trait.

As a mom, I cherish every moment with my children. I love to teach them, nurture them, cuddle them and play with them whenever the opportunity arises. During the tax season, a busier than normal time, the one who has paid the highest price is our oldest child. As she leans on the front of my desk, her big brown eyes beg me to spend time with her now that I am home. She doesn't fully understand yet that although Mommy is at home, she is working. But, I'd still rather be in a home-based office situation to see her mature and to nurture her along this way. ❧

CHILD CARE

Whether you work full-time, part-time or stay at home with your child, quality child care is a necessity. Although child care facilities must meet certain state standards, you should have your own list of preferences and expectations. Listen to your parental instincts when making your selection. Leaving your child is difficult anyway, but to do so with a child care arrangement that you are not completely satisfied with is even more stressful.

To begin your child care search, it is important to examine the options available to you. Below is a brief description of the most common child care choices, including registered family child care homes, child care centers, and live-in child care.

FAMILY CHILD CARE HOMES

Licensed family child care refers to child care in the private home of a licensed individual. The number of children a single provider may watch is regulated by each state, and may depend on the age range of the children. Typical is a maximum enrollment of six children (12 if the care provider has a full-time aide). To obtain licensing, most states require an initial visit to the child care site to ensure the safety of the children in the home and a criminal and child abuse record check, in addition to a certificate of completion from an approved infant safety and CPR course. If you have questions, contact your state's child care licensing agency.

Family child care homes vary widely, from the neighborhood mom who takes in a few children to help earn extra money to professionally-run businesses. There are some definite advantages of working with group child care homes:

- The provider is licensed and therefore must follow certain guidelines provided to retain licensing.
- A small, family-like environment.
- Can be less expensive than other forms of child care.
- Social interaction with other children.
- May be more flexible. Some home care providers offer weekend and evening care.

Disadvantages may include:

- Since you're often dealing with only one provider, if he or she becomes ill or takes a vacation, you must work around that person's schedule.

❧

Although child care facilities must meet certain state standards, you should have your own list of preferences and expectations.

❧

CHILD CARE

- Child care may be treated more casually because the provider is in her own home and not directly supervised.
- If the provider is caring for her own children, there is the possibility that her child could be favored.
- The provider may not stay in business for the length of time your child needs care, i.e., may stop providing services if economics or family needs change.

CHILD CARE CENTERS

Child care centers are licensed for the care of more than 12 children. Staffing requirements ensure that children are cared for by qualified teachers. Caregiver to child ratios are 1:4 for infants, and ratios for toddlers range from 1:7 to 1:12, depending on state law. Typical ratios for toddlers are 1:12 and, for age 5 and up, one adult to every 15 children.

Besides following an adult-to-child ratio, child care centers are expected to fulfill educational requirements and provide more than a baby-sitting environment. Many child care centers will give you written reports that include everything from the number of diaper changes to the achievements of special milestones, such as a first step. Child care centers must also follow specific fire, building, and zoning codes.

Some child care centers go beyond minimum requirements to gain accreditation by the National Association for the Education of Young Children (NAEYC). This requires meeting nationally recognized quality standards and includes a site evaluation by a NAEYC staff member.

Some advantages of choosing a child care center may be:
- Convenient location for parents.
- Licensing of the center's caregivers.

STEPS FOR CHOOSING CHILD CARE

- List things you feel are important for you and your child.
- Screen potential caregivers on the phone to see if they meet your basic requirements and make appointments with those you would like to visit.
- During your visits, use a checklist to evaluate programs. Visit more than once and at different times of the day.
- Count the number of children and staff at each of your visits.
- Ask about the provider's experience and education.

- Check references by talking to parents with children in the program and calling the child care licensor of the program.
- Read the caregiver's written policies and procedures carefully.
- Consider substitute plans in case your child is ill or your child's care provider or the child care center is on vacation or closed.

The above information is reprinted with permission from "Choosing Child Care," provided by Child Care Resources in Seattle, Washington.

CHILD CARE

- The provider's educational background may include early childhood education and/or previous child care experience.
- Programs are offered for every age, so your child can stay at the same center through the years.
- Licensing requirements necessitate constant supervision.

Disadvantages may include:

- Larger and less of a "homey" environment for infant care.
- Lack of "sick" care. Most centers have very strict sick care rules and will not accept ill children. (This can be an advantage too!)
- More caregivers—so your child may have less of an opportunity to bond with a provider.
- May cost more than family care.
- Because of the size of large center-based child care, flexibility of policies for individual families may be more difficult.
- Many centers have high staff turnover.

ABOUT LICENSING

While licensing is no guarantee that the child care facility is right for your child, you are assured that the care provider has made the effort to comply with state regulations and is confident of her ability to provide an environment for her charges that meets those guidelines. A child care license limits the number and ages of children in care. A license requires that all child care providers are checked for criminal and child abuse records. Before a license is issued, child care centers and group homes are checked for health and safety hazards.

IN-HOME CHILD CARE

There are several options for those who prefer to have their child care in their own home. The two most well-known options are nannies and au pairs.

To working parents, a nanny is the ultimate in convenience and care. A nanny comes to your home, watches your child, and may perform light housekeeping duties. Most nannies are found through local agencies which screen, interview candidates and ultimately link you with a provider. Annual salaries for a full-time nanny hired through an agency can range from $10,000-$22,000 or more. Most agencies also charge a one-time placement fee.

Before hiring a nanny, you should talk with an accountant or bookkeeper familiar with household employee tax laws. The IRS can also provide Publication 926 and Form 942, which states "that in any year you pay a household employee $1000 or more you must pay federal employment taxes." These taxes consist of Social Security, Medicare, and unemployment taxes. On top of federal taxes, you may also be responsible for state taxes. Some nanny agencies act as the nanny's employer, freeing you from the hassles of filling out multiple forms.

Parents also acknowledge that there is little or no supervision with an employee caring for children in the house. There is a company whose web site allows you to monitor, via home video recorder, your child and care provider. Another option is to use an in-home camera to view the day's happenings. Of course, these only will allow you to view interactions in one area of your house at any time, and may cause suspicions of interference with your care provider.

An au pair is a foreign student who exchanges child care services for living arrangements and/or a small salary for a maximum of one year. The nation's au pair organizations are licensed by the U.S. Information Agency in Washington, D.C. Au pair pay is mandated by the agency, and weekly stipends rose to $139.05 in September 1997. Other costs include full room and board, an education stipend of $500, additional insurance cost if your au pair uses the family car, and other minimal costs associated with au pair care.

Au pairs are able to perform child care and light housekeeping duties related to child care approximately 45 hours per week. They also may drive your automobile, if you provide the insurance, and can help with transporting children.

The advantages of care in your own home may be:

- Convenience—someone will come to, or live in, your home.

- There is less travel and preparation time for parent.
- Your child is in a familiar environment.
- Some in-home providers may do light housework and other duties.
- In-home providers may be experienced and have some type of child education background.
- Providers are thoroughly screened by nanny placement services, and most services offer a guarantee.
- Some caregivers will also provide care for sick children.

Disadvantages may be:
- The cost.
- Lack of regulations and supervision.
- Household space requirements and loss of family privacy with a live-in.
- Reliance upon one individual for child care.
- Your child may not receive the same socialization skills compared to being in a group setting.

&a& RESOURCES &a&

■ CHILD CARE ACTION CAMPAIGN

330 7th Ave., Ste. 17
New York, NY 10001
This group offers "A Child Care Primer for Parents," a guide to assist you in selecting child care. For $5, it includes checklists designed to help you evaluate the quality of programs, child care tax credits, subsidies and employer benefits that help pay the cost of care.

■ CHILD CARE AWARE

800-424-2246
2116 Campus Dr. N.E.
Rochester, MN 55904
Child Care Aware works with the National Association for the Education of Young Children to encourage national standards of accreditation of child care workers. You can request their brochure which helps parents evaluate child care centers, and gives you questions to ask when making a decision about which center is best for your family. Also under the Child Care Aware umbrella is the

National Association of Childcare Resource and Referral Agencies, which makes referrals to child care referral agencies nationwide.

■ THE CHILD CARE REGISTRY

800-CCR-0033 or (510) 248-4100
The Child Care Registry provides national background checks on child care providers. The registry provides a seven-year check of information including verification of the provider's identity, date of birth, social security number, employment and educational history, driving record, and criminal and civil judgments in the jurisdictions where he or she has lived. The normal turnaround time is four to seven business days. The cost of the service is $140 plus $8 for Federal Express delivery or $2 for fax transmission of findings. You may pay by credit card.

■ INA VISION (INTERNATIONAL NANNY ASSOCIATION)

(609) 858-0808
Station House, 900 Haddon Ave.
Collingswood, NJ 08108
Web site: www.nanny.org
A bimonthly newsletter of the International Nanny Association, "InaVision" contains articles such as updates on child care legislation, ways to avoid nanny burnout and tips on making the nanny-employer relationship work. They have a good brochure on common questions parents often ask about in-home child care. A yearly subscription is $35 and includes INA membership. An annual conference includes workshops and exhibits of interest to nannies and families.

■ NANNY NEWS

800-ME-4-NANNY
P.O. Box 277
Hopewell, NJ 08525
E-mail: NannyNews@aol.com
Nanny News isn't just for parents; the national bimonthly publication is helpful for nannies as well. The newsletter is 12 pages (no advertising) packed with information. Each issue covers current topics of interest to families with in-home child care, activities for kids, professional advice for nannies, and more. Subscriptions run $29.95 for one year (six issues); a two-year subscription is $39.95, and the magazine offers a money-back guarantee.

■ NATIONAL ASSOCIATION FOR SICK CHILD DAYCARE CENTERS (NASCDC)

(804) 747-5900
From her organization's national headquarters in Virginia, President Gail Johnson offers this referral network for sick-care facilities across the country. Typically, the centers adjoin a regular child care facility with daily fees from $25 to $55.

AU PAIR AGENCIES

■ AU PAIR CARE

(415) 434-8788
1 Post St., 7th Floor
San Francisco, CA 94104
Au Pair Care was founded in 1989 by AYUSA International, a nonprofit educational organization. The process of matching au pair candidates and families takes about six to eight weeks, from initial application to the au pair arrival. The careful selection process, working through offices all over the world, places

capable, dependable people between 18 and 26 years old with experience caring for children.

Travel costs are included in the program fees, but are based on arrival in New York, and do not include air fare to your city. Au Pair Care determines the domestic portion of airfare which is due 30 days prior to the flight.

A host family application is filled out and returned with a $100 application fee and $125 interview fee. A confidential reference form should be provided directly from the friend or other personal reference used. The program fees of $4,070 cover screening and selection, English language testing, proper family matching, visa forms, travel to New York, health insurance while in the U.S., orientations for au pairs and families, community counselor's services and cultural and social activities for au pairs. A program fee deposit of $1,200 is required upon matching and the balance of the fees are due 30 days prior to arrival. They do have a payment plan if you prefer to spread out the payments.

Telephone calls and free time should be arranged in the beginning and car insurance added if the au pair is to use the family car. Repeat families do not need to submit an application or interview fee.

■ AU PAIR HOMESTAY
800-479-0907
1015 15th St. N.W., Ste. 750
Washington, DC 20005
The Au Pair Homestay program has been operating since 1986 to provide caregivers from around the globe. It is part of World Learning Inc., a nonprofit organization founded in 1932 as "The Experiment in International Living." This organization is the oldest of its kind and invented the homestay concept. A 20-minute video is available to further explain their program. Au Pair Homestay participants, now numbering over 2,000, presently come from over 20 countries.

Families seeking an au pair are considered on a first-come, first-served basis. You must qualify as a host family by completing a family application kit, providing two character references, and a check for $250. Prematched or returning families submit a $175 deposit.

After your application is reviewed, an interview in your home with the community coordinator is set up.

A program fee of $3,950 covers health and accident insurance, orientation, seminars, year-long support, counseling/advising from community coordinators, educational materials, local and special occasion activities and round-trip airfare from Washington, D.C. There will be an additional cost to bring the au pair to your city. Automobile insurance will need to be adjusted if the au pair is expected to use the family car. An au pair works approximately 45 hours per week with two weeks off per year.

■ AU PAIR IN AMERICA
800-928-7247
102 Greenwich Ave.
Greenwich, CT 06830
For more than 10 years, Au Pair in America has been helping families with child care. Most au pairs are from western Europe and the United Kingdom. Au Pair in America has a four-day training program which includes child safety and child development. The screening process includes reference verification,

medical examinations, criminal background checks and personality profiling. The program fee is $4,200. Au Pair in America estimates total costs to run about $10,500 annually for Au Pair care. Their staff will send you a colorful brochure with all the details regarding the program and application forms.

■ AU PAIR PROGRAMME USA
800-574-8889
(801) 255-7722
6955 Union Park Center, Ste. 360
Salt Lake City, UT 84047
Web site: www.childcrest.com
Local counselors in cities throughout Europe, Australia and South Africa screen au pair applicants, accepting for Au Pair Programme USA only those with top references, English skills, and good educational backgrounds. In the U.S. a placement counselor assigned to each host family presents several au pair files for the family to consider. Each file holds the applicant's application, essay, references, family photos, and physician's report. Au pairs have completed 32 hours of child care training and additional child care experience, and are covered by medical insurance for the 12-month period they will be in the U.S.

Au Pair Programme's applicants fix meals, drive children to school and lessons, straighten children's rooms and do their laundry.

Costs to Au Pair Programme USA, including the au pair's weekly stipend, tuition allowance, transportation costs, and program fee of $4,180, average $220 per week when allocated over the program's one-year period.

■ EF AU PAIR
800-333-6056
One Memorial Dr.
Cambridge, MA 02142
EF Au Pair provides English-speaking European and Australian au pairs with legal visas to American families for one year of intercultural child care. The au pairs are thoroughly screened and trained. EF Au Pair's unique matching process ensures you are the only family reviewing a particular au pair's application; therefore it is certain that the au pair is available. Upon arrival in the U.S. and before going to their host family, all EF au pairs participate in an intensive four-day training program. Their program includes eight hours of child safety training and 24 hours of child development instruction. EF Au Pair provides year-long local and worldwide support for your family and au pair. Local child care coordinators have monthly contact with the au pairs and are available for host family support.

The expense is about $220 per week which covers 45 hours of child care (regardless of the number of children), airfare, weekly stipend, and insurance. Au pairs provide their own medical insurance. Host families are required to pay a nonrefundable $250 application fee and up to $500 in tuition for the au pair to fulfill a U.S. government sanctioned educational component.

The au pairs taking care of children under 2 years of age must have six months of infant care experience. Au pairs cannot care solely for infants under three months of age.

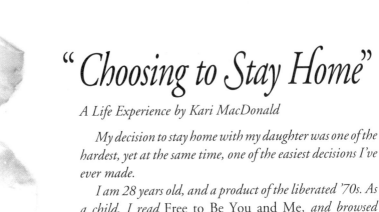

"*Choosing to Stay Home*"

A Life Experience by Kari MacDonald

My decision to stay home with my daughter was one of the hardest, yet at the same time, one of the easiest decisions I've ever made.

I am 28 years old, and a product of the liberated '70s. As a child, I read Free to Be You and Me, *and browsed through copies of my mother's* Ms. *and* New Woman *magazines. I attended the University of California and then started work as a financial analyst. Work was exciting and challenging, and I received regular promotions. I loved my job, loved to solve problems, and loved to chat with co-workers and wear Jones New York suits. My entire identity was as a professional, working woman.*

When I announced to my boss that I was pregnant, he first looked at me in disbelief, then rushed to confirm that I would be returning to work after the birth of the baby. "Of course," I assured him. "We can't afford for me to stay home." Besides, putting my child in child care was just what you did. I accepted that I would have some additional stress in my life, but that I would follow in the footsteps of all the working mothers before me.

However, many things happened to change my mind. The first, of course, was the birth of my daughter, the most precious and perfect child ever created. She was literally a dream come true—more than I had ever hoped for. I spent hours staring at her, marveling at her, and knowing that I never wanted to leave her.

The second was the circumstances of my husband's job. As he completed medical school during our daughter's first year, the intense years of residency loomed ahead. The stories of the 36-hour shifts, the 120-hour work weeks and walking around like a zombie while being paid poverty wages are all true. With one parent gone all the time, didn't my daughter deserve at least one parent's undivided time and attention?

Still, the cost of living being what it is, I began looking for

child care when my daughter was eight months old. Four-to-one caregiver-to-infant ratios appear reasonable on paper, but when I observed them firsthand, I felt they were woefully inadequate. The caregivers I observed ranged from loving but harried women, to inexperienced teenagers, to retired women helping out to fill their time. I have no doubt that most teachers love the children and do the best they can. But "the best they can" was still not good enough for me. I wanted my daughter to have all of someone's time, attention and energy. Most of all, I wanted that someone to be me.

I won't lie and say that staying at home with my daughter is easy. We are living on a strict budget with no room for extras. We have no savings and a ridiculously high Visa bill. We tear fabric softener sheets and paper towels in half to extend their use. We make our own cleaning solutions and I've taken to washing my hair every other day to save shampoo. I shop at the cheapest pack-your-own grocery store and buy all store-brand foods. No snacks, chips, ice cream, frozen food or individually packaged convenience foods are allowed. All of my daughter's clothes and toys are hand-me-downs or are purchased at resale shops. When my husband needs a haircut, it sends us scrambling to make room in the budget somewhere. I haven't bought myself anything in more than two years, and my underwear sorely need replacing.

Despite these lifestyle adjustments, I've never been more at peace with my decision. I realize that the choice is clear: "things," like name-brand foods, toys and Windex, versus time spent with my daughter laughing, playing, and learning during these few crucial developmental years. As long as we can, we will continue to scrimp and save and sacrifice, because she is worth it all, and even more.

I constantly battle with myself and others over this decision to stay home. Most of my co-workers are incredulous. "You're not the type," they say. "You'll be bored stiff." Internally, I wonder if I shouldn't be contributing somehow to society, being an educated, able-bodied adult. I keep reminding myself that raising a kind, moral, educated, and happy child is a great contribution.

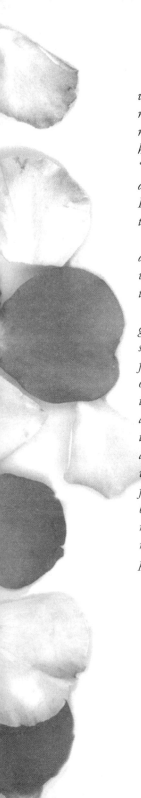

My ten-year high school reunion was this year. I didn't want to go, because I didn't know what I would say about my life. "I used to be a very successful financial analyst. I'm married to a man who is about to be a physician. I stay at home all day and change diapers, do laundry, and recite "The Itsy-Bitsy Spider." I felt like I had to justify what I was doing with my life. What I found was not disdain for what I did, but envy that I had the means to do what they wished they could also do.

Sometimes I feel guilty about staying home with my daughter. I have such a wonderful life with her, taking walks, singing, going to the park. "No one has the right to be this happy!" I say to myself.

Each day, I walk into my daughter's room to wish her a good morning and find her clutching her blanket and sucking her thumb, waiting for me. When she sees me, her face lights up with a huge smile, and she literally wriggles all over with pleasure. We have such fun during the day together, talking, laughing, crawling around, smearing food all over the high chair. She is a content baby, and a delight to be around. Being there to see the look on her face when she accomplishes a new skill is better than any promotion I would have received at work. When I receive compliments from others about how content and secure she seems, it's the best performance review I could ask for, and I know I've made the right decision. Just as I used to throw myself into my work, I've thrown myself into her. She is my job now, my project, and the love of my life. ❧

BABY
PRODUCTS

CHAPTER THREE

SHOPPING SMART FOR YOUR NEW BABY

Even veteran shoppers may be overwhelmed by the tasks of purchasing maternity and baby clothing, a crib, car seat, stroller, diapering equipment, special linens and toiletries, and nursing or bottle feeding accessories. (And that's just the bare minimum!)

Matching the bewildering array of items to purchase are the number of places where such purchases can be made. Expectant parents must choose between shopping at discount stores, department stores, warehouse stores, baby specialty stores, resale shops, or staying at home and buying through catalogs or over the World Wide Web. Here is a little information to help you choose where to shop for those purchases designed to help you welcome a new person into your home.

❧

Matching the bewildering array of items to purchase are the number of places where such purchases can be made.

❧

- **Baby specialty stores.** Often thought of as top-of-the-line, exclusive stores, specialty stores are often the best place to shop for baby furnishings. Staff is usually very knowledgeable about each line and model, and is willing to spend time to discuss which items will suit your needs. Prices are often not that much higher than at discount stores, and the personal service may more than make up for the markup.

- **Department stores.** People often have a favorite department store, which may be a good place to investigate for baby items, even though department stores may have limited baby furnishings departments. Sales can bring prices down to the discount store range. Staff is usually helpful, and returns are often handled with little problem.

- **Discount stores.** You won't find much in the way of helpful staff at discount stores, and often car seats and strollers are displayed up high, where they are difficult to examine. But discount stores do carry familiar brand names and enough variety to make you feel you're making an informed product decision. Pricing is generally low, with occasional sales that bring prices down even more.

- **Warehouse stores.** For low prices, warehouse stores can't be beat. But sales help is nonexistent, and displays are limited. You may find only one or two models available of only a couple of products. However, if you like what you see, buy it! Prices don't get much lower than at huge warehouse stores.

- **Catalog shopping.** A pleasure for those who just can't bear the thought of trudging through store after store searching for just the right thing, catalogs offer a wide variety of merchandise for expectant and new parents. From the upscale full-color catalog to the mimeographed type stapled at the catalog owner's kitchen table, you will find a variety of merchandise advertised in a wide variety of ways. Be sure to check return policies, and make sure that the shipping and handling charges don't overwhelm your purchase price. Otherwise, shopping by catalog—especially for nursing clothes and diapering products—can be a quick way to find marvelous things. (Also, you can't beat getting packages in the mail for a real day-brightener!) You may also want to check the Internet for a wide variety of products prior to shopping. Manufacturers' and retail stores' web sites generally list products, prices, and information.

- **Resale shops.** Some people are hesitant to shop at resale stores. There is a wide range, from the decidedly upscale resale store to jumbled thrift shops. If you plan your shopping trips wisely, you'll find that most resale shops carry top-quality, gently used merchandise that is very affordable. Remember resale shops when you no longer need your baby equipment and clothing—resale shop owners generally offer you about half the selling price either on consignment or will purchase outright.

- **Garage sales.** You can find baby equipment and clothing at rock-bottom prices at local garage sales, but you must check items over carefully—there is no returning a garage sale item. Be especially cautious about baby furnishings offered without manufacturer's directions and product information.

BABY PRODUCTS

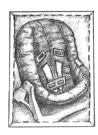

It can be difficult to choose baby products that meet your needs and budget. This section includes information on a variety of baby products, including their features and benefits. It is not meant to take the place of *Consumer Reports* or other scientific baby product reviews but rather to give you a starting point on baby product purchases.

Products included in this chapter are: strollers, car seats, cribs, swings, child carriers, nursing accessories and bottle feeding products, and great gift ideas. We hope this information will prove helpful as you evaluate your upcoming purchases. We do not endorse any one brand or product, nor do we validate the safety of any product. Readers should make their own choices based on personal preference and on the safety of each item. With that in mind...read on!

PURCHASING DECISIONS

How do you find products that best meet your needs and your budget? Start by asking yourself the following questions:

- Are you looking for products that will last through more than one child?
- Do you care about added convenience features, or do you want to purchase products for the lowest possible price?
- How informed are you about baby products on the market?
- Does your partner have an opinion on the baby products you purchase?

BABY PRODUCT TIPS

Once you've answered these questions regarding your purchasing decision, consider the following general tips which can help you decide where to shop and what to look for.

DURABILITY AND CONVENIENCE

If you are looking for products that will last beyond one child, you may want to consider purchasing a higher quality product that offers durability and convenience. Consider a duo stroller, a high-quality mattress or a crib that converts into a toddler's bed, and colors that will work as well for a boy as they do for a girl.

✌

This section includes information on a variety of baby products, including their features and benefits.

✌

PRICING

Although some department stores and discount stores offer low-priced baby products, you will probably not find available staff in these stores to assist and inform you about the individual items. You may be left to make your product decisions and choices alone. For those of you who know little about baby products, this may prove to be a frustrating experience. However, once you know what you are looking for, you may want to shop around for the best price.

PRODUCT INFORMATION

We found baby specialty stores more responsive to parents' needs since they can be a valuable source of information. The staff at most baby specialty stores is well-trained and available to assist you and answer your questions.

Several publications review baby products that will help you become more informed. *Baby Bargains*, written by Allen and Denise Fields, is an excellent source of information on baby products. Another useful resource is *Consumer Reports*. This magazine periodically reviews baby products. They also have a book entitled *Consumer Reports Guide to Baby Products*, which is updated almost every two years. It evaluates the safety, convenience and durability of hundreds of baby products. It also includes buying advice, price guidelines for products and recall information. Also check out manufacturers' web sites for specific product information. Becoming informed before you make a purchase may save you time and money, as well as aggravation.

OPINION

Check with your significant other before shopping. You may be surprised by your partner's opinions and besides, it is fun to shop for baby items together.

SOME GENERAL SUGGESTIONS

In case you don't have time to read the entire baby product chapter, here are some "biased" random opinions regarding products.

- Double check the buckle and harness system on your car seat. Make sure it is easy to get the baby in and out of the car seat without fumbling with buckles.

- Buying a stroller that is lightweight and has the features you want, although it may be more expensive, is well worth the purchase. For families on the go, a stroller is a lifesaver.

- Consider a swing with a bassinet feature. The bassinet can be used when the infant is newborn and placed directly in the crib, alleviating a separate bassinet purchase. Swings with this feature are only about $30 more than the swing-only seat.

- If you don't have a walker, it is probably the one purchase you should skip. The American Academy of Pediatrics recommends that children not use walkers due to the high rate of walker-related injuries.

REFERENCE NUMBERS

CUSTOMER SERVICE AND CONSUMER INFO	
Juvenile Products Manufacturers Association	609-231-8500
Aprica	310-639-6387
Baby Jogger	800-241-1848
Britax	888-4-BRITAX
Century	800-837-4044
Combi	800-992-6624
Cosco	800-544-1108
Emmaljunga	800-848-3864
Evenflo	800-837-9201
First Years	800-533-6708
Fisher Price	800-828-4000
Gerber	800-443-7237
Gerry	800-525-2472
Graco	800-345-4109
Infantino	800-365-8182
Johnson & Johnson	800-526-3967
Kelty	800-423-2320
Kolcraft	800-453-7673
Little Miss Liberty	800-RND-CRIB
Little Tikes	800-321-0183
Medela	800-435-8316
Nojo	800-854-8760
Peg Perego	219-482-8191
Playskool	800-PLAYSKL

CAR SEAT SAFETY/PRODUCT RECALL NUMBERS	
D.O.T. Auto Safety Hotline	888-327-4236
National Highway and Traffic Safety Administration	202-366-2768
Child Safety Seat Resource	800-772-1315
Consumer Product Safety Commission	800-638-2772

❧

Here are some quick references to product information and car seat recall numbers.

❧

CAR SEATS

By Cathy Morris
Placer County (CA) Buckle Up Baby Car Seat Project Coordinator

Vehicle crashes are the number one preventable cause of unintentional death and injury to children. When used correctly, child car seats hold a child securely, spread the crash forces over a wide area of the child's body, and keep the child from striking the interior of the vehicle in a sudden stop or crash.

A common question asked by new parents is: "What is the best car seat?" Initially, the answer seems simple. The best car seat is the seat that fits your child, fits in your

WHAT TO LOOK FOR

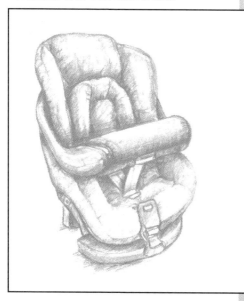

WHAT PARENTS LIKE
✓ STURDY AND SAFE
✓ EASY TO GET BABY IN AND OUT
✓ ALSO A CARRIER

WHAT PARENTS DON'T LIKE
✓ TOO HEAVY, BIG AND BULKY
✓ HARD TO BUCKLE AND UNBUCKLE
✓ HARD TO PUT IN THE CAR
✓ UNCOMFORTABLE FOR A NEWBORN

vehicle, and one that you will use correctly and consistently. However, once some parents start shopping for the "best" car seat, they can find it to be a frustrating experience. This is because vehicles are designed for the safety and comfort of "non-car seat" passengers. Be aware that safety belts are designed differently—types of belts, locking mechanisms and insertion points. Also remember that vehicles seats are designed differently as well, with fabric, plushness, pull-down armrests, and slope of the seat all factors that can affect the fit of a car seat.

When parents begin trying different child car seats they may find that a particular brand does not fit their particular vehicle, while another brand may fit perfectly. The following tips may help you when choosing your child's car seat:

First, decide the type of child car seat you need:

- **Infant-only,** from newborns to 18-22 pounds or 26 inches in length. If your baby's head reaches the top of the seat before the weight limit, you must move your baby to a rear-facing convertible seat. Most infant seats are rear-facing only and are designed to recline to around a 45-degree angle. Sometimes a rolled towel must be added beneath the base of the seat to maintain the angle. Some infant seats have a removable base. The base is belted in the car, and seat can be lifted in and out of the base. These seats can also be installed without the base.

- **Convertible car seats** fit babies from about seven pounds to 40 pounds. The seats convert from the infant rear-facing position to the toddler forward-facing position. Economically, this seat is the best choice. However, if this type of seat is used for a newborn, it's important that a five-point harness be chosen. This type of harness pro-

vides a snugger fit for the small newborn. When trying this seat in your vehicle, remember to try it in the rear-facing position as well as the forward-facing position.

- **Forward-facing car seats** are for children from 1 year old and at least 20 pounds and up to 40 pounds. These seats are designed to face forward. You cannot place this seat in the rear-facing position.

- **Booster seats** are for children who have outgrown their convertible car seats. You'll need to check manufacturer's information for specific weight and age requirements. Some boosters use the car's own three-point buckling system, while others use a shield or harness system integrated into the booster seat.

FITTING YOUR CAR SEAT

Before making a purchase, try adjusting the shoulder harnesses. Is it something you'll take the time to adjust every time? Consider whether the harness adjustment is easy for you to reach after the car seat is in the vehicle. A snug shoulder

---

TETHERS: HOLDING CAR SEATS FIRM

Some car seats have a tendency to move about, and not be completely secure in a car. Tethers are an excellent way to prevent any movement. Car seat manufacturers may recommend a tether, depending on the type of seat belt, but you may choose to install one to keep your baby more secure. The tether strap attaches to the car seat and is bolted into a predrilled anchor point, usually covered with a plastic rivet, in your car's back deck or van's floor. Cars built before 1987 will need a hole drilled; do not do this yourself. Take your vehicle to your dealership or certified auto mechanic.

Several manufacturers, including Evenflo, Gerry, Cosco and Century, will supply a tether on request; Britax and Fisher-Price car seats include tethers. Britax's seat even has a tether for a rear-facing infant. Visit your local baby specialty store to see car seat tethers and discuss this important car seat option.

harness is crucial—it's what holds your baby inside the car seat. How do you know if the shoulder harness is tight enough? There should only be room for one of your fingers between the shoulder harness and your child's collar bone.

Try the seat in your vehicle. The safest place is in the back seat. Put your body weight into the car seat while you fasten the safety belt. Pull all slack out of the safety belt to make it tight. Next, try to move the seat—there should be no more than an inch of movement side to side or an inch forward. If rear-facing, check the angle of the seat. You may need to add towels under the front of the seat to maintain an angle of around 45 degrees. If the seat is forward facing, make sure the seat is fully upright. You may need to move the car seat to a different location to achieve a tight fit. You may have to add a locking clip to the safety belt to lock the safety belt in place. The locking clip will be located somewhere on your new car seat. The car seat instructions tell you when you need to use the clip, and explain how to use it.

AIR BAGS

Air bags are effective in saving lives. However, babies and young children can be at risk if seated next to one. Air bags inflate quickly and forcibly, and a child's small body may not tolerate the force. Therefore, when there is a passenger side air bag in the vehicle, babies and children (12 and under) should be restrained in the back seat. Never place a rear-facing car seat in the front seat if the vehicle is equipped with a passenger side air bag.

If your car seat has been in a crash, it must be replaced. A crash can cause unseen structural damage to the car seat and it may not restrain your child in a

subsequent crash. Do not use a second-hand car seat unless you know the history of the seat. If you've used your car seat consistently for five years, safety experts recommend replacing the seat.

CORRECT USE OF CAR SEATS

Many parents use car seats incorrectly. It's critical to read the car seat instructions and the vehicle instructions. The car seat's instructions will tell you how to properly secure your baby in the seat and will show you the correct path for the safety belt. The vehicle instructions will tell you how to use a car seat in your vehicle and if you need any additional attachments to make your car seat secure.

If your child is taken to child care by one parent and picked up by another, consider buying two car seats. This will help cut down on installation errors.

Remember to fill out the registration card that came with your car seat. Mail it to the manufacturer. You will be contacted if the seat goes on recall. If you think your car seat has a defect, call the manufacturer, and report it to the Auto Safety Hotline at 800-424-9393.

Laws vary from state to state regarding car seat usage. But common sense and the desire to keep children safe dictates that children should use a child restraint until they reach 4 years old or 40 pounds and, depending on the child's size, booster seats or seat belts after that. Even if your state does not require car seat usage, buckle your children!

FOR OLDER CHILDREN

For children old enough and heavy enough to ride without a car seat or booster, you must teach proper use of safety belts. The lap belt should fit low

CAR SEATS

over a child's upper thighs. Make sure the child sits straight against the vehicle seat back. Keep the belt snug. If the lap belt rides up onto the tummy, it could cause serious injuries in a crash. The shoulder belt should stay on the shoulder with less than an inch of slack across the chest. If the shoulder belt rubs against the neck, but not across it, it may be uncomfortable for the child but is not harmful. You can fold a soft cloth over the belt to reduce discomfort. If the shoulder belt goes across the child's neck or face, raise the child with a belt positioning booster. Never put the belt under the child's arm or below the back. Either of these kinds of misuse could cause serious injury in a crash.

POPULAR BRANDS

BRITAX

Britax is new to the U.S., but has been in business in Europe and Australia for more than 30 years. The company has gained international recognition for their excellent products and commitment to safety. Britax car seats are sold exclusively in children's specialty stores. All stores that carry Britax seats must attend training sessions on the installation of their car seats, and be fully prepared to educate customers in the installation and proper use of the seat.

Britax car seats are designed with cars in mind, taking into account that many back seats now have shoulder/lap belts rather than lap belts, and bucket rather than bench seats. They also offer tethers and tether kits for most models.

The five-point restraint Freeway seat is designed for children 20-40 pounds. It has a patented lock-off clamp that

INFANT CAR SEAT

locks the shoulder belt in place, eliminating the need for a locking clip. The forward-facing reclining seat has deep side panels that not only protect against impact, but catch the child's head if he falls asleep.

Britax also carries a rear-facing infant seat, the Rock-a-Tot, and the Cruiser, a transitional seat for children 30-60 pounds. All Britax seats have beautiful cloth covers and are well-padded. The seats are more expensive than most, ranging from $80-$200, but the additional safety features and education are well worth it.

CENTURY

Century offers a wide variety of car seats from infant to toddler sizes. The infant car seats are the 565, 590 and 4525 models. The 565 is a basic model without a canopy, but it does have a handle. The 590 model has a canopy and detachable base. The 4525 models are called "SmartFIT." They have a stay-in car base that is sculpted to fit today's cars, and a curved handle for easier carrying. They also have a level indicator near the handle to determine if the seat is properly installed. If the ball is under the arrow, the seat is correctly installed; if not, the seat is tipped too far forward or backward. Century's infant car seats run from $50 to $80.

Century's convertible car seats begin with the 1000 series. Their least expensive model costs about $60 and has a five-point harness with no shield. The top of the line model runs about $160, and offers a wide variety of luxury features including a pillow, shield and extra padding. Century also offers a car seat named Smart Move, designed to let infants ride in a more reclined position, at a 47-degree angle rather than current infant car seats' more upright angle. The car seat is designed to meet the needs of both infants and toddlers. It costs around $140.

Century also offers an infant car seat/stroller combination named the 4-in-1 System. It can be used as a car seat, an infant/car seat stroller, a carrier and a toddler's stroller. This product runs around $150. We found it at baby specialty stores.

COSCO

Cosco is the only car seat company to offer all five types of child restraints: car bed/car seat, infant-only, convertible, auto booster, and travel vest. The Dream Ride is the only car bed available, allowing premature or other special-needs babies to lie flat. If parents can't find this model in their area, call Cosco at 800-544-1108. It can convert later to a car seat, and costs around $55. They also offer three infant car seats: TLC, Arriva

and Turnabout, which has a 360-degree rotating handle grip for ease of carrying. Their convertible car seats—Touriva, Regal Ride and Olympian—feature five-point harnesses, T-shields or overhead shield designs, and have comfortable pads. Some models add an infant insert or removable pillow. Prices range from $30-$75 for infant seats and $40-$100 for convertibles.

One of Cosco's newest products in the Travel Vest, designed for use by children from 25-40 pounds. Just four pounds, the vest can be used with either a lap or shoulder belt. The child wears the five-point harness while seated directly on the car's seat. It is perfect for those times when you don't want to lug your car seat around—for traveling, carpooling and to use at Grandma's. This vest costs $30 to $35, and is available at Toys R Us and major department and discount stores.

FISHER-PRICE

Fisher-Price is back in the car seat market, with a simple line featuring both infant and convertible models. Their infant seat has a five-point harness and built-in locking clip. Its uniquely engineered sliding track system allows you to adjust the car seat's belts with the touch of a button, and costs approximately $70.

Fisher-Price's "Safe Embrace" convertible car seat retails for around $140, and includes a built-in tether strap to secure the seat into your car. Its five-point harness has two buckles for greater adjustability. The car seat's unique color-coding system shows parents where the car seat and auto restraint straps should be placed for both rear- and forward-

---

POINTS TO CONSIDER

- Try out your infant car seat's handle. Many of the handles used to carry the car seat are extremely difficult to move from front-to-back or vice-versa.
- The advantage of car seats with a detachable base is that the seat is removable from the car without undoing the seat belt each time.
- Consider purchasing a car seat with a built-in locking clip and/or tether system. These devices provide the most secure fit in your car.
- If you can't afford a car seat, you may want to check with your hospital or community agency to see if any programs are available. Midas Muffler and Easter Seals also have special low-cost car seat programs.

---

facing positions. These seats are available at major retailers.

EVENFLO

Evenflo is a large manufacturer of a variety of juvenile products. In their car seat selection alone, they offer more than 15 styles. Their infant car seat offers cloth padding, a handle and canopy. The seat can also be used as a baby carrier, and in some cases a rocker. The seats have a base that is permanently installed in the car, enabling you to snap the car seat in and out without adjusting the belts. They are also designed to be used without the base, but *Consumer Reports* recommends using the base for additional safety. The Joy Ride car seat can be installed directly into the car, using the lap belt, or can be used with the Travel Tandem Base. Prices begin at $50 for the basic Joy Ride, a little higher for the Travel Tandem. The On My Way car seat comes with the base and an ergonomic curved handle, making it easy to carry the baby. The seats cost about 10% more than the Joy Ride. Both the Joy Ride and On My Way also have the

option of the Travel System, which includes a stroller. The car seat snaps into the stroller, which has a large storage basket, and can be used as a toddler stroller when the baby gets older. The Travel Systems cost about $150.

Evenflo makes three styles of convertible car seats: the five-point harness, the T-shield and the overhead shield. The five-point harness offers the advantage of having a buckle that attaches to the harness rather than the base of the car seat, making it easily accessible. The five-point harness car seats run from $60 to $120, depending on the features you choose. In reviewing Evenflo's car seats, we found only one T-shield model which buckles at the base of the car seat, costing about $60. Evenflo sells a large selection of car seats with overhead shields. A large plastic shield is pulled down in front of your child's body. You buckle the child in through the base of the car seat. The overhead shield model costs between $80 and $120. Evenflo's convertible car seats cost more for additional padding, additional places to adjust the harness, and headrests.

CRIBS

Expectant parents generally decide on their child's crib based on its looks. There are, however, safety features to be considered. Most were mandated by the CPSC in 1973. Major manufacturers also follow voluntary standards as developed by the Juvenile Products Manufacturers Association (JPMA). Products that meet these standards usually carry a JPMA certification sticker, but a crib without a sticker doesn't necessarily mean that it does not meet the safety standards. What all this

WHAT TO LOOK FOR

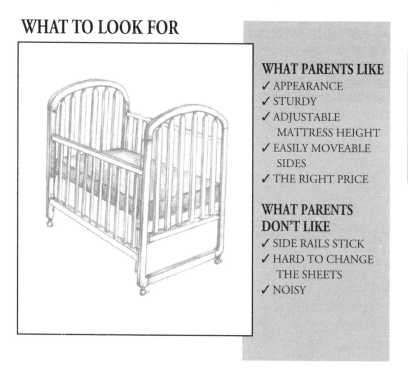

WHAT PARENTS LIKE
✓ APPEARANCE
✓ STURDY
✓ ADJUSTABLE
    MATTRESS HEIGHT
✓ EASILY MOVEABLE
    SIDES
✓ THE RIGHT PRICE

WHAT PARENTS DON'T LIKE
✓ SIDE RAILS STICK
✓ HARD TO CHANGE
    THE SHEETS
✓ NOISY

CRIBS

means, basically, is that if you purchase a new crib, you can safely base your choice on convenience, price and looks. The rest has been taken care of for you. The federal government came up with the following requirements that are still in effect today:

- Crib slats must be no further apart than 2-3/8".
- A lowered dropside must be 9" above the mattress support at its highest setting. The raised dropside must be at least 26" above the support at its lowest position.
- A dropside must take at least two separate actions to activate. If it is too easy to drop, an older baby could activate it.
- The mattress must fit snugly. You should be able to fit no more than two fingers between the crib interior side and the mattress.

Voluntary standards cover aspects such as corner posts and mattress supports. Corner posts should be either practically flush with the top of the end panels or very tall, such as on a four poster bed. If they are not completely flush, they should be no more than 1/16" above it. Mattress supports should be firmly secured to the brackets at the end panels. Also, the end panels should extend lower than the mattress support at its lowest position. This prevents accidents caused by a child becoming trapped between the end panel and the support.

There are a few features of convenience that you may consider when choosing a crib. Wheels make a crib easier to move. Round, ball casters move better, especially on carpet, than narrow, disk-shaped wheels. The dropside release mechanisms vary from model to model, and some are easier to work than others. Try them out at the store when shopping. Keep in mind that you may be holding an infant when putting the side down. A mechanism that can be worked with one hand is preferable.

Cribs are available with either one or two dropsides. A one dropside model is less expensive; if your crib is going to sit against a wall, it may be a better choice. The extra money isn't worth it if you aren't going to use both sides.

Ease of assembly is also a consideration. Some cribs require only a screwdriver to put together while others are more complicated. Some stores offer the option of having the crib assembled at your home when it is delivered. There is an extra fee for this service, but it may be worth it.

To help you choose a crib, you can write to the CSPC for their free brochures called "Tips for your Baby's Safety" and "Nursery Equipment Buyer's Guide." Their address is U.S. Consumer Product Safety Commission, Nursery Equipment Buyer's Guide, Washington, DC 20207. Specify which brochures you want and send along a self-addressed stamped business-size envelope.

MATTRESSES

Crib mattresses need to be purchased separately, and there are a few things to look for. Mattresses are either foam or inner-spring. It is just a matter of preference which you choose. Inner-spring models may keep their shape better, although a high-density foam can be just as good. There are many variations of inner-spring models, which contain anywhere from 60 to 360 coils. A large number of coils doesn't guarantee firmness. You will want to purchase as firm a mattress as you can afford, and the only way to measure firmness is by giving it a "squeeze" test.

Squeeze the mattress in the center and around the edges to test firmness. Vent holes in the sides are also good to have. They help keep the mattress fresher and reduce pressure on the seams. New mattresses on the market are firmer on one side than the other. The softer side is for infants up to 20 pounds. The other side is firmer and more durable for older infants and toddlers. Whichever mattress you choose, it should fit snugly in your crib.

CRIB SAFETY

Even with the current safety regulations, *Consumer Reports* magazine reports that more infants die each year in accidents involving cribs than any other child product. General consensus is that most of these involve older model cribs that were manufactured before 1978. If you are purchasing a used crib or using a family hand-me-down, you'll need a tape measure to check to see if it meets the CPSC requirements. Also check to see that there are not cutouts or decorative items attached to the head or footboards. These can pose a choking or strangulation hazard. All bolts and screws should be present and fit tightly. Another thing to check for, especially on cribs manufactured before 1970, is that they may be coated with paint that contains lead. If the used crib you are considering does not meet the current safety requirements, don't use it. Special note: If your infant is in child care and is using a crib there, check the crib to see if it meets the safety standards.

There are a few things to remember so that you use your crib safely. First, position it away from windows, heating elements, lamps, wall decorations, cords, and climbable furniture. When your baby is alone in the crib, keep the dropside up and locked. Hanging toys and mobiles should be out of the baby's reach, and as soon as the child can pull herself up on hands and knees, remove any toy that goes across the top of the crib. Don't leave pillows, stuffed animals or large toys in the crib. A tiny infant could smother in them, and an older child can use them as steps to climb out. Also, as soon as your child can stand in the crib, you should remove the bumper pads. They can also be used as steps to climb out. A rule of thumb is that when your child either reaches a height of 26" or can climb out of the crib, it's time to make the move to a regular bed.

When considering bedding, be aware of a warning issued by the CPSC in 1994 which strongly discourages soft bedding because they found it could cause asphyxiation in small infants. The warning is based on research done at Washington University in St. Louis. They have found that soft bedding may be responsible for up to 25% of infant deaths from SIDS. The infant can become wrapped in the bedding, which leads to re-breathing of exhaled air that can eventually lead to death from carbon monoxide poisoning. To avoid this the CPSC recommends:

- Putting the baby to sleep on his or her back on a flat, firm mattress without any plush, fuzzy bedding.
- Don't use soft, fluffy products such as pillows, sheepskins or toys under the infant as he or she sleeps.

To check on a particular model for recall information, call the CPSC at 800-638-2772. Many manufacturers also have consumer information hotlines, which are listed in the reference numbers section in this chapter.

CRIBS

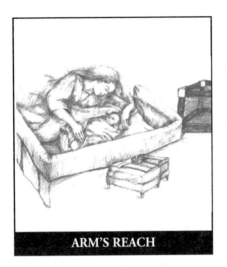

ARM'S REACH

SPECIAL CRIBS

ARM'S REACH CO-SLEEPING SYSTEM

Invented by a mom and endorsed by Dr. William Sears, the Arm's Reach patented system links its special bassinet right to your bed mattress. Arm's Reach is a dream come true for new parents who want to sleep close to their infants but may be afraid of rolling over on them. It is also perfect for nursing moms or those recovering from C-sections. Available for under $200, the system folds into a travel bag, and can be converted to a changing table or play yard. Current information can be found on their web site, www.armsreach.com. The Arm's Reach system is available through specialty stores and catalogs.

THE BUMPA BED

The Bumpa Bed is a crib mattress with built-in bumpers. It is manufactured by the same company that makes the Baby Jogger. It's formed from a solid piece of breathable foam and fits right

into the crib. Having built-in bumpers eliminates the dangers of tie-on strings and sagging bumpers. It also comes with custom made, quilted cotton sheets that velcro right onto the mattress. This saves the parents the hassle of lifting the mattress in and out of the crib and retying bumpers when changing sheets. After the child has outgrown the crib, the Bumpa Bed can be placed on a toddler frame or on the floor. The bumper sides prevent rolling out of bed. The bed also had a foam insert that makes it usable as a guest bed or a juvenile couch. The bed is very light, and has a carrying case which makes it ideal for travel. Retailing at around $140, the Bumpa Bed is available from the factory, 800-241-1848, and at some baby specialty stores.

THE DURA-CRIB™

An alternative to the rectangular crib is finally here! Little Miss Liberty Round Crib Company, created by actress Jean Kasem (wife of LA disc jockey Casey Kasem) and named after their daughter Liberty, offers Dura-Crib, a very attractive round crib. While researching the history of cribs, Jean learned that the first cribs were round or oval-shaped.

With safety as its primary feature, Dura-Crib is made of stress-resistant polyplastic components that will not flake, yellow, peel or blister. There are no small, breakable parts or corners, and the crib uses less floor space than traditional models. The round crib also offers easy, two-sided access and increased visibility for baby. The canopy model, with its beautiful coordinating bedding, is the ultimate crib for the parent who simply must have the best of everything for baby. Each crib comes with a custom

THE DURA-CRIB

round mattress. Suggested retail prices begin at $300 with prices exceeding $1000 when you include custom bedding on a higher-end model.

NATURE'S CRADLE

After more than five years of extensive research, development and testing in the hospitals, Infant Advantage brings Nature's Cradle into the home. This patented FDA-approved sleeping environment is designed to ease baby's transition into the world by simulating the sounds and motions experienced in utero. Nature's Cradle is a complete crib mattress, sheet and "sleeping environment" kit. It actually moves and produces sounds that change during the first 16 weeks of using the product. Each week the movement and sounds lessen until about four months when the child sleeps on the mattress without the simulation technology.

According to its manufacturer, Nature's Cradle infants sleep longer at night, cry less, and sleep through the night sooner than babies who sleep in a traditional crib or bassinet. Parents with premature or colicky babies may want to contact the company for their research and the benefits this cradle may specifically offer your family. This is a truly remarkable product with solid information backing it. Suggested retail price is about $359. Contact Infant Advantage at 800-272-3538 for a retailer near you.

CONVERTIBLE CRIBS

Both Child Craft and Gerry have introduced cribs which convert into youth beds. Child Craft's new "Crib 'N' Double Bed, retailing at about $349, goes from crib to day bed to double bed. It may be the only bed you need to purchase for your child. It also has coordinating furniture pieces to complete your child's nursery. Gerry's "Room to Grow" is similar as its crib converts to a twin bed. It also has a changing table which becomes a bench/toy chest. Both manufacturers offer their products in gorgeous wood with a classic look.

A smaller furniture manufacturer named Pflop House Pfurniture offers a unique crib which sits on the floor and converts to a toddler bed and, with a full-sized mattress, becomes a platform bed. Quality and safety come first with this company. As a newcomer to the baby market, you may need to contact Pflop House directly at (303) 964-9608 to find their crib and other products, including a two-drawer chest/changing table/travel cradle and a rocking chair with a "sidecar" for baby to rock gently along with you.

PORTABLE CRIBS

Portable cribs are very popular items with parents. The new portable cribs are also playpens, but are easier to set up, and they fold up into a small bundle. Portable cribs are great for the babysitter, grandparents and for travel.

POINTS TO CONSIDER

- There are no separate Consumer Product Safety Commission (CPSC) standards for portable cribs. Most of the new models, however, meet voluntary safety standards set by the manufacturer.
- The most important thing to consider when shopping is that a portable crib should be portable! They should set up quickly (within a few minutes) and fold up into a convenient carrying size. The best ones come with a travel/carry bag.
- They are rectangular like a crib, instead of square.

PORTABLE CRIB

- They can be used either as a temporary bed or play area for babies up to 30 pounds or under 34 inches in height. When used as a playpen, the play area is slightly smaller than in a conventional playpen.
- Portable cribs should not be used in place of a regular crib for everyday use.

POPULAR BRANDS

Most portable cribs are made with a plastic or metal frame with woven fabric and mesh sides, and include a mattress and fitted sheet. Basic models have two mesh sides and two fabric sides, while more deluxe models may have four mesh sides and/or roll-down flaps that can be secured when the child sleeps. Some also have sun shades for outside use and attached bags for toys. One feature you might consider is a portable crib with a bassinet that fits in the top of the crib. It's a nice way to get three products in one, and the bassinet can also be used as a changing area.

COSCO

Cosco's three Zip 'N Go travel play yards set up in less than a minute. The deluxe models have lockable wheels, canopies, side bags to hold toys and accessories, and side shades. Manufacturers' suggested retail prices range from $50-$80.

EVENFLO

The Evenflo Happy Cabana is easy to put together and affordable. It has a removable cover for indoor or outdoor use, lockable wheels on one side, which makes moving the crib easier, a toy bag, and a mattress with a stylish fitted sheet.

The mesh sides have pull-down flaps and the top rail is padded. They also have the Happy Cabana Bassinet with all of the above features, plus a removable bassinet. The Happy Camper line includes the basic Happy Camper without the toy bag, bassinet, wheels, or flaps and the Happy Camper Bassinet which has all of the deluxe features except for the sunshade. Evenflo notes that all of their cribs set up in less than a minute.

FISHER PRICE

Fisher Price's Travel Tender with Soothing Bassinet has some interesting features. It's a lightweight, compact portable crib with four mesh sides, and wheels on one side for easier moving. It also has a bassinet that vibrates to simulate the motion of a car, to help soothe a fussy baby. The bassinet can be switched on and off, and uses a D battery. Fisher Price portable cribs now come in three colors, and cost about $120.

GRACO

Graco's Pack'n'Play portable cribs are popular and easy to use. For around $60, Graco's basic Pack'n'Play has four mesh sides, is lightweight, and very easy to assemble. Other models have the options of wheels on one side, sunshades, bassinets, bug netting and cargo bags with individual pockets. They also make one extra-large model that is 36 inches square, instead of the standard rectangular style. The most deluxe model is about $160. All Graco portable cribs have padded mattresses with fitted sheets and come in a wide variety of colors.

GERRY

Gerry portable cribs are not like other brands, in that they are wooden like a real crib. Their wheeled Fold-Away Crib folds to fit through doorways, but in general the crib is not light or compact. It has a fold-down side for putting in and taking out the baby, and a lightweight foam mattress. This crib is a good option for a grandparent's house, or other place the baby visits frequently. Because the other styles of portable cribs are so popular, it can be difficult to find sheets to fit the Gerry crib. It does have the advantage of having the "feel" of a real crib, with the option of attaching bumpers or mobiles, which might make the baby feel more at home while sleeping at the sitter's or Grandma's house, while still portable enough to wheel away into the closet when not in use.

PORTABLE CRIBS

MORE PRODUCT INFORMATION . . .

Want a comprehensive look at all juvenile products on the market today? The national best-seller *Baby Bargains* takes you through the maze of your baby product purchases, including recommendations by the authors, Denise and Alan Fields, who are new parents themselves.

Another excellent resource is the *Consumer Products Guide to Baby Products*, which includes reviews and product testing results of the most popular baby purchases. Both books are available at bookstores nationwide.

SWINGS

An infant swing is a product that isn't absolutely necessary to have, but many parents swear by them. It can be used to stimulate a baby's senses, rock a tired baby to sleep or soothe a colicky baby when nothing else can. Early swings were crank operated with vinyl seats. Most have been changed over the years to make them more convenient, accessible and comfortable for the infant. Most models are battery operated, with seats that can be removed from the swing to be used as a separate baby seat. The trays now swing away to make it much easier to take the infant in and out.

WHAT TO LOOK FOR

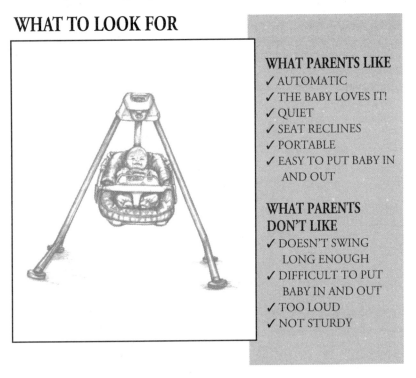

WHAT PARENTS LIKE
✓ AUTOMATIC
✓ THE BABY LOVES IT!
✓ QUIET
✓ SEAT RECLINES
✓ PORTABLE
✓ EASY TO PUT BABY IN
  AND OUT

WHAT PARENTS DON'T LIKE
✓ DOESN'T SWING
  LONG ENOUGH
✓ DIFFICULT TO PUT
  BABY IN AND OUT
✓ TOO LOUD
✓ NOT STURDY

One thing to keep in mind is that not all infants like swings. Before purchasing one, it might be wise to borrow one to see how your baby reacts to the swing.

POINTS TO CONSIDER
- If space is limited, look for a swing with detachable legs for easier storage.
- Parents mentioned that they liked swings that detach for use as a carrier.
- Some swings are vinyl; others have removable, washable covers. Parents again commented that they preferred the cloth removable covers over vinyl. They are easier to clean, and parents felt their babies looked more comfortable.

POPULAR BRANDS

CENTURY

Century swings are only available as battery operated. The motor runs on two D batteries for up to 100 hours. All their patterns coordinate with other Century products such as their strollers and car seats. For the fashion-concerned parent, this is an advantage. Each Century swing model also comes with a machine-washable pad and detachable links and toys, which give your baby something to look at and to play with. All models offer at least a two-position posture seat that reclines for your baby's naps. Their most expensive model offers a four-position angle and rocking base. These swings range from $75 to $100.

COSCO

All Cosco swings are wind-up models, with whisper-quiet winding that gives 30 minutes of swing time. Their Quiet Time Elite, for babies up to 25 pounds, has a push-button T-bar/tray that rotates out of the way to make it easy to get baby in and out of the swing. The Dream Ride Plus is multipurpose: a car bed/car seat, swing and cradle swing all in one for babies up to 20 pounds.

FISHER PRICE

Fisher Price recently began offering its 3-in-1 Cradle Swing. This swing has the option of swinging side to side like a cradle, or forward and back like a traditional swing. The frame isn't open-top, like Graco's, but it is designed to be very accessible and give the baby an unobstructed view. The seat reclines in two positions, has a soft cloth cover, and removes from the base so it can be used as a carrier, and a rocker if placed on the floor. The 3-in-1 Cradle Swing also has a flip-top tray with detachable activity bar. This swing folds compactly for storage as well. We saw the swing offered for about $100.

GERRY

Gerry offers an open-top glider as its alternative to the traditional swing. The glider is smaller than traditional swings and makes less noise as it glides. It has a padded, two-position seat with a tray that lifts and pivots for loading and unloading. Gerry claims the glider will run for 100 hours on its four batteries.

GRACO

Depending upon the model, all of the swings recline to two or more positions. Nearly all models feature a flip-open tray that makes it easy to get the baby in and out, and removable cloth seat covers. Graco's low-end swings have a closed top and crank winding mechanisms that have been recently improved to be more quiet, with a run-time indicator. Their battery-operated swings have an open top, which makes it much easier to get the child in and out, especially when he's asleep. Parents have the choice of two or three speeds, toy bars for the tray, or music with some models. One of the most practical Graco swings is their Three-in-One Swing. This style features a removable cradle—a lifesaver during the early weeks—and a swing that can also be used as a baby carrier. If parents choose this model, they can use the cradle as a bassinet and eliminate the need for one additional purchase. The cradle also fits easily into a crib. Graco swings generally run $60-$100.

STROLLERS

A stroller will probably be one of your most useful baby products. It is also one of your most important, as you will use a stroller for a longer period of time than almost any other baby product (depending on the brand). There are a variety of brands and styles of strollers on the market. You'll find everything from umbrella strollers to old-fashioned buggies to double strollers. This is one of the products that you may consider buying what you really want, if it is in your budget. Sometimes, for a little extra money, you receive more features and a stroller that will last (and that you want to last) for more than one child.

WHAT TO LOOK FOR

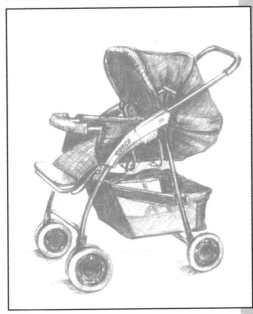

WHAT PARENTS LIKE
✓ FOLDS EASILY
✓ MANEUVERS EASILY
✓ RECLINES, SO INFANT MAY LIE DOWN
✓ HANDLE IS REVERSIBLE
✓ DURABLE

WHAT PARENTS DON'T LIKE
✓ HARD TO MANEUVER
✓ TOO LARGE AND HEAVY
✓ THE WHEELS STICK
✓ TOO BULKY
✓ DIFFICULT TO CLEAN

POINTS TO CONSIDER
- Check out the storage availability. The larger the basket, the better.
- Strollers with removable, washable pads are a real plus.
- Up-and-down adjustable handles come in handy, especially if one parent is much taller than the other.
- Since many parents want to take their newborns out for a stroll, finding a stroller that completely reclines makes this possible. Remember, babies don't sit up until about five months old.

- Good quality wheels can make all the difference in a stroller. Large, sturdy wheels can make for a more enjoyable ride for you and baby.
- Practice opening and folding strollers before you buy. Some are difficult or awkward to use.
- Umbrella strollers are very affordable and make an excellent investment, as you can use them as your child grows. They are also very convenient to use when traveling.

POPULAR BRANDS

BABYJOGGER

Light and easy to push up hills and on rugged terrain, jogging strollers offer one of the smoothest, lightest rides available. They are suitable for walking, running, hiking, or even on sandy beaches. The tripod base makes them very easy to steer. These strollers are not always widely available; call BabyJogger at 800-241-1848 to find the nearest retailer.

Babyjogger is a well-known maker of jogging strollers. Their strollers have light aluminum frames that fold easily. The tires are large and have thorn-resistant inner tubes for use on all surfaces. The brakes are hand-operated caliper brakes, similar to bicycles. Babyjogger also offers many stroller accessories including sunshades, baskets, and a trailer conversion kit so that it can become a bike trailer. There are even models for twins and triplets! Babyjoggers are available in many colors and start at about $250 for a single and $350 for a double.

CENTURY

Century offers several stroller styles, but the one they are best known for is the 4-in-1 System. Century was the first to develop this system which includes a car seat, infant carrier and stroller. The car seat snaps into the stroller base or the base that remains in the car. When in the stroller, the baby faces the parent and rides high up for easier viewing. These strollers fold easily, and recline in two positions. The type of handle and wheels vary from model to model. The 4-in-1 System is about $150.

Century also offers compact-folding lightweight umbrella strollers with large baskets, and the Adventure stroller, with oversize knobby wheels, suspension, and an large canopy.

COMBI

Combi makes one of the lightest, most durable strollers available. Their lightest stroller weighs just seven pounds, and their heaviest is only 18 pounds. By contrast, the typical Graco stroller is about 17 pounds. Combi strollers are well built and very portable. Most have a foot release, fold very compactly, and self-stand when folded up. All Combi

JOGGING STROLLER

strollers have aluminum frames, shock absorbers, and ventilated seats. Most models' seats recline to some degree. They also all have a large storage basket. Except for the umbrella stroller, all Combi strollers are also height adjustable. Combi also offers a double stroller that weighs only 20 pounds, but is fully adjustable, and each seat reclines independently. Basic Combi strollers start at $170, and go up to about $270 for the double stroller.

COSCO

Cosco's Rock n Roller strollers feature rocking and gliding movements which help calm fussy riders. With a seat that can be removed for use as a bassinet as well as adjusted to four seating positions, a canopy, large market basket, and forward- and rear-facing positioning, this is a versatile stroller you can use for years to come. The Rock n Roller is also available as a double stroller. There's even a model that includes a car seat for babies to 22 pounds. These models range from $50 to $170.

Cosco's carriage stroller can be used with newborns, and sits up for older babies and children. Their market stroller is a snazzy model with a huge basket and machine-washable toss-in pad, with a see-through window in its canopy.

EMMALJUNGA

Emmaljunga strollers were originally manufactured in Sweden. A very popular European brand, the Emmaljunga stroller offers old-fashioned high quality—many parents save their strollers as heirlooms. These classic, high-performance strollers are not cheap, but are well worth the cost. Emmaljunga stroll-

EMMALJUNGA

ers are classic buggies with oversize, shock-absorbing wheels that have a lifetime warranty. They have large, collapsible hoods, and extra-long sure-grip handles. Their five-point harness restraints are the type touted by *Consumer Reports* as the safest stroller restraints.

All of their strollers have washable, removable pads made of a material that allows fresh air to come in and moisture to evaporate quickly. They are Scotchguarded for stain control. The frames have an antimicrobial finish that prevents mold and rust. Emmaljunga strollers start at about $250, and are sold primarily through baby specialty stores.

EVENFLO

Evenflo offers several unique styles of strollers. Their Fresh Air Gear line of outdoor products includes the Hike 'n'Roll—a baby carrier that becomes a stroller—and the Tri-Wheel Stroller. This all-terrain stroller has three extra-large, rugged wheels, plus a two-position handle and a large canopy. The storage basket is moderately sized. When folded, this stroller will stand on its own.

Evenflo also offers the On My Way Travel System, a combination car seat/stroller. The rear-facing infant seat snaps into the stroller or the car base. Without the car seat, the stroller is lightweight, has an enormous carrying basket, and is reclinable. The handle is ergonomically designed for comfort. This system has a wide wheel base for extra stability. The combination system is also available with Evenflo's Joy Ride car seat, which is similar to the On My Way, but has a less comfortable handle. The On My Way Travel System costs about $150.

GERRY

If you are looking for a stroller that makes it easy for the parent, check out Gerry's Convenience Stroller. It features one-hand steering, cupholder, and trays for both the adult and child. Add in an extra-large basket, side storage pockets, and infant bolsters on the deluxe model, and you've got a stroller that is a pleasure to use. Prices range from $80-$100.

Gerry's carriage stroller models recline fully and include a big storage basket. The higher-end model has side storage baskets. Prices are $100-$120.

GRACO

Graco offers many types of strollers including basic strollers, full-size carriages, double and triple strollers, and umbrella strollers, all with washable pads and easy folding capability.

Graco's basic full-size strollers have extra head support, four sets of swivel wheels, and a storage basket. Depending on the model, you can also get adjustable-height handles, reversible handles, and larger storage baskets. All of the

strollers have a rain/sun canopy with a viewing window, and reclining seats.

Two double canopy stroller styles with reclining seats are available, including side-by-side and one-in-front-of-the-other. Double strollers start at $90.

Graco's popular LiteRiders have several styles from a basic umbrella stroller to a nearly full-size lightweight stroller. All have extra large storage baskets and ergonomic handles. Deluxe models have adjustable handles and extra large wheels, plus suspension for a smoother ride. At around $80, they are among the most durable, least expensive strollers.

The Outrider is a rugged sport stroller with sturdy frame, oversize, knobby tires, extra storage, and a comfortable handle. They also offer a jogging stroller with a single wheel in front.

PEG PEREGO

Made in Italy, Peg Perego strollers are beautifully designed. Their rust-resistant, aluminum frame strollers are just 16 to 22 pounds. The washable pads come in several attractive patterns. Peg Perego strollers have extra large metal wheels and large storage baskets. They also feature a "remote control" device in the handle that opens and closes the stroller with one hand.

The full-size stroller carriages have European styling, with adjustable and reversible handles. They come with an apron for cold days. The large, removable basket can hold a full grocery bag.

Peg Perego also offers double and triple strollers in various styles, in side by side and facing styles. The seats individually recline on all of these strollers, and the strollers are still quite portable. Peg Perego strollers start at $150.

HIGH CHAIRS

High chairs are essential for your baby once he or she is ready to eat solid foods and can sit up easily. This usually occurs during the fifth or sixth month. Parents have a wide selection of types of high chairs—from the basic to the sophisticated.

Basic high chairs are plastic with vinyl seats. They may require one or two hands to adjust the high chair. Most models today offer the one-hand option, which makes it much simpler for the busy parent. You can also purchase a "no frills" wooden high chair for your child. Although these chairs look beautiful, they may be more difficult to clean, and they also take up a little more room because they don't fold. There are

WHAT TO LOOK FOR

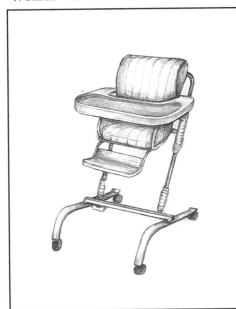

WHAT PARENTS LIKE
✔ LARGE TRAY
✔ EASY TO CLEAN
✔ ONLY NEEDS ONE HAND
✔ STURDY
✔ APPEARANCE
✔ ADJUSTABLE
✔ WHEELS

WHAT PARENTS DON'T LIKE
✔ HARD TO CLEAN
✔ TRAY STICKS
✔ SEATBELT STRAP IS DIFFICULT TO USE

also high chairs available that will "grow" or adjust to your child. Many baby product manufacturers offer this option. The advantage of these high chairs is that they may be used as a high chair, youth chair and also a play chair. They may be placed in several positions, extending the life of the high chair. The adjustable models also come with the convenience features of a large tray, non-splash sides and one hand adjustments. Many also come with wheels! You'll pay more for this type of high chair, but it will also last longer.

The final type of high chair is a portable high chair. Portable high chairs may either be strapped onto one of your chairs or placed directly on the table (it hangs on your table). If you travel or visit friends and family, a portable high chair is great.

One safety feature that is a must on any high chair purchase is the waist belt to secure your infant. According to CSPC, falls from high chairs are a leading cause of childhood injuries. Make sure you buckle your child in every single time you put him in the high chair.

POPULAR BRANDS

CENTURY

Century has two models of high chairs. The basic high chair has a wraparound tray, and is adjustable and foldable. The pad is vinyl and easy to clean. The more deluxe model has a thick, textured cloth pad and a six-position height adjustment. The restraint incorporates a crotch buckle for additional safety. This model has locking wheels for portability.

COSCO

Cosco manufactures both the basic model of high chair as well as others which are height-adjustable or convertible. Their Sit 'n Gro 3-in-1 Chair doubles as a youth chair for dining and converts to a junior chair for kids up to 8 years old. Cosco's Rise & Dine chairs include four-position reclining backs for use while feeding, napping and playing and three height adjustments. The seat's rotation T-bar secures baby to minimize slippage. The one-hand, wrap-around tray snaps into the last adjustment posi-

ADJUSTABLE HIGH CHAIR

tion and most models include locking casters. Options is five chairs in one—infant feeding seat, high chair, youth chair, booster seat and play seat.

EVENFLO

Evenflo's Right Height high chair can be adjusted to six different levels, and can be used as a high chair, play chair and youth chair. The tray can be adjusted into eight positions, all with one hand. This chair has a vinyl pad, a tri-buckle restraint system, and comes with locking wheels. The Phases high chair is even more versatile. A car seat or carrier can be locked into its base for an infant feeding chair; it can be used as a regular high chair; the tray can snap off and the chair can be pulled up to the table as a booster seat, and the entire unit can be broken down to become a table and chair set for a toddler. The tray has high anti-splash sides, and is one-hand adjustable. This chair also has a vinyl seat and tri-buckle restraint system. The Phases chair costs about $70.

FISHER-PRICE HIGH CHAIRS

Fisher-Price offers a high chair that can be adjusted to six different heights. It can also be used as a youth chair for sitting at the table. The tray has a splash guard in back, to protect the baby's clothes, and can be operated with one hand. This seat doesn't have wheels and isn't collapsible. The Fisher Price high chair costs about $70.

GRACO HIGH CHAIRS

Graco offers a wide variety of basic high chairs. Almost all of its models fold and have the one-hand entry-and-release feature. Most are height-adjustable, and have a T-bar restraint for additional security. Graco high chairs come in a wide variety of colors and patterns. Prices range from $60 to $80. Graco also makes a portable high chair, which sits directly on the dining room table and costs around $30.

GERRY

Gerry's Adjust-A-Height Chair is three chairs in one: a high chair, youth chair and play chair. It has six adjustable positions and a tray that can be adjusted and removed with one hand. The Play Top High Chair is really unique. It is a high chair that converts into a table and chair set. The high chair is made of sturdy wood, and has a large, one-hand release tray. The chair lifts out of the base to be used as a wooden table and chair. The play table has two surfaces, one smooth side for coloring, and a building block side. The low price, around $60, is a bargain for three pieces in one.

PEG PEREGO

Peg Perego was one of the first manufacturers to offer an adjustable high chair. The high chairs are about $175, but loaded with features that make them a worthwhile purchase. All models have swivel wheels and spacious trays. The Prima Pappa chair can be used from infancy and is reclinable in four positions. This chair has seven height positions. The chair also folds up very compactly. The well padded cloth cover comes in two patterns. Peg Perego also has deluxe high chairs that are adjustable and compact. These chairs are upholstered, and have push-button release restraining belts. They even have a handle on the back of the tray, to make it easier to move around on the wheels. There is also an optional toy tray that fits onto the regular tray.

BABY CARRIERS

Baby carriers are a nice item to have for situations when a stroller isn't practical, or you need to have your hands free, yet keep the baby close to you. Young babies really seem to enjoy them. Carriers come in a variety of styles. The classic front pouch keeps the baby close to your chest—very soothing to babies in the early weeks. Most have the option of having the baby face in or out. Slings are growing in popularity. They keep the baby more horizontal, but still close to the body. They can make it easier for babies to sleep, and provide a private and convenient way to breastfeed.

WHAT TO LOOK FOR

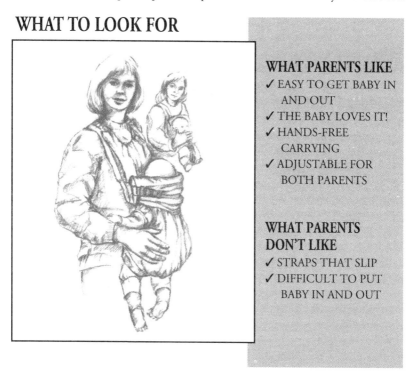

WHAT PARENTS LIKE
✓ EASY TO GET BABY IN AND OUT
✓ THE BABY LOVES IT!
✓ HANDS-FREE CARRYING
✓ ADJUSTABLE FOR BOTH PARENTS

WHAT PARENTS DON'T LIKE
✓ STRAPS THAT SLIP
✓ DIFFICULT TO PUT BABY IN AND OUT

Backpacks are for babies who are sitting up well. Most styles have an external aluminum frame, and are designed to rest the baby's weight on a parent's hips rather than the shoulders and back, which is much easier with an older, heavier baby.

POINTS TO CONSIDER

- Try out the baby carrier before you buy, if possible. Some are difficult to get on and off, especially once a baby is in them. With backpacks, pay attention to where your baby's knees and feet are in relation to your back. It is very uncomfortable to be constantly kicked!

- If you're very short or very tall, fitting a backpack frame can be problematic. It is very important that the weight rest on your hips or you may injure your back. Be sure to adjust the straps properly.
- Examine the seat when buying backpacks. Some packs are all one piece, while others have an adjustable seat. While adjustability is a nice feature for a growing baby, the seats are often adjusted with straps. Unless the straps are of equal length, the seat will tilt your baby to one side, or the baby may even start to fall out of a leg hole.
- Check that the straps on slings and carriers have a locking mechanism. Some people have had accidents when they placed the baby in the carrier and the weight of the baby caused the straps to slip out.

POPULAR BRANDS

BABY BJORN

The Baby Bjorn is a little more expensive than many front pouch carriers, at about $70, but parents feel it is well worth it. This carrier has clips on the side, enabling the carrier to be completely open on one side for loading and unloading. The clips also allow you to detach the carrier from the straps and lay the baby down without removing the baby first. It has a safety tab to prevent the straps from slipping. The straps are well padded and are designed to fit your back snugly, keeping weight distributed evenly and preventing back strain. They also have a model made especially for taller people to ensure a comfortable fit.

EVENFLO

Evenflo offers two carriers as part of their Fresh Air line. The About Face dual facing baby carrier is a front pouch where the baby can face in or out. It has extra padding in the seat and legs, and a zipper for easy nursing. The Hike'n'Roll system is unique—it's a backpack that converts into a lightweight stroller, with adjustable padded straps and a chest strap for additional support. The frame has a kickstand which provides a stable base to load the baby, and folds to become the stroller handle. There are also molded fenders on the wheels, which protects the backpack wearer from dirty wheels. The Hike'n'Roll costs about $80.

FISHER PRICE

Fisher Price's Perfect Support Carrier is a classic front pouch that gives the option of having the baby face in or out. It has a soft padded shell that offers additional head support and makes it easier to get the baby in and out of the carrier. This carrier has a removable bib and is washable. The Deluxe Perfect Support Carrier has all the features of the regular carrier with the added option of a sling. The carrier also comes with a removable weather protector. The deluxe carriers cost about $40, and the basic model slightly less.

GERRY

Gerry Snugli carriers are a favorite with many parents. Gerry carriers are affordable, ranging from $15 to $50. The Snugli Double Take is a soft front carrier with padded straps. The baby can face in or away from the parent. This carrier is only designed for infants 0-12 months. The better-equipped model adds the option of using the carrier as a backpack as well as a frontpack. Suitable for children up to 20 months old, it has built-in pillows to support the child's head and an adjustable seat. The Gerry Trailtech is a backpack with a loading stand, lightweight frame, and a storage bag. The backpack has five hip positions to fit adults from 5'-6'2". This carrier can be used until your child weighs 40 pounds. The Trailtech costs about $50.

INFANTINO

Infantino is famous for its 6-in-1 carrier, which fits into a car seat, attaches to a grocery cart, and converts to a backpack. The carrier costs about $20, comes in many attractive colors, and includes a free video to instruct parents in the proper use of the carrier. Infantino also offers the Side Traveler, in which the baby faces in towards the parent, but rests on the parent's hip, rather than the chest. Some of their carriers have other features as well, including large storage capacity, breathable mesh seats and a weather protector that keeps the baby warm in winter, but can be zipped out for summer. All Infantino carriers have padded leg openings, removable terry bibs, and high-back headrests.

KELTY

Kelty is well known for its infant carriers among recreational backpackers. They offer five different carriers suitable for use on light day trips up to several day backcountry hikes. The Kangaroo is a front carrier with the option of having the baby face in or out. It has a clip-on carrier that attaches to a jog-bra harness. It also has a built-in hood that protects against weather and provides some privacy for nursing. The other four Kelty styles are backpacks intended for older babies. The lower end models are for use on short trips, while the deluxe models are for serious hiking. All are very lightweight, with an ergonomic curved aluminum frame, stable kickstand base and adjustable shoulder and waist straps for both the child and adult. The carriers are all a striking spruce color with purple trim, and have reflective piping. A Kelty carrier costs about $130.

NOJO

Nojo is the maker of the original Babysling, created by Dr. William Sears. The sling can be worn in several positions including classic cradle hold, snuggle hold in which the baby faces the mother, hip carry where the baby rests on the parent's hip, and kangaroo carry where the baby faces out. The Babysling is adjustable and has a patented "stopper" which secures the tail of the sling and prevents slipping. Nojo also makes the Suburban 3-in-1 carrier which holds babies up to 30 pounds. This is a classic front carrier with the option of having the baby face in or out, and a backpack.

OVER THE SHOULDER BABY HOLDER

The only sling to be awarded the National Parenting Center's seal of approval, the Over The Shoulder Baby Holder is a deep sling with generous padding. A special feature is the patented nylon rod sewn into the bottom portion of the strap's tail which keeps the strap from slipping. The OTSBH, in three sizes for ease of carrying, is available in nearly 50 fabrics. You'll find these $39 slings at specialty stores or order from the manufacturer at (714) 361-1089.

NURSING PRODUCTS

Feeding your baby is probably one of your most important responsibilities as a parent. Experts agree that breastfeeding is ideal for babies, and there are many products that can make it easier to breastfeed longer, even if you are a working mother. This section discusses breast pumps, breast pillows and other nursing accessories.

BREAST PUMPS

Breast pumps can make it convenient to continue breastfeeding. By storing and freezing the pumped milk, your baby can receive the benefits of breast milk in a bottle, even when you can't be there. Many hospitals sell and rent breast pumps, as do local maternity/nursing stores and lactation consultants. Make sure to choose a breast pump that will meet your needs and maintain your milk supply. Consult a lactation consultant if you have any questions or concerns.

MEDELA

Medela, the largest and best known of breast pump manufacturers, makes high-quality electric pumps, handheld battery/electric pumps, and manual pumps. Most are available for purchase or to rent. Medela pumps are lightweight and portable, are available in models suitable for light, occasional use, or long-term separations. Many models have an option to double pump both breasts at once, to save time. A Medela pump has a built-in vacuum release, designed to simulate the way a baby would breastfeed.

The Lactina pump comes in two models: the Select and the Plus, both of which can also be used as a double pump. The only difference between the two is the speed. The pump has autocycle pumping action, which simulates the action of a baby's mouth. This pump can be used either an electrical outlet or the PowerPak battery accessory, which is a rechargeable battery and has an adapter for use on the go, or in a car.

The Pump-in-Style is a high performance professional breast pump with an insulated storage area that fits the pump, four milk storage bags or bottles and a cooling unit, all in a sophisticated carrying bag. This pump offers double pumping, a double pump kit, the collection bottle and cooling elements to chill the expressed milk. It has adjustable suction and Autocycle pumping action and, like any other Medela pump, you can pump directly into milk storage bags. A PowerPak is also available for this model.

The Mini-Electric is a lightweight, portable pump, designed for short-term separations. A battery adapter is available. In addition to autocycle pumping and adjustable suction, it has universal threads, allowing it to be attached to any standard baby bottle, and is small enough to fit in a purse. A new double mini pump is also available.

The SpringExpress is a manual pump for occasional pumping. It has a spring inside the piston to create suction more easily. These pumps are dishwasher-safe, and can be used with any standard baby bottle. They are useful for a night out, or during illness, but are quite labor-intensive for everyday use.

AMEDA-EGNELL

Ameda-Egnell is another large manufacturer of breast pumps. For over 50 years, their pumps have been used in hospitals and through rental stations. The Egnell Elite is a lightweight, quiet, efficient pump. It offers variable suction, and a cycle that imitates a baby's natural sucking. It also comes with HygieniKits for hygienic pumping. The Elite also comes with an adapter so the pump can be used in a car.

The One-Hand Breast Pump is a unique and convenient way to pump milk. The pump is small enough to fit in a purse. The amount of suction and cycling are controlled by a hand squeeze. Because it is one-handed, a mother can pump one breast while nursing on the other.

AVENT

Avent makes two styles of breast pumps: manual and battery powered. The manual breast pump is operated one-handed with a lever. You can pump directly into a storage liner to be frozen, or into an Avent bottle. The battery breast pump has an AC adapter for traveling. It features adjustable suction and a suction release button for added control. A special valve prevents splash back. Avent pumps are designed primarily for occasional pumping.

NURTURE III

The Nurture III is an electric pump with cycling action controlled by lifting a finger on and off a valve. The suction has four adjustments. The Nurture III also has the option of pumping both breasts at once. The pump is lighter than the Elite, and more economical.

WHITE RIVER

White River manufactures two styles of breast pumps. The Model 9050 features variable vacuum control, automatic cycling, and a patented Soft-Cup system that simulates a baby's suckling. The easy-to-clean pump comes with a carrying case.

The Model 0500D is a manual pump with the Soft-Cup system. This is a more labor intensive, but more economical choice. The pump can also be converted to an electric pump with White River accessories. Conversion kits are available for all White River pumps, as well as attachments for double pumping.

BREASTFEEDING ACCESSORIES

There are a number of accessories available to make nursing more comfortable and convenient. Doctors have noted that mothers nurse their babies longer and have a more positive experience when they use these products.

NURSING PILLOWS

Breastfeeding pillows provide back, arm and elbow support during nursing. They elevate the baby to get the baby in the proper position for nursing. They can also help mothers recover from a Cesarean section by lifting the baby off of the incision.

My Brest Friend is a nursing pillow that wraps around the mother's waist. It comfortably fits most body types, and doesn't slip out of place easily. It can be used for classic cradle hold nursing, or shifted to the side for football hold nursing. The contoured cover is washable soft cotton-flannel. When your child is older, it can also be used as a travel pillow, or for supporting a baby learning to sit. My Brest Friend costs about $40 and is sold at many maternity and nursing specialty stores.

The Nurse Mate Nursing Pillow is specially designed to make nursing twins easier. It has extra-wide cushions, a washable cover, and adjusts to many positions. The Nurse Mate for Twins costs about $50.

Nojo's Deluxe Nursing Pillow is a thick C-shaped pillow that rests on the mother's lap. The pillow was developed by a nursing mother and helps to prevent backache by raising the baby closer to the mother. The pillow is filled with non-allergenic fibers and is washable.

SLINGS

Slings are a useful nursing accessory both at home and away. Slings are designed to keep baby close to the body in a variety of positions, while providing excellent back support for the parent. The wide span of fabric also provides privacy during nursing. Nojo, Over the Shoulder Baby Holder, Gerry, Parenting Concepts and Fisher Price are just some of the popular sling manufacturers. For in-depth descriptions of slings, refer to the Baby Carriers section of this chapter.

NURSING STOOLS

Elevating the feet may alleviate back, shoulder, leg and arm strain by lifting the lap and the baby closer to the breast. The Medela footstool comes in oak or white finish and costs about $35. It can also be used as a computer stool, to alleviate back pain while working.

BREAST PADS/BREAST SHELLS

Breast pads are designed to absorb leaks. Breast pads come in disposable or washable styles.

Johnson's and Evenflo are well-known makers of disposable breast pads. The pads adhere to the inside of your bra with an adhesive strip. They are multi-layered to keep skin dry, and can be thrown away in the trash. A box of 36 costs around $5.

Medela's Washable Bra Pads are seamless pads designed to keep moisture away and allow air to circulate. A package of four pads costs about $8.

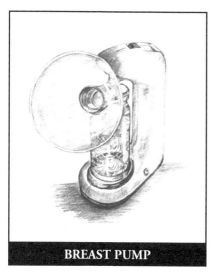

BREAST PUMP

Ameda-Egnell sells 100% cotton reusable nursing pads that are contoured to conform to breast shape for a natural look. They absorb milk well, to let skin breathe. A package of six pads costs about $10.

Milk Diaper nursing pads are also 100% cotton, washable and reusable. They have eight layers of cotton for maximum absorbency. A pack of two pairs is about $6, and a five-pair pack is $14.

Breast shells treat sore, flat or inverted nipples. They keep fabric away from the breast to allow air circulation which improves sore nipples. Medela, Ameda-Egnell and Blis make various styles of breast shells.

MILK STORAGE BAGS

When expressing, it is crucial to store the milk properly to prevent bacteria growth. Milk storage bags are specially designed for expressed milk. They are presterilized and close tightly to prevent freezer burn. The bags are of high quality to prevent splitting and cracking during freezing. Many are designed to hook directly to a breast pump; the bag can then immediately be closed and refrigerated or frozen. Many are printed with measurements, so you can determine how many ounces you've pumped.

Medela makes collection, storage and freezing (CSF) bags that attach to any Medela breast shield so you can pump directly into the bag, and then immediately freeze the milk. A pack of 50 bags is about $18.95.

One of the most popular storage bags is manufactured by Mother's Milk. The bags last for four to six months, have a built-in twist tie, and a place to write the date. You can buy 25 in a pouch for under $8.

Avent's breast milk storage bags are safe for use in the freezer up to three months, and can be fitted directly into a disposable bottle for use. The bags are closed with sealing clips and come with date labels.

SUPPLEMENTAL NURSING SYSTEM

The Medela Supplemental Nursing System is for adoptive and nursing mothers. A plastic bottle hangs around the mother's neck with two thin feeding tubes that carry expressed breast milk or formula to the baby, who "nurses" from the mother. This system can help an adoptive mother to bond with her child, or help a nursing mother to continue breastfeeding while she builds her milk supply. The system costs about $40.

BOTTLES AND ACCESSORIES

Bottles and nipples come in many shapes and sizes, and it can be difficult to choose between them. Many times, it's best to try a few different styles of bottles and nipples to see which works best. Some of the major brands of bottles and bottle accessories are Playtex, Gerber, Johnson's, Evenflo, the First Years, and Avent.

Bottles generally come in four- and eight-ounce sizes. Three styles of bottles dominate the market: the standard, plastic bottle; the disposable bottle, and the angled bottle.

Disposable bottles have a plastic shell that is reused, and disposable plastic liners that are inserted inside the shell. The liners are sterile, which assures a hygienic feeding. The disadvantage of disposable liners is that while they are graded by ounces, it can be difficult to determine how much liquid you've added, or how much a baby drank. Playtex, Evenflo and Avent are the available choices in disposable bottles. Playtex and Evenflo liners, shells and nipples are interchangeable.

Angled bottles are built like a standard bottle, but at the nipple end they are bent at an angle. Manufacturers claim these bottles reduce gas in babies because the nipple remains full of liquid due to the angle. It makes it easier to feed the baby in an upright position, while still tilting the bottle. They reduce a parent's arm strain because you don't have to lift your arm to tilt the bottle. Evenflo and Johnson's were the first to come out with this system, but now most major bottle manufacturers make an angled bottle.

NIPPLES

Nipples are a very individual choice among babies. It is impossible to predict which a baby will like, and it is usually best to try several. Nipples comes in rubber and silicone. Rubber nipples are orange, and silicone nipples are clear. Silicone is preferred by many babies because it is softer in the mouth. Silicone doesn't collapse as often during feeding, and the size of the hole is not affected by heat or cold. It is usually a good choice for formula or milk feeding. Rubber nipples are often used for juice, but some babies like them for milk as well. The holes can be adjusted to increase or decrease flow by manually enlarging the hole, or boiling the nipple to tighten the hole.

Nipples also come in many shapes. Each shape claims to simulate a breast, but again, nipple shape is an individual choice among babies. All shapes come in rubber and silicone. Most brands offer slower flow for younger babies, and faster flow for older babies, by varying the size of the hole.

Babies often have an easy time grasping the nipple on disposable bottles without gagging. Many breastfeeding mothers have had good luck with this nipple shape, but some breastfed babies have a difficult time alternating between rubber nipples and their mother's.

Johnson's makes an infant nipple that is narrow and elongated. This nipple is believed to be better for premature babies because there is a smaller tip at the end to grasp, and a slower flow.

The standard nipple is the one most often seen attached to a bottle. These are made by Johnson's, Gerber, Evenflo, First Years, and Playtex. The best thing about these nipples are that they are so easily attainable and interchangeable. Many babies, especially those that are exclusively bottlefed, use these nipples without a problem.

Gerber Nuk nipples are unique in that they have a round top and flat bottom. Again, this is supposed to simulate a human nipple, and the shape the nipple takes on during suckling. The nipple is designed to fit comfortably inside a baby's mouth and help reduce gas.

THE AVENT SYSTEM

The Avent System combines breastfeeding and bottlefeeding, which is ideal for the working mother, or to allow the father or other person to participate in feeding. The system includes breast pump, reusable bottles, disposable bottles, several styles of silicone nipples, cups, pacifiers, and accessories.

Avent bottles come in four- and eight-ounce sizes. They offer reusable bottles as well as disposables with special sterile liners. The disposables have a unique base that allows the bottle to hold either size liner, and provides support during the filling of the liner.

The natural-shaped nipples have an anti-collapsible tip, and are designed to make it easier for a baby to alternate between breast and bottle. The reusable bottle nipples have an anti-vacuum skirt with an air valve to prevent gas. Avent offers several nipple options including the newborn nipple with one hole; the Slow, Medium, and Fast Flow nipples, with increasing numbers of holes; and the unique Variable Flow Nipple with slots instead of holes. By turning the bottle, you can vary the flow to suit the baby's needs.

Avent offers several other bottle accessories. A steam sterilizer uses the power of the microwave oven to sterilize up to four bottles, nipples and caps in under ten minutes. The electric steam sterilizer

BOTTLES

can hold up to six standard bottles, nipples and caps. The Bottle and Baby Food Warmer is a convenient way to heat foods, and is safe for disposable bottle liners. Avent also offers a training cup set with interchangeable spouts and a straw adapter to transition a baby to cup drinking. All Avent products can be purchased singly or in sets.

BOTTLE ACCESSORIES

There are a host of products to make bottle feeding easier. Drying racks have many posts to rest bottles, nipples and caps. Allowing these products to air dry helps resist bacteria growth. Bottle warmers are a convenient, safe way to heat bottles. Microwaves are not recommended because they can cause heat spots which may burn a baby's mouth. You can safely place a bottle in a warmer and have it ready for the middle of the night feeding as well.

One crucial accessory for bottle feeding is a dishwasher basket, available in most drug stores, which keeps nipples, rings and caps from falling to the bottom of the dishwasher.

Insulated bags are designed to keep bottles warm or cool while traveling. They can also be used to store pumped breast milk. There are also special bottle caps for powdered formula used for mixing formula on the road. You fill the bottle with sterile water, and the cap with pre-measured powdered formula. When you're ready to mix, you open the valve and shake.

All major bottle manufacturers make these products for their bottles and nipples. Most are very reasonably priced.

WHAT YOU NEED TO KNOW ABOUT JPMA

The Juvenile Products Manufacturers Association (JPMA) wants all parents to be confident that the juvenile products they purchase are designed and built with baby safety in mind. For this reason, JPMA initiated a voluntary Safety Certification program. This program is in effect for high chairs, play yards, walkers, strollers, gates full-size cribs and portable hook-on chairs. The program is being expanded to include non-full size cribs, toddler beds, bath seats and bedding products.

JPMA's seal is available to manufacturers who voluntarily submit products for testing. Only after the product passes rigorous testing can it display the certification seal.

Parents can learn more about safe use of their baby products by requesting a free copy of Safe and Sound For Baby, by including a self-addressed, stamped envelope to: JPMA Safety Brochure, 236 Route 38 West, Suite 100, Moorestown, NJ 08057.

The brochure is also available in Spanish.

DIAPERS AND DIAPERING

Seven thousand. That's the minimum number of diapers you should expect to change before your baby becomes a fully toilet-trained child. While not always a pleasant experience, keeping your baby dry and clean is a necessary parenting task that expresses caring and love.

DISPOSABLE DIAPERS

Disposables are undoubtedly one of the greatest inventions ever for busy parents. They are easy to put on, fit well, and keep baby dry. There are even disposables especially made for newborns with a cutout area to avoid rubbing on the baby's umbilical cord stump.

One caveat: the newer disposables are so absorbent that the baby may not feel wet even when the diaper is soaked. The rules are the same, even for disposables—you must change the baby every time he wets in order to avoid a diaper rash.

Proponents of disposables point out that the savings by not washing and using energy to run washers and dryers make up for the landfill problems caused by disposables. The fabric diaper boosters point out that disposables in landfills can cause contamination of groundwater and rodent-borne disease from the feces often left in diapers. Disposable manufacturers recommend that all fecal matter be flushed before the diaper is tossed out, but all parents know that isn't always practical.

CLOTH DIAPERS

Cloth diapering has benefitted by new diapers and diaper covers which make leaky cloth diapers and stiff plastic pants a thing of the past. A cottage industry of mail-order cloth diapering suppliers has grown to fill the demand for high-quality cotton diapers, often with terrycloth linings, and diaper wraps and pants of soft, breathable fabrics that still provide leakage protection. All-in-one cloth diapers, while more expensive, are convenient and great for parents nervous about diaper pins.

Less expensive cloth diapers, in flat and prefolded styles, are available in most baby stores, discount and drug stores. Pull-on pants in nylon are less apt to crack and stiffen and are usually a better choice than plastic.

Keeping your baby dry and clean is a necessary parenting task that expresses caring and love.

DIAPER SERVICES

The greatest luxury of all is using a diaper service. Your baby's diapers are picked up and a new batch of sanitized diapers are brought right to your door. Especially during the first few months, when your days may seem to be an endless round of diapering, a service can be invaluable. Compare prices and features of your local diaper services before making your decision.

Most services require that you order diapers one month before your baby's due date. Diapers should be delivered a week ahead of time. Most diaper companies require a minimum service period and need notification of at least one week before cancelling the service.

❧ RESOURCES ❧

■ BABY BUNZ & CO.
800-676-4559
P.O. Box 113
Lynden, WA 98264
Since 1982, Baby Bunz has offered Nikky diaper covers, diapering products, and baby clothes and toys. Their beautiful catalog features cotton, polyester, and lambswool felt diaper covers from $12.50 to $18.95. The aptly named "Cottonclouds," "Heavenly Bottoms," and Spoil Me! Snugglebottoms" are cotton diapers in styles to suit your baby's needs. Unique offerings include a 25" x 31" pure wool "puddle pad" for $22. Baby Bunz's product line also includes Hyland's homeopathic remedies and the Weleda natural baby care products.

■ BABYWORKS
800-422-2910
(503) 645-4349
11725 N.W. West Rd.
Portland, OR 97229
E-mail: Bbworks@aol.com
Babyworks' catalog is a pleasure to read. Besides offering a wide array of cloth diapers and accessories, you'll also find cloth diapering tips, washing sugges-tions, "trouble shooting" hints, and an essay about the environmental impor-tance of using cloth diapers. Babyworks offers the Nikky line, wool diaper cov-ers, nylon waterproof pants, and Bumkins all-in-one diaper-plus-covers, as well as many varieties of cloth diapers and diaper doublers. There's even a swim diaper, diaper pack, baby blankets, bibs and capes.

■ BIOBOTTOMS
800-766-1254
617-C 2nd St.
Petaluma, CA 94952
Web site: www.biotottoms.com/
children@biotottoms.com
Biobottoms' 60-page color catalog is filled with rugged, comfortable clothes and shoes for children. One page is devoted to diapering products, includ-ing Biobottoms' exclusive felted lambswool diaper covers with velcro tabs, available in white or with rainbow stitch-ing at the edges ($18-$18.50). Their "Cottonbottom" is a all-in-one, cotton lined with a polyester moisture shield, available in white or pastels for $15.50-$16). They carry Gerber prefolded six-

layer diapers (per dozen: $19/infants; $25/toddler) and Happy Me diapers with extra thickness in front for boys and in back for girls (per six: $21-$25).

DIAPER BUNNY
(607) 276-6755
11 Angelica St.
Almond, NY 14804
Owner Jonna Statt includes washing instructions and easy hints with each purchase. Chinese cotton prefolded diapers are $20.95/dozen (infant size) and $24.95 (regular size). The catalog also includes Di-D Klips for pinless diapering. Other products carried include MotherEase fitted diapers with snap covers, snap-in diaper doublers, and Prorap diaper cover. Diaper Bunny's own pull-on diaper cover is made of lightweight, waterproof Ultrex. These covers are available in watermelon or jade colors, and cost just $3.95 each.

ECOBABY
800-596-7450
9319 Northview Terrace
Santee, CA 92071
Web site: www.ecobaby.com
Founded by a mother seeking natural products for her infant son, Ecobaby is a full-color catalog that offers children's and nursing clothing, toys, books, bedding and diapers. Kushies ($8.95/infant, $11.95/toddler) and Bumkins ($11.95) are convenient all-in-one diaper-wraps. Ecobaby carries a variety of cloth diapers and wraps, both wool and nylon. The catalog includes a section on setting up a cloth system and reasons to choose cloth.

THE HEALTHY BABY SUPPLY COMPANY
(612) 225-8535
323 W. Morton St.
St. Paul, MN 55107
E-mail: MKostohr@netcom.com
For those interested in natural health care, this is a wonderful catalog, as it includes a host of natural baby and bath care products, herbs and herbal oils, vitamin supplements, and books. Two pages are devoted to cloth diapers—prefolded, contour, and fitted with snaps. You'll find Prorap diaper covers ($6.95), the nylon/polyester EZ Cover ($4.95), and a 100% cotton wrap ideal for sensitive skin ($8.50). There's even a "recipe" for making baby wipes from paper towels.

MOMMY'S LITTLE HELPERS
800-859-3559
9250 Watson Rd.
St. Louis, MO 63126
E-mail: MommysLH@aol.com
A bare-bones catalog jam-packed with advice and information, Mommy's Little Helpers offers a plethora of diapers, covers, liners, and all-in-ones. Unique offerings such as the $9.30 all-organic "snap-to-fit" diaper, with velcro waist closures that fit newborns to 35-pounders, make this a special catalog. Mommy's Little Helpers stocks eight different kinds of diapers and eight wrap models, including the Biobaby wrap, with a "belt" that holds the diaper in place. The catalog includes a full page each on folding techniques, washing hints and "number crunching" to help you decide how many diapers you'll need to purchase.

DIAPERS & DIAPERING

■ MOUNTAIN AIR NATURALS

(406) 388-1056
113 North Davis
Belgrade, MT 59714
E-mail: mtnair@aol.com

A homegrown catalog that features hand-drawn illustrations, diapering hints and "mom-made" products, Mountain Air Naturals is a great find. For $20, their "Trial/Gift Set" includes three newborn diapers, a diaper cover, two wash cloths, a nylon tote bag and five note cards. The catalog includes flannel, terry/flannel and birdseye diapers; diaper clips (a pin alternative); a variety of diaper covers; washable nursing pads, and "dolly diapers" for your older sibling's favorite dolls.

■ SIMPLE ALTERNATIVES

800-735-2082
10513 S.E. 30th St.
Bellevue, WA 98004

Simple Alternatives presents a small selection of top-quality products. Included is "Diapering Details"—a great read if you're uncertain about which type of diapers to use. Made of 100% cotton flannel and thick terrycloth, their "Barefoot Baby" diapers are durable and absorbent. Their sampler pack includes a Barefoot Baby diaper, a Snugglup diaper cover, a Bumkins all-in-one diaper/cover, a Bumkins vented diaper cover, a Nikky diaper cover, six Barefoot Baby wash cloths, a package of baby wipes, and a small container of Nature's Second Skin baby ointment for $45.

■ TUSHIES

800-344-6379
675 Industrial Blvd.
Delta, CO 81416

An environmentally-friendly disposable diaper? That's right. Tushies' diapers are free of any gels, perfumes or dyes, with a cloth-like cover and cotton padding. If Tushies are not carried in a store near you, you can join the Tushies Club, and get regularly scheduled delivery of Tushies to your home. Club prices for Tushies are $42.95/case (270 newborn, 160 small, 120 medium, 88 large). You can also order Weleda, Earth Friendly, and Healthy Times baby products from Tushies.

■ WEE BEES

(303) 794-0966
P.O. Box 712
Littleton, CO 80160
E-mail: webees9@mail.idt.net

The Wee Bees catalog opens with five pages on the owner's good-natured diapering hints (and Rhonda Wiebe, with six children, knows diapers!). Inventory is small but well-chosen, and includes diaper service diapers with four cotton layers on the sides and eight in the center ($18/12 newborn; $25/12 regular; $31/12 toddler). Their nylon pants with snaps on both sides won't crack or harden and are economical at $8 for a pack of two ($10 for toddler size). Pull-on pants are $6.25 for two ($7.50 for toddlers). They also carry Mother-Ease snap-to-fit and Aplix (heavy duty velcro-type closure) diaper covers. The catalog closes with washing and diapering instructions, and several commonly asked questions.

TOP TEN GIFTS TO GIVE AND RECEIVE

Most of these gift suggestions may not seem like necessities, but we found them extremely helpful. Also, the recommendations are biased as they are products we ourselves, or parents we know, really appreciated. Take a look:

❶ **The Diaper Genie.** The Diaper Genie is now the number one best-selling individual juvenile product. It's easy to see why! For parents who use disposable diapers, this product removes odors from your home. Newly improved, it now can store more diapers, making it easier to use. It costs about $29 and is available at baby and discount stores.

❷ **Baby Bits computer software.** For any parent who has a computer and wants to make recording their baby's milestones simple, Baby Bits is a must! Baby Bits software allows parents to easily document everything from the first breath to the first step. Parents can even physically "record" their baby's cry or words with this software. The software comes with an expandable binder and 50 sheets of acid-free archive-quality paper. Suggested retail price is $40, with a portion of each sale going towards the SIDS Alliance. There is also a junior version which runs only about $18. Available only for Windows systems, Baby Bits can be purchased at specialty stores.

❸ **A locking clip.** Retailing at about $3, this is probably the most useful and inexpensive item you can purchase. A locking clip is to be used with a car seat to hold the seatbelt in place. It keeps your baby and the car seat secure. You can find a metal locking clip in the plastic bag attached to the back of almost all new car seats. It should be used at all times. We found this item at discount stores and local baby stores.

❹ **A Kelty Kids diaper bag or back pack.** We were especially excited about the Kelty Kids line of products as they seemed durable, functional, yet stylish in a '90s way. For parents on the go, the diaper bag should keep you organized. And, the Kelty backpack is one of the best-selling items at specialty stores nationwide.

❧

...there are also some great items to consider buying as a gift or simply to pamper yourself.

❧

DIAPER GENIE

❺ **A gift certificate for a cleaning service.** What all new parents need is time and order. Surprise yourself or a friend with a cleaning service gift certificate.

❻ **Books, books and more books!** One of our favorites is *What to Expect the First Year*. In our opinion, this is by far the best, easiest-to-read book for your baby's first year. Other books such as Dr. Berry Brazelton's *Touchpoints* and Dr. Jane Healy's *Your Child's Growing Mind* are wonderful also. Gift and baby books are also nice to receive.

❼ **A night of baby-sitting.** Offer your time and your care. It is probably the least expensive and most appreciated gift you could give to tired new parents.

❽ **A nightgown.** Between nursing, sleepless nights, and wanting your old body back, a mother needs pampering. A silky or brushed flannel button-down nightshirt or pajamas just may make the perfect pick-me-up every mother needs.

❾ **A car seat with a built-in locking clip and/or tether.** Safety comes first in every parent's mind. A car seat which has a built-in locking clip and/or tether helps the baby stay secure in a vehicle. Although these car seats may cost a little more than other models, it seems the benefits far outweigh the cost.

❿ **The Arm's Reach co-sleeping unit.** Sleeping near baby during the first months of life may be important to parents-to-be. The Arm's Reach co-sleeping unit makes it easy for parents to sleep near baby without fearing they may roll over on baby. Its own separate unit, the crib easily fits on any bed. It can also be used as a portable crib and/or bassinet when parents decide not to co-sleep with their baby. Available through the Right Start catalog and specialty stores, the Arm's Reach system costs under $200.

CARING FOR YOUR BABY

YOUR CHILD'S HEALTH CARE PROVIDER

Your most important, fundamental goal is to keep your children healthy. Your child's well-being must come first, which means:

- Get regular well-child checkups and immunizations.
- Be aware of symptoms that can contribute to illnesses.
- Make sure your child receives proper care when he is ill.

Choosing your child's health care provider is an important decision. You should feel comfortable with the provider's communication style, office hours, staff, credentials, and medical background. Parents may choose between pediatricians or family practitioners when looking for a medically trained primary care physician.

🌢

You should feel comfortable with the provider's communication tion style, office hours, staff, credentials, and medical background.

🌢

PEDIATRICIANS

Pediatricians don't just see small children. A child can see a pediatrician until she is out of high school. To become a pediatrician, a doctor must graduate from a four-year medical school and then serve three additional years of residency training in pediatrics. Pediatricians who pass the written examination given by the American Board of Pediatrics are issued a special certificate, and use the initials "FAAP" following their names. Choosing a physician within a "network" allows you access to specialists affiliated within the primary health system.

FAMILY PRACTITIONERS

Another choice for your child's doctor is a family practitioner. The benefit is that this health care provider can treat everyone in the family. So, when your child comes down with strep throat and you do too, one provider is aware and can treat your entire family. A family physician must graduate from medical school and then serve three years of residency training. Family physicians who have successfully passed an oral and written examination given by the American Board of Family Practice are known as Board Certified and the initials "ABFP" follow their name and title.

HEALTH INSURANCE

Once you've decided on your physician, evaluate your health insurance opportunities. If at all possible, choose your health insurance based on your provider. If you do not have a choice, you may find yourself limited to the physicians your insurance company contracts with. Most insurance companies have a booklet which lists the providers covered. You can also speak to your physician or the office staff to explore the possibility of adding another insurance carrier. Also, keep in mind that open enrollment takes place at many organizations annually, so you can switch insurance carriers if your health needs change.

If you are not covered by insurance, you can either seek public assistance, free or low-cost state or local government-sponsored clinics, private health insurance policies, or pay-as-you go for your children. While counties or community health centers typically sponsor well-child clinics, it may be more difficult to find clinics that treat ill children. Physicians accepting new patients should be willing to see you on a pay-as-you go basis with an office visit running generally around $60 to $75. It may be recommended to visit the health care provider's office ahead of time, interviewing the pediatrician at no cost, and getting the child registered, so if treatment is necessary the system is in place.

CHOOSING A CARE PROVIDER: A CHECKLIST

From a practical point of view, here are some other questions you may want to consider when choosing a provider:

- What is your provider's educational background and experience? Does she have any area of specialty?
- Are specialists available with a referral from your physician?
- Is there a large network of specialists if your child needs special care?
- Is your provider near your home or office? Proximity is key when dealing with sick children.

- How accessible is your provider? Ask about the provider's days off and the backup plan for when he or she is away. What are the provider's office hours?
- At what hospital(s) does your physician have admitting privileges?
- How open and friendly is the office staff?
- How well does the provider listen and respond to your questions?
- What is the provider's off-hours policy?

QUESTIONS AND ANSWERS
An Interview With a Pediatrician

All pediatricians are not alike, and your challenge is to find one who relates well to both you and your child.

Every pediatrician is committed to helping parents raise healthy children; however, individual pediatricians take different approaches so you may want to interview several doctors before selecting the one who best meets your needs. A pediatrician should be selected before your baby is born. This will allow the pediatrician the opportunity of giving your newborn her very first examination. The information below was obtained through an interview with Peter Wang M.D., a pediatrician practicing in Sacramento, California.

Q: *How do I choose a pediatrician?*

A: One way to choose a pediatrician is to ask your friends and neighbors about their pediatricians. You can also ask your obstetrician for a recommendation. Before your baby is born, it is possible to interview different pediatricians until you find one with whom you are comfortable.

Here are some things to look for in a doctor:

- Someone who will explain things clearly, including diseases, development, anticipated problems, and behavioral issues.

- He or she should be available and accessible most of the time; find out about backup procedures when the doctor is unavailable.
- Experience.
- A doctor who likes and works well with children.
- Someone who shares your basic philosophies on baby care, feed-ing/nursing, and medication.

Q: *What type of relationship should I expect to establish with my child's pediatrician?*

A: You definitely should be able to discuss any of your concerns with your doctor. The doctor should explain your child's sickness—why it has developed, what symptoms to expect and when. However, parents need to also understand that some illnesses are difficult to diagnose or predict. They should be willing to accept a sincere, "I don't know what is going to happen in the next few days. We just have to observe the child closely." Part of the doctor's job is to alleviate the parents' fears and worries, but at the same time to be completely honest.

Q: **May I call the pediatrician during non-office hours?**

A: Yes! Doctors and their associates should be available at all times for emergency situations. Most doctors try to educate their parents during regular office visits to explain the situations in which they should call, and those in which they should wait. If a parent has a real concern, however, he/she should not feel guilty for calling during non-office hours.

Q: **Are there times when an appointment is not necessary and I can call for additional advice over the telephone?**

A: There are times when you may want to call and speak with the nurse or leave a message for the doctor to call you back. When you call the office because your child is sick, you should be prepared to give the following information:

- Your child's age and approximate weight.
- Your child's temperature, when appropriate.
- The duration of the illness, and what measures have been taken so far.
- Whether your child has an underlying condition, such as diabetes, or takes medication on a regular basis.
- Have the phone number of your pharmacy on hand in case a prescription is needed.
- Have a pencil and paper ready so that you can write down the instructions.

Q: **What happens during the doctor's first visit with a newborn?**

A: The doctor has two main purposes in checking the newborn:

❶ To make sure the child is capable of meeting the challenges of life outside the womb.

❷ To screen out possible birth defects.

When a totally dependent fetus becomes an independent newborn, dramatic physiological changes occur. For more than 95% of newborns, the doctor will inform the parents that their newborn is healthy and normal. Most newborns develop normally; however, 5% of newborns need some kind of medical intervention to help them survive this critical period. There is a 3% to 5% chance that a newborn will have a birth defect or irregularity. Sometimes this situation can be life-threatening. If you had complications during pregnancy or delivery, your baby should be examined at birth. If your pregnancy was trouble-free, the exam can take place anytime during the first 24 hours of the child's life.

Before you leave the hospital, a blood sample is drawn from the baby for a blood count. Thyroid function tests are also administered, and enzyme tests are run to detect PKU (phenylketonuria), galactosemia, and sickle-cell anemia. Other tests for disorders such as congenital hypothyroidism and congenital adrenal hyperplasia may be run as well, depending on your area's newborn screening guidelines.

Q: *What else should I expect during this first visit?*

A: Your doctor will examine your baby every day during your hospital stay and discuss with you the baby's current condition and symptoms that babies normally develop later. These may include:

- jaundice
- molding of the skull
- cephalohematoma (bleeding under the scalp)
- forceps marks
- puffy eyelids
- subconjunctival hemorrhage (bleeding in the white of the eye)
- hemangioma (birthmark made by blood vessels)
- mongolian spots (bluish spots on the buttocks)

Q: *Once we leave the hospital, what are some of the things I may notice with my infant?*

A: Some of the more common occurrences are:

- frequent hiccupping
- spitting up
- sneezing
- initial weight loss
- vaginal discharge or blood
- transient hair loss

In addition, your baby may experience these common skin conditions:

- heat rash
- neonatal acne
- diaper rash
- skin peeling
- other infant rashes

Q: *What are some issues I should discuss with the doctor and/or nursing staff before leaving the hospital?*

A: You should ask for information and advice on the following:

- feeding: breast or bottle
- burping techniques
- clearance of air passages if baby gags or chokes
- care of umbilical cord
- crying
- sleeping patterns
- infection protection
- postpartum adjustment
- bathing techniques

IMMUNIZATIONS

By Kenneth A. Frank, M.D.

All normal and healthy children should be immunized against diseases which may be crippling or fatal. Benefits of immunization are partial or complete protection against the consequences of disease, which range from trivial and inconvenient symptoms to paralysis and death. No immunization is completely effective or completely safe. Minor reactions to immunizations are frequent; severe reactions are extremely rare. It is more likely a child will have severe health problems from serious illnesses than to have significant problems from the immunization against the illnesses. Minor illnesses, even those with some fever, are usually not sufficient reason to postpone immunization, but you should discuss any illness with your pediatrician. Immunizations should not be given if an individual is hypersensitive to a vaccine component or has altered immune response. "Vaccine Information Sheets," prepared by the Communicable Disease Center for each vaccine, are designed to inform parents of the benefits and risks of the immunizations. If you have any questions, ask your provider.

Most states require that children be immunized before enrolling in school, preschool, child care centers or family home day care, unless exempt for medical or religious reasons. As a parent or guardian, you will be required to complete a certificate showing proof of this. Below is information about the different diseases for which your child may be immunized.

&.

The American Academy of Pediatrics recommends that all normal, healthy children in the United States receive immunizations.

&.

DTAP/DPT IMMUNIZATION:
DIPHTHERIA, PERTUSSIS, TETANUS

Diphtheria occurs primarily in children. This throat infection produces a toxin which damages the heart, kidneys and nerves, and may cause death.

Pertussis (whooping cough) is most severe in young infants. The illness produces protracted coughing, and may cause lung damage, seizures, brain damage and death. Immunization protection wanes in adulthood so adults can be a reservoir for the disease. It is always present.

Tetanus (lockjaw) is caused by a toxin produced by a wound infection. The toxin may cause severe, painful muscle spasms, breathing problems and death.

There are two vaccine types available:

- **DTWP** (or more commonly **DTP**). In addition to containing diphtheria and tetanus toxoid, this vaccine also contains inactivated "whole cell" pertussis organisms.
- **DTaP** contains diphtheria and tetanus toxoid, as well as more purified cellular components of pertussis, not the whole organism. It is believed that DTaP has fewer adverse side effects, such as fever, than DTWP.

POLIO IMMUNIZATION:

Polio is a viral infection of the nervous system which may produce extensive paralysis and death. The polio vaccine has been very successful; wild polio virus is no longer causing disease in the Western Hemisphere. There are two types of polio vaccine:

- **Oral Polio Vaccine (OPV)** is an attenuated live virus vaccine. In addition to protecting the recipient against paralytic polio, it also induces intestinal immunity.
- **Enhanced Inactivated Polio Vaccine (eIPV)** is a killed polio virus vaccine. It protects the recipient against paralytic polio but does not induce intestinal immunity.

MMR IMMUNIZATION:
MEASLES, MUMPS, RUBELLA

Red measles or "rubeola" is the most serious common childhood illness. The illness lasts ten days, with a high fever and generalized rash. Complications are pneumonia and encephalitis, which can produce deafness, blindness, retardation and death.

The mumps virus causes painful swelling of the salivary glands. It may cause inflammation of the pancreas. Fortunately, complications are rare. Infection in adult males may cause sterility.

Rubella, also called "German measles" or "three-day measles," is usually a mild illness with fever and rash. Infection in a pregnant woman can result in disastrous defects in the fetus.

HIB IMMUNIZATION:
HEMOPHILUS INFLUENZA TYPE B

Invasive hemophilus influenza type B disease is one of the most serious bacterial infections in the young child. This bacterium causes meningitis, which has a high mortality rate. There is a high rate of residual neurological effects among survivors. HIB may also cause serious infections of the throat (epiglottis), lungs, bones and joints. This vaccine has dramatically reduced infections from this organism.

HBV IMMUNIZATION:
HEPATITIS TYPE B

Hepatitis is a liver disease caused by several types of viruses. The serious forms can result in chronic liver damage, liver cancer and death. Vaccines are available for two types of hepatitis.

Hepatitis B Vaccines (HBV) protect against hepatitis B which is transmitted through blood and body fluids. Hepatitis B is the leading cause of liver cancer in the world. Infected mothers may pass the virus to their infants at birth. The risk can be greatly reduced by giving the newborn infant a dose of hepatitis B immune globulin (HBIG) on the day of birth and then vaccinating the infant with the hepatitis B vaccine series. This vaccine series has recently been added to the list of required vaccines for those children entering school for the first time.

CHICKEN POX IMMUNIZATION:
VARICELLA VACCINE LIVE (VVVL)

Chicken pox is a highly contagious, common childhood illness with fever and a blistery rash as the primary symptoms. The complication rate of this disease is low; yet 25 children die each year in the U.S. due to chicken pox, and many more may end up with brain damage. More commonly, chicken pox causes significant economic problems with disruption of child care and school attendance. Shingles at an older age is a long term complication of chicken pox. Talk with your pediatrician about the pros and cons of this vaccine.

OTHER VACCINES

- **Hepatitis A Vaccine (HAV)** protects against infectious hepatitis (hepatitis A) which is spread via ingestion of fecally contaminated material. Symptoms include fever, malaise, jaundice, decreased appetite, and nausea. Although not recommended for routine use, it is advised for those traveling to Mexico and third world countries.

- **Influenza Vaccine** is given yearly in the fall to high-risk individuals to prevent influenza. This includes those with asthma and other chronic lung diseases, major heart disease, sickle cell anemia, diabetes, chronic

renal or metabolic disease, and immunosuppressed individuals including those with HIV infection. Influenza spreads in epidemics during the winter time. Symptoms vary but usually include fever, chills, headache, malaise, muscle aches, cough, and stomachaches. Since the influenza virus mutates frequently, a yearly shot is needed to build resistance to newer strains.

- **Pneumococcal Vaccine** is recommended for children 2 and older with increased risk of acquiring systemic pneumococcal infections—those with sickle-cell disease, functional or anatomical absence of the spleen, nephrotic syndrome or chronic renal failure, HIV infection and conditions associated with immunosuppression. Pneumococcus is a bacterium which can cause bacteremia, meningitis, otitis media (ear infection), pneumonia, and sinusitis. Some doctors recommend vaccination in older children with recurrent ear infections.

- **Meningococcal Vaccine** is currently recommended for children 2 and over who have functional or anatomical absence of the spleen and those with complement component deficiencies. Meningococcus is a bacterium which causes meningococcemia and meningitis. Shock, coma, and death are common.

﷼ RESOURCES ﷼

■ AMERICAN ACADEMY OF PEDIATRICS

800-433-9016
(847) 228-5005
P.O. Box 927, Dept. C
Elk Grove, IL 60009-0927
Send a self-stamped envelope to request information on immunizations from the medical perspective. This resource also offers the most current recommendations in the immunization schedule.

■ CENTERS FOR DISEASE CONTROL AND PREVENTION (CDC)

800-CDC-SHOT
Web site: www.cdc.gov/nip
Through this free service of the National Immunization Program, you can request information by fax, mail or recorded information on hundreds of topics—everything from the theory of immunizations to specific information about each vaccine, including disease and immunity information, statistics, and side effects. You may request up to five documents at any one time. We found this to be the most comprehensive resource available on immunizations.

■ CENTERS FOR DISEASE CONTROL AND PREVENTION NATIONAL IMMUNIZATION HOTLINE

800-CDC-2522
If you have questions about vaccinations, the hotline puts you directly in touch with a knowledgeable operator who can fill you in on recommended vaccinations, answer questions about side effects, and refer you to free or low-cost immunization clinics nearby. CDC will mail out free brochures including a parent guide to immunizations, common misconceptions, and recommended vaccination schedules. The hotline is staffed from Monday through Friday, 8:00 a.m. until 11:00 p.m., Eastern Standard Time.

■ NATIONAL VACCINE INFORMATION CENTER

800-909-SHOT
512 W. Maple Ave., Ste. 206
Vienna, VA 22180
Web site: www.909shot.com
This is a nonprofit center founded by parents whose children responded negatively to immunizations. They represent the small number of children who have had significant reactions, and offer several packets of information regarding immunization reactions. The group's toll-free number can also help you access their six-minute tape on preventing vaccine reactions ($12).

■ VACCINE ADVERSE EVENT REPORTING SYSTEM (VAERS)

800-338-2382
If your child has suffered a serious reaction to a vaccination, call for a report form. You can do this yourself. Your child's physician is also required by law to report the reaction.

"A Measure of Love"

A Life Experience by Mary J. Patt

It's 11:00 p.m., and I am sitting on the carpet beside the white wooden crib that has been shrinking steadily for 23 months. My daughter's porcelain face, framed by golden ringlets, lies so close to mine that I can see her eyes dancing beneath the lids as she slips into REM sleep. Her right hand, poking out between two slats, is closed tightly around my left index finger. She squeezes it involuntarily the way she did as a newborn, when her hand was one-third this size. She is wearing her favorite vegetable pajamas, which are getting tighter by the week. With each warm breath, a garden of carrots and peas and tomatoes and corn and radishes rises and falls across her chest.

I am so in love with this child that my heart hurts. I can't let go of the moment. I want her to fit in the crib and remain my baby forever. But her body, mind and spirit have their own agendas, as they should. In a few days she'll be moving on to a toddler bed, just as she has moved on to toddler aspirations. Her favorite phrases this week ("All by self....Show Julie....Julie do it...") suggest that my husband and I have been doing our job of helping her to grow into a confident and purposeful human being. But only years and years of trial and error, on all our parts, will tell.

Since the beginning we have been torn between comparing her to other children (to assure ourselves that she is "normal") and not comparing her to other children (because each one develops so differently). Numbers cannot describe the unfolding of a unique soul. How could I possibly quantify the questioning light that has been shining in my daughter's eyes since the first moment I took her in my arms? How could I tally the myriad expressions that shaped and reshaped this beautiful face long before she had words to describe pleasure, pain, amusement, fear, anger, curiosity, and surprise?

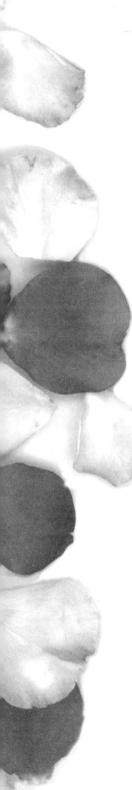

A baby is a constant reminder to stop analyzing life and just immerse oneself in it. While we have wasted precious time worrying about how much self-esteem Julie will have as a teenager, or how we'll afford a great college education, or whether the world will be destroyed by pollution and overpopulation during her lifetime, she has been busy finding joy and awe in each bug, book, and bird that has come her way. When she was tiny, so many parents of older children stared wistfully at her and sighed, "It all goes so fast. Cherish the baby days." Suddenly we find ourselves in their place, looking at newborns and wondering how she could ever have been that featherweight and fragile.

In several hours she will stand up and call out from this crib: "Momma. Dadda. Ooouuuuut!" She will hit the ground running, demanding juice, a book, a song, a hug from Big Bird and several more from us. We will embrace her as she embraces life, as she begins her daily dance with the essence of all things. And we will renew our trust in her to find her own path, to come up with her own definition of success.

There are so many things I cannot know about her future. All I do know is that she loves her life now. She loves her Mom and Dad and Grandmas and Grandpa and other children and, of course, some furry friends—alive and stuffed. To-night, as she tucked several animals into some pretend beds she had made out of old cloth diapers, she whispered to them what she usually hears from me. "Good night. Sweet dreams," she told them as she gently patted them on the back.

What she doesn't know is that her Dad and I never go to bed without creeping back into her room, separately, to whisper our hopes and dreams into her sleeping ears. To-night I kiss her soft hand before letting go with a silent prayer I have repeated many times: "God bless your soul, tonight and always, Julianne. Know that your father and I love you and we always will. Sleep long and deeply and sweetly. Count your blessings, and we'll see you in the morning for another wonderful day." ❧

BREASTFEEDING

By Dianne Neilson, R.N., I.B.C.L.C.

Breastfeeding is the most special gift you can give your baby. Although it is natural, nursing is really a learned skill that you acquire together with both time and patience. Breastfeeding provides frequent, close physical contact that helps to promote feelings of security and increasing health for you both.

The ideal first food, breast milk has immune properties that increase your baby's resistance to infections such as respiratory viruses and ear infections, as well as diseases that occur later in life—diabetes, lymphoma, Crohn's disease, and ulcerative colitis. Breast milk is associated with less constipation, stomach upset, and diarrhea. Many breastfed babies experience fewer or delayed allergies and research has shown the incidence of SIDS in breastfeeding babies is significantly reduced.

Exclusive breastfeeding for a minimum of four to six months is recommended by the American Academy of Pediatrics, the U.S. Surgeon General, and the World Health Organization. These three influential organizations recommend continuing breastfeeding, supplemented with solids, through the baby's first year of life.

Conveniently, breast milk is always ready, warm and fresh. There is nothing to mix, measure, heat or carry, no added cost or product waste. The hormones stimulated during nursing promote feelings of relaxation and well-being and help the uterus to contract after birth, minimizing blood loss and improving recovery. Also, the milk production process utilizes the nursing mother's calories, helping her to return to her prepregnant weight more quickly and easily. New research indicates breastfeeding may have a beneficial effect in reducing risks of breast and uterine cancer and osteoporosis. The benefits are many and the experience too wonderful to miss.

> ≈
>
> *Although it is natural, nursing is really a learned skill that you acquire together with both time and patience.*
>
> ≈

PREPARATION FOR BREASTFEEDING

Prior to the birth of your baby there are a few things you can do to get off to a good start. It is recommended that you not stimulate or even wash your nipples with soap in the last few weeks of pregnancy as your body is naturally preparing them for breastfeeding.

Attend a breastfeeding preparation class to get basic information, especially on latch-on and positioning. Having a current breastfeeding book purchased prior to the baby's birth is also recommended. During their last trimester, many mothers also purchase two to three supportive bras designed for nursing.

Other than that there is little to do. Attending a La Leche meeting, talking with friends who have successfully breastfed, or speaking with health professionals who are knowledgeable and supportive about breastfeeding can be helpful.

GETTING STARTED

Once your baby arrives it helps to be patient. Offer your baby an opportunity to breastfeed as soon as possible after delivery—within the first hour is ideal. Breastfeed skin-to-skin with your baby—your body will keep your baby warm. Colostrum is the valuable first milk your body produces for your baby's first days. Present in small quantities, colostrum has antibodies which give your baby early protection against germs. It also has a laxative effect and helps to move the first dark, tarry stools. This also helps to minimize jaundice.

Most often mothers notice increasing breast fullness by the third or fourth day postpartum. By this time babies are ready for more milk. Some mothers' breasts will feel warm and lumpy and a low-grade fever may be present while milk volume increases. On this day nurse often (up to 10 times a day, or every one and one-half to two hours), keeping baby awake to nurse longer than five to 10 minutes. Continue frequent nursing for 48 hours. The swelling normally lessens within this time.

Babies need to nurse a minimum of eight times a day after that. Babies nurse for different lengths of time so watch your baby, not the clock. If your baby falls asleep after nursing for five minutes, and wants to nurse again within an hour, you may find it easier to keep him awake the first time so he feeds 15 minutes or longer. Then he may sleep two to three hours before waking to nurse again. Most mothers like to use both breasts at each feeding, starting on the last breast nursed.

Most importantly, parents need to know that their baby is getting enough milk. You don't need to see it or measure it—you will know. You will learn to recognize the sounds of your baby swallowing, especially after your milk increases. The most reassuring sign is frequent soiled diapers. By the fifth day it is important that your baby is having three or more soft yellow bowel movements in a 24-hour period, as well as six or more wet diapers. At checkups, reassurance comes from the baby's weight measurements. After losing 5% to 7% of their weight in the first few days of life, babies begin to put the weight back on at approximately an ounce a day, regaining or passing their birth weight by 10-14 days old.

THE COMFORT FACTOR

Breastfeeding needs to be comfortable. Often mothers feel tender when baby first latches on. If the tenderness disappears after slowly counting to 10, then it is usually a sign that baby has latched on well. If the tenderness continues, baby needs to be relatched. Babies need to have more than just the nipple in their mouths—they need to mouth enough areola to compress the pockets under the areola that hold the milk in the breast. Their lips need to be flanged out around the breast with their noses and chins touching the breast at all times. Mothers find it helpful to relax and lean back once baby is latched on, which helps the baby to stay on the breast fully.

Pillows are important to support baby and mother's arm as they relax while nursing. Many mothers find putting their feet up on a short stool can help baby to stay up on the breast. With good latch-on and positioning you are not only comfortable and can enjoy nursing your baby, but your baby also nurses more effectively, getting more milk in a shorter amount of time. Massaging your breasts while nursing also helps increase the amount of milk your baby drinks.

If you experience pain, are unsure if baby is getting enough milk, or have questions and concerns about what you are experiencing it is best to contact a breastfeeding/lactation specialist who can provide you with individualized guidance and support.

LACTATION CONSULTANTS

Lactation consultants are specially trained in breastfeeding education, management and support. Their goal is to help you breastfeed successfully and to help you work through any problem. Most lactation consultants are International Board Certified Lactation Consultants (IBCLC), which means they have met the necessary qualifications set by the International Board of Lactation Consultant Examiners and meet continuing education requirements. Fees for private lactation consultants vary yet usually start at $45-$60 per hour depending on the services you need. Most lactation consultants also sell and rent electric pumps and related supplies.

Some insurance companies may reimburse lactation consultant fees, breastfeeding supplies or breast pump rentals; be sure to ask your provider. If you are a WIC recipient, you may qualify for a breast pump or other supplies.

BREASTFEEDING

DISCREET NURSING IN PUBLIC PLACES

After the first couple of weeks, most moms are more comfortable with nursing but may have concerns about nursing in public. Often new parents are more concerned about making someone else uncomfortable even though they feel good about what they are doing. You might practice in front of a mirror to see what others will see. You can always wear your baby in a sling, handy for both carrying and nursing, or toss a sweater or baby blanket over your shoulder. Many mothers just pull their T-shirt up and rest the edges against their breast, covering it but not the baby. There are also beautiful nursing shawls and aprons and a variety of styles of nursing tops and dresses designed for easy access and discreet nursing. Often just finding a location like rest room lounges, dressing rooms, or even sitting in your car will be more comfortable than nursing in a crowded area. Most times mothers who nurse simply look like they are cuddling their babies. It really is simple to take baby anywhere.

WHAT TO WATCH

All things you ingest may affect your milk, your milk supply, or your baby. Some things can reduce the amount of milk your body will produce. Others can cause fussiness in babies or may harm your child. You do have choices.

Regular alcohol intake will often decrease a mother's milk supply and readily passes into breast milk. If you do drink an alcoholic beverage, always nurse first prior to drinking and wait two to three hours before nursing again.

Current recommendations for caffeine intake is a two-cup limit of caffeinated coffee (300mg) per day. Most medications are safe but always remind your prescribing physician that you are nursing. If you are unsure about the medication's safety, contact a lactation consultant or another health professional who keeps up with current information on drug and medication effects on lactation and the breastfed baby.

NURSING AND WORK

Dedication and planning can help nursing moms overcome challenges when returning to work. Waiting until your milk supply is fully established (six weeks or longer) increases your chances of successfully combining breastfeeding and work. Breast pumps allow you to save milk for later bottle feeding by your child's caregiver. It's best to begin pumping and saving milk a good two weeks before returning to work. Not only does this help you create a backup milk supply but it also familiarizes you with your pump and your body's response to pumping. (See the Products chapter for a review of breast pumps.) Breast milk can be stored in the refrigerator for three to five days or in the freezer for three to six months, if stored in glass or plastic bottles or milk storage bags.

Often the best time to pump is in the morning right after your baby has nursed. At this time most mothers' breasts are more full so there is usually extra milk. Pumping right after the baby nurses won't interfere with baby's next nursing time. Most mothers like the advantage of a double pump collection kit which minimizes pumping time, often draining both breasts in 10-15 minutes.

INVOLVING THE NEW FATHER

Fathers' support of breastfeeding is the most influential factor in mothers' feeling successful about their nursing experiences. Some dads claim to feel left out of the breastfeeding experience. Of course, not much can be done about sharing the actual act of breastfeeding but knowing that their baby is getting the best food available anywhere usually makes both parents feel good. Fathers can participate in so many other activities with their babies when they are not nursing—babies also need to be cuddled, sung to, rocked, burped, bathed. Babies especially love to sleep on their fathers' chests and have preferences for skin to skin contact.

At work, plan to pump and then nurse evenings, mornings, and on your days off. Pumping at the times your baby would nurse is ideal but you often need to coordinate with work times that are available to you. It's wonderful if you can visit and nurse your baby on your lunch break.

When you pump and save your breast milk, it can be used to provide breast milk exclusively for your baby, or your baby can have formula while you're at work and nurse while at home. In either case, make sure the baby will take a bottle when the time comes to return to work. Introducing your three- to four-week-old baby to a bottle assures acceptance. Offer a bottle once or twice a

week to keep your baby familiar and to help with the adjustment between breast and bottle.

Before returning to work it is usually a good idea to inform your employer of your plans to pump. Hopefully, your employer can help you locate a private, comfortable area for pumping.

Finding supportive child care is essential. When you feel more confident with your care provider, the easier it is for you to leave your baby, the less anxiety you will have, you'll be able to express more milk, and your baby will be happier to nurse on your return. The key is to be flexible and creative, and trust your intuition in trying to create a balance between work and motherhood.

☜ RESOURCES ☜

■ HOLLISTER/AMEDA EGNELL
800-323-8750
755 Industrial Dr.
Cary, IL 60013
Ameda Egnell, now part of the Hollister pharmaceutical firm, has been manufacturing breast pumps for over 50 years. Their "Breastfeeding Answers" covers everything from what a breastfeeding mother should eat to how to manage breastfeeding and working. You can request a free subscription to the "Circle of Caring" newsletter, which covers topics of interest to lactation consultants and nursing moms. The company's Elite breast pump is the only one on the market controlled by a microprocessor, allowing the user to find just the right combination of suction and cycling. Many other pumps and accessories for purchase and rental are available.

■ LA LECHE LEAGUE INTERNATIONAL
800-LA-LECHE (525-3243)
1400 N. Meacham Rd.
Schaumburg, IL 60173
La Leche is the world's largest source of information on breastfeeding and related topics. It is a nonprofit organization founded in 1957 that offers support groups, monthly meetings, breast pump rentals, a catalog and educational materials. A $30 membership includes six issues of the newsletter "New Beginnings" and a 10% discount on most purchases. Their book, *The Womanly Art of Breastfeeding*, is a comprehensive guide to nursing your baby.

BREASTFEEDING

■ MEDELA BREAST PUMP RENTALS AND ACCESSORIES

800-TELL-YOU (835-5968)
4610 Prime Pkwy.
McHenry, IL 60050
Medela's Breastfeeding National Network is a 24-hour, seven-day-a-week warmline. Staffers provide information on where to buy or rent Medela breast pumps, accessories or nursing bras, and lactation consultants in your area.

Most local Medela outlets carry the "Pump in Style" breast pump that looks like a purse but comes with everything needed for double pumping. Medela also has a line of specialty feeding products for babies with special feeding problems. Local Medela dealers offer a free breastfeeding information guide and a catalog of the full product line.

■ NURSING MOTHERS COUNSEL

(415) 599-3669
P.O. Box 50063
Palo Alto, CA 94303
Web site: www.nursingmothers.org
This network offers information and support for nursing mothers. The Nursing Mothers Counsel will mail a free breastfeeding informational packet, including recommended reading. The group offers phone counseling and referral to Medela breast pump rentals. The nonprofit group is made up of women volunteers who have had firsthand experience with breastfeeding. The organization is also a source of support for combining nursing and returning to work.

■ WOMEN, INFANTS AND CHILDREN (W.I.C.)

This federal supplemental food program helps pregnant women up to six months after delivery, nursing mothers up to 12 months after delivery and children from birth to age 5, who have a nutritional or medical need and low income (up to 180% of the poverty level). They also provide education and assistance with breastfeeding. Eligibility is determined at the first clinic visit. Classes, counseling, nutritious foods and referral to health care are offered. Your local health department, hospital or care provider can refer you to the nearest WIC agency.

BECOMING A HUMAN MILK DONOR

Though the days of the wet nurse are long gone, one satisfying way a mother can share her breast milk is by participating in the Human Milk Banking Association of North America's donation project.

For babies unable to tolerate formula whose mothers cannot nurse, donor milk can be lifesaving. Donors may choose to express daily over weeks or months, or may make a one-time donation of stored milk. Before donating, women are screened and tested to rule out blood-borne diseases.

For more information about milk banking, contact the Human Milk Banking Association of North America, Inc. toll-free at 888-232-8809. Their address is 8 Jan Sebastian Way #13, Sandwich, MA 02563.

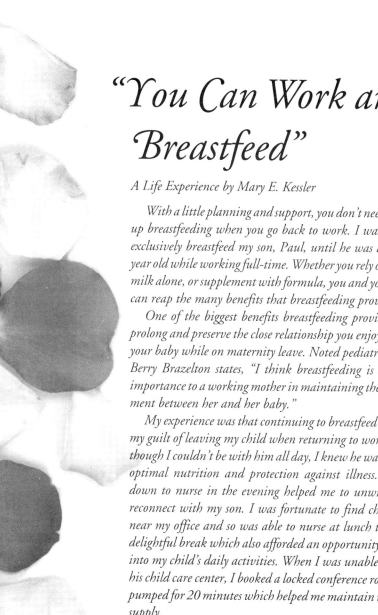

"You Can Work and Breastfeed"

A Life Experience by Mary E. Kessler

With a little planning and support, you don't need to give up breastfeeding when you go back to work. I was able to exclusively breastfeed my son, Paul, until he was almost a year old while working full-time. Whether you rely on breast milk alone, or supplement with formula, you and your child can reap the many benefits that breastfeeding provides.

One of the biggest benefits breastfeeding provides is to prolong and preserve the close relationship you enjoyed with your baby while on maternity leave. Noted pediatrician T. Berry Brazelton states, "I think breastfeeding is of extra importance to a working mother in maintaining the attachment between her and her baby."

My experience was that continuing to breastfeed reduced my guilt of leaving my child when returning to work. Even though I couldn't be with him all day, I knew he was getting optimal nutrition and protection against illness. Sitting down to nurse in the evening helped me to unwind and reconnect with my son. I was fortunate to find child care near my office and so was able to nurse at lunch time—a delightful break which also afforded an opportunity to tune into my child's daily activities. When I was unable to go to his child care center, I booked a locked conference room and pumped for 20 minutes which helped me maintain my milk supply.

I also got more rest! With no formula to mix or bottle to warm, I could nurse Paul during the night while I was half asleep and catch another 40 winks during his morning feeding, snuggled in bed.

One question people often ask me is how I was able to continue to breastfeed without worrying about juggling work and pumping. My answer is I didn't concern myself *with caring about what people thought, nor did I tell very many people what I was doing. As the regional vice president of a bank, I found myself in a traditional environment and yet I found a way to balance my personal needs with my work expectations.*

A good support team is essential. At home, my husband, Michael, cooked and cleaned up after many meals, giving me time to nurse the baby. My child care provider was knowledgeable about breastfeeding and did not sabotage my efforts. I also arranged for a long enough maternity leave that allowed me to establish my milk supply and energy level. I found that easing back into work with a flexible schedule allowed additional nursing time. Finally, I found that I really needed to rest as much as possible to maintain my milk supply.

Most important, I found it was essential to keep my priorities straight. Nursing a baby is one of life's greatest joys and it lasts for just a few short months. For me, making the commitment to breastfeed was worth every minute of the extra effort it took.

Mary's Tips for Fast, Easy and Effective Pumping:

To maintain your milk supply and provide milk for baby, pumping the breasts is important. Here are a few hints I found helpful:

■ Rent a top-quality electric pump. Some insurance companies will reimburse part of the cost. With a double hookup, you may be able to pump six to eight ounces of milk during a typical coffee break.

■ Find a private space at work so you can relax (an office with a door that locks, a conference room, seldom-used restrooms).

■ Two piece suits work best for pumping and covering up an occasional leak.

■ Assist your "let-down" reflex with your baby's picture or an item of clothing.

■ A Playmate cooler with reusable ice works well for private storage of milk and pump components that require daily cleaning, as well as a snack and drink for mom.

■ Sterilize the plastic parts of the pump in the dishwasher every night to save time.

To help you stay organized, here is a list I found helpful each morning:

Work Checklist

■ Cooler
■ Ice
■ Pump kit (assembled to save time during pumping breaks)
■ Empty bottles to store milk
■ Snack and drink for mom
■ Briefcase, purse, etc.

Child Care Checklist

■ Breast milk pumped the previous day
■ Baby food, juice for an older infant
■ Baby's "lovey" and/or pacifier
■ Mom's lunch (if nursing at lunchtime)
■ Mom's "bib" for protecting work clothes from spit-up (made from an old towel)
■ Weekly: diapers, wipes, clothes, etc.

After-Work Checklist

■ Refrigerate and label pumped milk
■ Sterilize pump kit and used bottles in dishwasher
■ Refreeze ice
■ Pack cooler for tomorrow!

QUESTIONS AND ANSWERS
Sleep: Getting a Full Night's Rest

For parents and children, sleep is essential. It is not until parents are faced with sleepless nights and children wake up haggard and grumpy that the true appreciation of a full, good night's sleep sets in. During pregnancy, we hear parents talk about sleepless nights. But what we may not hear is that the patterns we set for our infants can carry on into the toddler and school age years. Starting life with healthy sleep patterns makes an enormous difference in a child's and parent's life. To explore sleep needs and habits, we asked John Kuhn, M.D., some of the most common questions about sleep.

Q. How do you get your baby to sleep?

A. To start healthy sleep patterns, parents may consider keeping a normal, healthy baby out of close proximity once they are ready to move baby out of the parents' bedroom. Because parents are so in tune with a baby's sounds, every noise or movement can result in parents not sleeping fully or deeply. Also, as baby awakens and makes sounds in the morning, parents may rise immediately, rather than let the baby explore himself and his surroundings and perhaps return to sleep. Babies will let parents know when they need to get up.

Other culprits in forming poor sleep habits include pacifier use and/ or using a parent as a prop to help baby get back to sleep. How you fall asleep is how you put yourself back to sleep. So, if a child falls asleep laying next to Dad with a pacifier in his mouth and wakes to find neither the pacifier nor Dad, a child may react by desiring both. Then, a parent wakes up to a screaming child and rushes to pop in the pacifier and hold the child again, and so the vicious cycle is formed. By putting the child to bed either awake or partially awake in his own bed, you are teaching the child to fall asleep alone, and when the child wakes he can put himself back to sleep alone.

Q. Are security blankets or special animals okay for children to use to sleep with?

A. Security blankets are a very good idea. Don't ever let your baby take a bottle to bed because it can become the "security blanket" and can be very harmful and difficult to stop. I definitely would encourage a "blanky" or soft animal. These are extensions of us, and make for a transference of the feeling of closeness. Of course that makes it difficult to take them away. We've all seen the 3-year-old carrying a special friend. Sooner or later they wear out and can be left behind. It's interesting that the memory of these items stays in the parents' minds so vividly—we know their importance.

Q. What about the family bed?

A. Years ago, in less sophisticated societies, families slept together. We needed warmth and huddled in the cave or in an unheated home. Now, with a more sophisticated society, sleeping together is not physically necessary. Many families sleep in the same bed by personal choice.

The only thing I stress is to be consistent in your choices. If you have a family bed, a child cannot sleep with you one night and then not be allowed another. You also need to think about when you will have your children sleep in their own room and about any sleep problems that may occur when making that transition. And, finally, you may want to consider your own sleep habits. Are you a light sleeper? Do you awaken every time your child does, or is it comforting for you to have your child next to you? These may all be factors in your sleep decision.

Q. How much sleep is necessary for my child?

A. This is a purely individual question. There is no hard rule for each age group. Sleep needs are dependent on your child's personality and your tolerance level. The biggest indication of whether your child is getting enough sleep is how she wakes up in the morning. Does she wake up on her own? Is she sluggish, sleepy, cranky? Look at the morning results and then base your child's bedtime generally around those criteria. Also, you can put your child to bed earlier than when she actually falls asleep. After following a bedtime routine, you can allow your child to play or read a book quietly in his room and then put himself to sleep when tired.

Q. Why is a bedtime routine so important?

A. Children thrive on routine and consistency. We all do better when we know what is going to happen. When it is time for bed, have a routine you follow—reading a story, brushing teeth, singing a quiet song, getting a drink of water, then going to bed. It is vital that you stick to the routine. Do not change the order of bedtime rituals or forget one of the steps, but instead go through the same routine every night. Then once you've done the final tuck-in, leave the child's room and do not go back. Children will always want one more story or one more drink, but what they really want is you. A parent provides a security blanket, and at bedtime a child is alone and senses a loss of control of his environment, so sleep can be scary. By making bedtime positive and consistent, a child learns good sleep patterns.

PACIFIER PROS AND CONS

❧

Parents are

cautioned

against

pacifier

overuse,

which causes

babies and

their families

to become

overdependent

on the

"plastic

plug."

❧

Before your baby is born, it is easy to decide not to use a pacifier. With a squalling infant who seems to need vast amounts of sucking time, however, you may change your mind rather quickly. For some, pacifiers are a magical device which instantly stop crying once they are popped in the baby's mouth.

Parents are cautioned against pacifier overuse, which causes babies and their families to become overdependent on the "plastic plug." A little experience will tell you if your baby's cries are for hunger, boredom, crankiness, or just a request for a little cuddling. Pacifiers are perfect for that cranky cry which sucking can soothe. Breastfeeding moms, especially until their milk supply is well established, should always try feeding a cranky baby before offering a pacifier.

Choose your baby's pacifier with safety foremost in mind. Don't use the nipple of a bottle as a pacifier. Choose one designed specifically for your baby's age. The pacifier should have shield vents and a sturdy design which will resist breakage. The orthodontic-type pacifiers have the disadvantage of only fitting in the right-side-up position. It's up to you (and your baby) to determine which shape is most comfortable.

Never tie a pacifier to a string around your baby's neck. To avoid possible strangulation, keep any ties attaching pacifier to clothes very short—6" or less. The makers of Mam pacifiers recommend replacing pacifiers every two months owing to the breakdown of the nipple due to baby's saliva, coupled with exposure to heat and sunlight. Pacifiers need to be washed either in the dishwasher or in hot, soapy water. It's best to have more than one pacifier so frequent cleaning is possible.

Some babies prefer the natural pacifier—thumbsucking. As it often starts well before birth, thumbsucking is a difficult habit to break. Parents can try to substitute a pacifier for thumb, but success is unlikely. Unless thumbsucking continues well into childhood, permanent malformation of teeth is unlikely. An advantage of thumbsucking is that the thumb is always available as baby requires, as parents who have spent many nights waking hourly to reinsert pacifiers will attest.

For those non-thumbsucking babies who refuse pacifiers altogether, parents are on their own as far as comforting techniques go. The old familiars of rocking and gentle motions are age-old methods to calm baby.

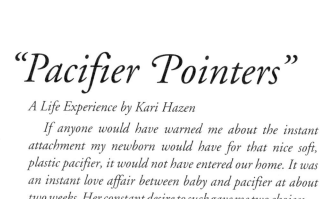

"Pacifier Pointers"

A Life Experience by Kari Hazen

If anyone would have warned me about the instant attachment my newborn would have for that nice soft, plastic pacifier, it would not have entered our home. It was an instant love affair between baby and pacifier at about two weeks. Her constant desire to suck gave me two choices— a baby at the breast constantly or a pacifier. Although I loved breastfeeding, I also desired some independence—and the opportunity to go to the grocery store without a screaming infant. With one trip to the nearest pharmacy I came home with pacifiers galore. My life, or so I thought, would become quieter and simpler with a content baby.

My daughter became one of those children who constantly had a pacifier in her mouth. She slept with it, she played with it and used it for security. I was not quite sure of the "rules" of pacifier use, as my first child wanted nothing to do with the plastic security blanket. I had visions of my second-born starting kindergarten with a pacifier, or graduating from high school with a moldy piece of plastic in her mouth.

What I didn't realize was the impact the pacifier would have on my sleep habits. Night after night, as soon as my daughter would wake up "pacifier free," a loud shriek would be heard throughout our household followed by sobs. Once she began to talk, she shouted, "Binky! Binky!!" throughout the night. Almost on autopilot, I would make a zombie walk to her bedroom, place the pacifier in her mouth and return to bed exhausted. My husband and I concocted a plan—we would buy several binkies and place them in her crib. She would have so many to choose from, including "glow-in-the dark" models, that she would not have to wake us up.

The night we put our plan into place, we snuggled in bed thinking "finally, a full night's sleep." To our despair, it became obvious that the habit of one of us placing the pacifier back in her mouth was already formed, so after 15 minutes of screaming I got up and gave her a pacifier.

There were other problems that arose from the pacifier. I'll never forgot the night my husband called me at an evening meeting: "Go to the store and buy a pacifier right away and come home." That was the entire conversation. When I arrived 30 minutes later, the furniture was rearranged in an attempt to find the lost pacifier. My husband wordlessly handed me a screaming child who instantly became content with a pacifier back in her mouth.

I am the first to admit we "enabled" our daughter's habit. One well-known parenting book suggests saying goodbye to the pacifier at age 1, as it may be very difficult after this time period. I read it, looked at my daughter, and decided I did not have the energy to remove it.

Once she turned 2, I began slowly weaning her from the pacifier. She didn't use it during the day unless she asked for it. I began to put it in a drawer after I brushed her teeth, so she knew where it was when nighttime arrived. During this time, I read an article that stated pacifier use contributed to a greater number of illnesses. Since my daughter had a dozen ear infections by the time she was 18 months old, I thought the sooner we said goodbye to the pacifier, the better. It's strange that after all my worrying, eventually it just went away. As she matured, she simply didn't need it as much.

We bought a Muppet board book entitled "Bye-Bye Pacifier" and it explained how great life is without a pacifier. There were, and still are, times my daughter asks for it and I explain it went bye-bye. The only downside is that she still does not typically sleep through the night. Those habits formed in her earlier days of waking, being comforted, and settling back to sleep, have stayed with her.

I know several other parents whose children used a pacifier without a problem. A friend who is a nurse told me the sucking reflex is very strong up to age 2. She explained that all children are different, and so are the parents' experiences. I wish, though, I had known some of the side effects of a using a pacifier. Maybe I would have tolerated more of the fussiness in her earlier months and would sleep better today. ❧

FEEDING BABY

FORMULA

Scientifically, baby formulas are meant to imitate mother's milk. For women who cannot breastfeed, or for those who choose not to nurse, formula is a safe and appropriate choice. It is recommended that cow's milk not be used until a child is one year of age because of the high amount of sodium and protein it contains and its lack of other vital nutrients for infants. Most starter baby formulas are milk-based and allergies can occur.

Several brands and types of formula are on the market. Discuss with your baby's pediatrician the different choices available and ask for a recommendation.

If you decide to bottle-feed your infant, you should know which formulas are the most nutritionally balanced. No formula is identical in composition to breast milk; however, some are closer than others.

Commercial formulas are manufactured and available as:
- Single-serving bottles with sterilized nipples
- Ready-to-pour from a can into your own bottles
- Liquid concentrate to dilute with water in bottles
- Ready-to-mix from a powdered concentrate.

BABY FOOD

When should a parent introduce solids to the baby? The typical introduction period is when your baby is four to six months old. Discuss with your pediatrician any questions you may have regarding solids and what is best for your child.

When you're ready to introduce baby food, you may choose to pursue one of two avenues. One is to purchase commercial baby food from the grocery store; the other is to make the food yourself. The choice is an individual one.

COMMERCIAL BABY FOOD

Purchasing commercial baby food offers some great advantages, especially during your child's infancy. The texture is the perfect consistency for babies during this early stage. Single-ingredient foods make it easy to detect any food allergies.

The convenience of commercial baby food is undeniable. Most full-service grocery stores carry major brand-name baby

ꙮ

For women who cannot breastfeed, or for those who choose not to nurse, formula is a safe and appropriate choice.

ꙮ

BOTTLE FEEDING SAFETY

- Always check the expiration date on the formula.
- Follow the manufacturer's directions when preparing formula.
- Do not use leftover formula; bacteria which develops in formula may cause infection.
- Do not heat formula in a microwave oven. The formula may heat unevenly and burn the baby's mouth or throat.
- Do not use formula that has been frozen or shows white specks or streaks.
- Keep the bottles and nipples clean, and wash your hands before preparing formula.
- Refrigerate unused portion or prepared amount of formula until feeding.
- Follow manufacturer's guidelines for the refrigerator life for formula.

foods that offer a wide variety of single foods and combinations. Read labels carefully so that you can avoid ingredients such as added sugars, salt, modified food starch, MSG, preservatives and artificial colors and flavors. It is possible to buy commercial baby food that consists of only the food and water.

To minimize germs, portion baby food from the jar to a dish. Don't feed baby from the jar unless she will finish the entire contents. After opening, the unused portion of baby food fruits or juices will keep in the refrigerator for three days; vegetables may be safely stored for two days. If you warm your baby's food in a microwave oven, be sure to stir thoroughly and test the temperature before giving any to your child.

ORGANIC BABY FOOD

Many parents prefer to feed their baby certified organic baby food in order to avoid food treated with synthetic pesticides and fertilizers. Federal standards for production, processing and certification of organic foods, and independent

certification that you will see noted on organic baby foods, such as Earth's Best, let consumers know the food is truly synthetic pesticide- and fertilizer-free. You can also make your own baby food with organic produce found at health food stores and farmer's markets.

HOMEMADE BABY FOOD

Taste some store-bought baby food and ask yourself, "Is this what I want for my child?" If taking food from a jar is not exactly your idea of a delicious, nutritious, satisfying meal, then read on.

For less then $15, you can purchase a baby-food grinder from most stores that carry baby products, including some grocery stores and pharmacies. Other than this, you need not invest more than a little time in order to offer your baby homemade food. Simply grind up the fresh vegetables, fruits, grains and meats you already have at home. Don't salt or sweeten baby food—babies' taste buds are different from adults'. Add a small amount of formula, breast milk or water if too thick. The easiest way to store homemade baby food is to prepare each food in bulk, freeze in ice cube trays, then store the cubes in plastic bags in the freezer. The cubes can be defrosted as needed for your baby. When on the go, instead of grabbing a few jars of baby food, go to your freezer.

Remember it is best to stick with one new food a week in case of allergies and for the purpose of identifying which food may be causing the problem. Once foods have been introduced, you can start mixing them.

If organic is what you want, you may want to shop at either a health food store or a natural food co-op for fruit and vegetables. Some grocery stores also sell organic foods.

FOODS TO AVOID

Certain foods are best avoided until your baby is one year old because they are either highly allergenic, contain too much fat or are difficult for a baby to digest.

Avoid:

- wheat: until 6 months
- corn: until 6-9 months
- citrus fruits and juices: until 1 year
- egg whites: until 1 year
- honey: until 1 year
- raw vegetables: until 1 year
- peanut butter: until 1 year
- pudding and fruit desserts: avoid at all ages since they contain excess sugars and empty calories.

CHILD SAFETY

Accidents continue to be the leading cause of death among American children ages 1-5; however, up to 90% of accidents are adult-preventable. As a parent, be aware of situations in which accidents are likely to happen. Get down on the floor and see the world from your child's point of view. This will open your eyes to the potential disasters waiting to happen.

- Teach safety at an early age.
- Check every room of the house and eliminate hazards.
- Be aware of the increasing abilities of your child.
- Never leave a child in a home alone.
- Be prepared in the event an accident does occur.
- Learn infant CPR and first aid!

Children get into everything. From the moment they begin to scoot across the floor, everything within reach is fair game. Take time to review your environment and begin child-proofing before you bring your baby home from the hospital.

Auto safety: Use an approved, properly installed infant carrier or child's seat from birth to four years, or 40 pounds, and booster seat or seat belt thereafter. Auto deaths account for the largest group of fatal injuries among American children. The possibility of death or injury is reduced 70% when a child is in a safety seat. Never place an infant in a car seat or carrier on a counter or table top.

Changing tables: Never leave a baby unattended on a changing table. The day you turn your back will be the day your baby rolls over for the first time.

Choking: Avoid hard candy, hot dogs, grapes, nuts, popcorn, chips, and other small food items that your child could choke on. Learn CPR and know what steps you should take if your child chokes.

Cleaning supplies: Keep all cleaning supplies in a high, locked cupboard.

Cribs, strollers and walkers: Check current safety standards. Make sure equipment is sturdy and properly assembled. The American Academy of Pediatrics recommends foregoing the use of walkers because of the number of injuries they cause. Never use an infant carrier as a car seat. Do not place a crib near

❧

Children get into everything. From the moment they begin to scoot across the floor, everything within reach is fair game.

❧

draperies or blinds where a child could become entangled and strangle on the cords. Don't use pillows, and make sure the mattress fits snugly in the crib.

Cupboards: Put safety latches on all cupboards that contain items children should not get into, especially in the kitchen and the bathroom. Anything that could be considered a poison (Ask yourself: would I want to put this in my mouth? If not, treat it as poisonous.) must be in a high, locked cabinet.

Electrical outlets: Keep them all covered...even ones that are up high; children are great climbers. Consider using self-closing outlet covers that cover outlet holes automatically upon removal of appliance prongs.

Gates: All gates should be permanently mounted into wood or a wood stud. If you have plaster walls find the stud and mount a board to the wall and then mount the gate.

Hanging cords: Wrap up all cords from telephones, answering machines, lamps and appliances out of reach to avoid strangulation. Be sure any cords from draperies or blinds are tied up and out of reach.

Lead: If your home was built before 1978, it's quite possible that your walls are coated in lead paint, which can cause a wide range of problems in children. Contact the National Lead Information Center, 800-LEAD-FYI (532-3394), for a lead information packet. Old lead and chrome-plated water pipes in the home can cause lead poisoning in children. Call the Environmental Protection Agency's Water Safety Line at 800-426-4791 for more information. Non-glossy vinyl miniblinds contain lead which creates lead dust on the blinds. The Consumer Product Safety Commission advises replacement with blinds labeled "made without lead."

Medications: Keep all medications in a locked tool box or fishing tackle box and place the box out of reach of the child. Even vitamins can be deadly; the number one cause of poisoning deaths in young children is iron overdose. Just a few pills can cause deadly results.

POTENTIALLY DANGEROUS HOUSEHOLD SUBSTANCES

- alcohol, rubbing and drinking
- ammonia
- bleach
- detergent
- floor wax
- furniture wax
- gasoline
- lighter fluid
- lye
- medicines
- mouthwash
- oven cleaners
- paint thinners
- pesticides
- toilet cleaner
- turpentine

Contact your state's Poison Center for answers to your questions regarding these and other dangerous substances. If you have non-emergency questions about household chemical products, you may call the Chemical Manufacturers Association's Chemical Referral Center at 800-262-8200 weekdays 9:00 a.m.-6:00 p.m. EST.

Plants: Some plants are safe and some are toxic. Know the difference. You can ask your pediatrician for a list of poisonous plants.

Poisons: Always keep a bottle of syrup of ipecac on hand. It is available without a prescription and should be used to induce vomiting upon the advice of your area's Poison Center. Find the number and keep it near your telephone.

Pools: Pools should be fenced all the way around, and the doors leading to the pool should be locked. Never leave a baby or young child by the pool unattended.

Purses or pocketbooks: Always store up high since many contain medications, mace, pepper spray or weapons, and have straps that could cause a choking hazard.

Sleepwear: Since January 1997, infant and children's sleepwear is no longer required to be made of flame-resistant material. Now "longjohns" and rompers made of cotton can be labeled for sleepwear if tight fitting. If you buy cotton sleepwear, make sure the garment fits snugly, as that is the key to fire resistance.

Stairs: Keep a gate at both the top and bottom. If the posts are more than four inches apart, consider plexiglass or safety netting.

Stoves: Use only the back two burners or adhere a child stove guard. If burner knobs are accessible to a child, remove them and only use when cooking. Any freestanding stove should be secured to the floor or wall. Call the stove manufacturer for appropriate hardware.

Strings: To prevent strangulation, never put a pacifier or other items on a string around a baby's neck. Maximum length for any strings, ties, belts, etc. is seven inches.

Toys: Any toy can be unsafe if it is misused or given at an inappropriate age level. Keep older children's toys away from infants.

Water: More than 200 children have drowned in five-gallon buckets of water since 1984. Keep children away from buckets of water and use toilet latches to avoid accidents. Never leave an infant or young child alone in the bathtub. Babies can drown in less than two inches of water! Your home's hot water heater should be set to 120 degrees or lower to prevent scalding.

Windows: To keep your child from falling out of an open window, prevent windows from opening more than four inches with a window lock out of the child's reach. Window screens are for bugs only; they are not strong enough to keep children from falling.

⋅⋅ RESOURCES ⋅⋅

■ **AMERICAN ACADEMY OF PEDIATRICS**
800-433-9016
P.O. Box 927
Elk Grove Village, IL 60009
The American Academy of Pediatrics offers safe baby tags ($4.95/set) which can be easily attached to a diaper bag or stroller. The cards include first aid guidelines for emergencies and have room for you to list your infant's health information. Several safety-oriented videos are available, including "Baby Alive," "Child Safety Outdoors" and "Infant and Toddler Emergency First Aid."

■ **AMERICAN TRAUMA SOCIETY**
800-556-7890
(301) 420-4189
8903 Presidential Pkwy., Ste. 512
Upper Marlboro, MD 20772-2656
The American Trauma Society is an injury prevention advocate. The society provides posters, brochures and other materials showing common injuries, their prevention and treatment. It will also refer you to other resources, if necessary. It has materials suitable for schools, homes and public service organizations.

■ **CHILD HEALTH ALERT**
(617) 239-1762
P.O. Box 610228
Newton Highlands, MA 02161
Child Health Alert is a six-page newsletter containing summaries and evaluations of late-breaking reports from medical journals, meetings, and public health press releases. Topics covered include medications, product recalls, infections and other illnesses, environmental issues, immunizations, nutrition and parenting concerns. To maintain its independence, there are no advertisements. A one-year subscription (10 issues) costs $29; you can request a free sample issue.

■ **CONSUMER PRODUCT SAFETY COMMISSION (CPSC)**
800-638-CPSC
Washington, DC 20207
Web site: www.cpsc.gov.
This government commission reviews product safety. They offer free brochures such as "The Baby Safety Checklist" and "The Safe Nursery." All are available by sending a postcard with your name and address (call first to find out the names and numbers of publications you'd like to receive). Many are available over the Internet. This is the agency to report unsafe children's products, receive recent product recalls and general product safety information. To check on recalls and seasonal safety information, check their web site. CPSC regulates most mainstream products except for car seats.

■ **THE DANNY FOUNDATION**
800-83-DANNY
P.O. Box 680
Alamo, CA 94507
Web site: www.dannyfoundation.org
E-mail: dannycrib@earthlink.net
The Danny Foundation exists to educate the public about crib dangers. Call or write for your free brochure, "Is Your Crib Safe?" which discusses proper mattress fit, acceptable space between crib slats and appropriate corner post heights.

■ DEPARTMENT OF TRANSPORTATION AUTO SAFETY HOTLINE

800-424-9393

Web site: www.nhtsa.dot.gov

This federal government hotline is staffed by members who can tell you whether your safety seat has been recalled. Part of the National Highway Traffic Safety Administration, they can provide registration forms if you never registered with the manufacturer to be alerted of any future recalls. When you call, have the manufacturer name, model number and the date the seat was made.

■ JUVENILE PRODUCTS MANUFACTURERS ASSOCIATION (JPMA)

(609) 231-8500

236 Route 38-West, Ste. 100

Moorestown, NJ 08057

Web site: www.jpma.org

The Juvenile Products Manufacturers Association is a national trade association comprised of manufacturers of baby products. The JPMA logo appears on products which have been lab tested for safety. For information regarding JPMA, safety standards and a list of JPMA's Directory of Certified Products, send a self-addressed stamped business-size envelope to the address above.

■ NATIONAL LEAD INFORMATION CENTER

800-LEAD-FYI

Lead is an insidious poison that can be found in older homes' paint, water pipes, even miniblinds! Call the Lead Information Center to receive a free information packet about lead and how to go about minimizing your family's risk of exposure.

■ MIDAS MUFFLER SHOPS PROJECT SAFE BABY

800-868-0088

P.O. Box 92292

Libertyville, IL 60092

Under the "Project Safe Baby" program, Midas sponsors community education programs on car seat safety. When you purchase a car seat from Midas for $42, you are eligible to return it for $42 in services. Check with your local Midas dealer about the car seat program. Call Project Safe Baby for a free brochure or video ($2.50) entitled "Tips for Safer Travel with Children."

■ SAFETYBELTSAFE U.S.A.

800-745-SAFE

P.O. Box 553

Altadena, CA 91003

This nonprofit group provides information on safe car seat installation and use. A representative will call to answer your questions about car seats if you leave your name, phone number, city and state. Safetybeltsafe can also answer questions about an individual seat.

■ WINDOW COVERING SAFETY COUNCIL

800-506-4636

Long window-blind cords can be a strangulation hazard in the home. To prevent this, furniture should be moved away from windows, cords shortened or cut, and drapery cords anchored to the floor. This safety council is making available, at no charge, retrofit tassels or tie-downs to make existing cords safe. You can find them at participating retailers; more information can be obtained through the 800 number.

SPECIAL CONCERN RESOURCES

CHAPTER FIVE

"Alicia"

A Life Experience by Carrie Camacho

I was ten days past my due date when my gynecologist ordered a non-stress test to make sure everything was okay. Once the test was completed, I had an ultrasound and then was told that an emergency C-section was needed because the baby's heartbeat was showing signs of stress and there was very little amniotic fluid left.

Within 30 minutes I was prepped for surgery, allowed to make two phone calls and then wheeled into the operating room. I was frightened, but also excited. Once Alicia was born, and seeing she had all her fingers and toes, the fears I had about the non-stress test were eased. After a difficult night of pain, nausea and very little sleep, the pediatrician came in and told me they were running genetic tests because they thought our new daughter had Down syndrome. I was devastated! I waited until that evening when my husband came to see us to tell him what the doctors suspected. I'll never forget the look on his face. We just stared at each other, not knowing what to do or say. We decided to wait for the test results to see if there was anything to worry about. When Alicia was four days old, the test results came back positive.

I think the most difficult part was having to tell our family and friends. We didn't want people to feel sorry for us; we felt sorry enough for ourselves. Then, when she was seven days old, we found that Alicia had a heart murmur. I was trying to be positive in thinking that Alicia was looking good; yet I didn't know how much more bad news I could take. When Alicia was ten days old, the cardiologist informed us that she had three heart defects that were repairable. We just cried! Such tragic news in ten short days. Trying to be there for each other when we were barely there for ourselves was so difficult, not knowing what to do or say.

For the next six months, Alicia went to the cardiologist once a week, then gradually every two weeks, then every three weeks. It was such a struggle for her to put on weight. Her

heart was working three to four times harder than it should, so her body was really burning off the calories. I attended a monthly support group for parents of children with heart defects. They helped me to understand that I wasn't the only one with an ill child. There were others who had much worse conditions than Alicia.

At six months and one day, Alicia had open heart surgery. Nobody in either of our families had ever had any operation so critical. Family members rallied to our support and donated blood for Alicia. Her surgery went well with the exception that we were told she might have to wear a pacemaker. Seven days after surgery, Alicia was released from the hospital the day before Thanksgiving. Needless to say, Thanksgiving is a special time of year for us.

Alicia has steadily improved over the past two years. She has quite a personality. Alicia and I are learning sign language so we can better understand each other. Lacey, her younger sister, is a big help and an excellent role model for Alicia. Alicia is also Daddy's girl. She seems to melt everyone's heart.

I have received help from the community that I can't imagine being without. It was difficult having a handicapped child, especially our first. Professionals in the community helped us to help Alicia. They showed us methods we could use when playing with her. It's really neat to see her learn something from us through playing.

As I look back over the last two and a half years, the negatives have turned into positives. We have all learned so much and become better and stronger people. The struggle to learn, and to help Alicia, has enriched our lives. Everything she conquers also becomes a victory for us. Normal children will eventually learn to do things. Alicia has to be taught over and over until all of a sudden she catches on, and it is such a natural high. We tell everyone about her newest victory.

Once you work through the anger, denial, shock, depression and accept the fact you have a handicapped child, you can start healing yourself. That little bundle will open your eyes and your heart to a whole new way of life and an appreciation for the little things in life. 🐾

CHILDREN WITH SPECIAL NEEDS

By Janet M. Hier

Soft lights, romantic music, maybe a nice bottle of wine...and *voila!* Forty weeks later a squalling little child is presented to the world. Obviously not every moonlit tryst creates another human being. All sorts of microscopic errors can occur between the candlelight and the cradle. Some fertilized eggs fail to implant in the uterus, while others have defects that cause them to be shed in the menstrual flow even before the woman may know she is pregnant. In fact, some statistics have shown that the awe-inspiring process that leads from conception to birth is so fraught with peril that as few as 25% of all successful conceptions actually end with the birth of an infant.

Although these numbers may make it seem as though the chances for ever having a baby are pretty overwhelming, a glance at the birth rate proves this simply isn't so. The vast majority of infants are born after having "beaten the odds" and come into this world in a healthy state. Unfortunately, though, not all are born this way. The number of newborns with some sort of congenital abnormality readily detected at birth has been estimated at 3% of the population, with another 3% being diagnosed within the first year of life.

According to statistics from the American Medical Association Encyclopedia of Medicine, the 12 most common birth defects in descending order are:

- **Heart Defects:** Range from minor heart murmurs to severe heart valve errors requiring immediate surgical repair.
- **Mental Retardation:** Includes cerebral palsy, a disorder that can be caused by developmental defects in the brain or trauma at birth. It also includes the effects of Fetal Alcohol Syndrome (FAS), which has been recognized as the most common cause of mental retardation in the United States. At first FAS was thought only to affect the babies of severely alcoholic mothers, but recent research has shown that even relatively small amounts of alcohol can cause birth defects.

᥍

Statistics seem pretty irrelevant when the child in question happens to be yours.

᥍

- **Pyloric Stenosis:** A narrowing of the muscle at the bottom of the stomach that causes vomiting and problems with eating. Surgical correction is necessary and curative. This condition is much more common in boys than girls.
- **Anencephaly:** The brain fails to fully develop. Often detected during prenatal testing, anencephalic babies carried to term die soon after delivery.
- **Spina Bifida:** The backbone does not fully fuse around the spinal cord. How severely a child will be affected depends upon the size of the opening and its location. Research shows a decrease in occurrence of spina bifida when the mother takes folic acid before and during pregnancy.
- **Down syndrome:** A chromosomal defect that causes a characteristic appearance, heart problems and often some degree of mental retardation.
- **Cleft palate and cleft lip:** Immediate surgery and intervention help these children to breathe and suck properly. Later operations minimize disfigurement.
- **Clubfoot:** One or both feet are turned in an abnormal direction. Clubfoot is often corrected with special braces and shoes while little bones are still soft. Sometimes babies' feet turn because of their position in the uterus before they are born. This is not true clubfoot and may require no special treatment.
- **Hypospadias:** A malformation that causes urine to flow from a displaced opening along the penis.

- **Congenital dislocation of the hip:** This malformation is possibly due to several genetic factors.
- **Congenital deafness:** Some children are now being fitted with electrical devices implanted into the inner ear that enable them to perceive sounds.
- **Cystic Fibrosis:** A disorder in which the lungs fill with sticky mucus; other severe health problems occur. Some genetic markers for CF have recently been found, although there is no cure as yet.

Statistics seem pretty irrelevant when the child in question happens to be yours. Although some prenatal tests can detect a few abnormalities in utero, and surgical intervention has been successful at reversing certain problems even before birth, most parents have no warning their child will not be born "perfect."

Adjusting to this situation will take family members through a series of stages similar to those of the grieving process. Mothers, fathers, grandparents, siblings and even extended family members will all experience the seven stages of reaction at different times and in different ways. These stages do not necessarily occur in order, but they can generally be considered as:

- **Shock:** A period of helplessness and numbness. It can be especially difficult to concentrate through this stage. Some parents have referred to it as "running on autopilot." Write down everything you need to remember, from questions to ask the neurologist to a reminder to feed the dog every day. Using a small hand-held tape recorder at the

SPECIAL NEEDS

physician's office will give you something to refer to when it all seems to blur.

- **Denial:** Disbelief; a sensation that it is all a bad dream, rationalizing a child's developmental patterns to "he'll (crawl, walk, roll over) when he's ready!"
- **Sadness:** This stage can overwhelm parents at awkward times, causing embarrassment or even paralyzing grief. It is of the utmost importance that you find non-judgmental help for this stage, either through a support group for parents of children with similar problems, or by seeking professional counseling.
- **Anger:** Hair-triggering nerves and a general feeling of rage. Many people find this stage affects their relationships with coworkers, family members and spouses. Very few marriages are truly seamless unions, and this stage can amplify the tiniest flaws into tremendous conflicts. Seek help and support if the crisis negatively affects your marriage.

- **Anxiety:** Nervousness, sleeplessness, lack of appetite. The sense of isolation at this time is very strong. It may be difficult for outsiders to understand why you haven't "gotten over it." Hard as it may be to comprehend, it is vital for parents to take a break from the strain of coping with their child's needs. Other siblings also need a chance to "get away" without feeling guilty.
- **Bargaining:** A faith in God may be restored at this point, although it may not resemble what it was prior to the birth of a special child. Many parents will find themselves trying any and all treatments they can find at this time, from the most conventional and aggressive to very nontraditional, alternative sources.
- **Acceptance:** The ability to pull all the above together and still cope with your life. There is no set time as to how long these stages can take to work through, and not everyone feels them in the same order. Additionally, unexpected events such as emergency surgery or milestones like entry into kindergarten can cause emotional relapse.

❧ RESOURCES ❧

■ AMERICAN HEART ASSOCIATION
(214) 373-6300
7272 Greenville Ave.
Dallas, TX 75231
Web site: www.amhrt.org
Founded in 1924, the American Heart Association promotes education, supports research into heart disease, and

trains CPR instructors. For parents of children with congenital heart defects, the association provides information on feeding, dental care and general information about the condition. Information about other heart conditions such as rheumatic fever and heart murmurs is available.

■ AMERICAN LUNG ASSOCIATION

(212) 315-8700
1740 Broadway
New York, NY 10019

Many local chapters of the American Lung Association offer support for parents of children with pediatric asthma, including resource material and referral to support groups.

■ AMERICAN SOCIETY FOR DEAF CHILDREN (ASDC)

800-942-ASDC (2732)
(916) 482-0121
2848 Arden Way, Ste. 210
Sacramento, CA 95825

A nonprofit parent-helping-parent organization, ASDC provides support, encouragement and information to families of children who are deaf or hard of hearing. For a yearly $30 membership, families receive a quarterly publication with national news of interest to the deaf community, family profiles and children's activities. A convention is held every other year. The national office provides information on signing, language acquisition, special equipment, and advocacy issues.

■ AUTISM SOCIETY OF AMERICA

800-328-8476
7910 Woodmont Ave. #650
Bethesda, MD 20814
Web site: www.autism-society.org/

For over 30 years, the Autism Society of America has supported parents whose children have autism. Information and referral services are provided by phone. The society operates local support groups, and members receive the bimonthly "Advocate" newsletter. If you have questions, the society's "What Is Autism?" brochure, or one or more of the 21 packages of information on various autism-related topics, are sure to help you find answers.

■ BEACH CENTER ON FAMILIES AND DISABILITY

(913) 864-7600
3111 Haworth, University of Kansas
Lawrence, KS 66045
E-mail: Beach@dole.lsi.ukans.edu

The Beach Center supports families with special needs through research, training manuals, and a variety of reading materials. Their publications catalog includes booklets such as "Research Brief: Fathers, Their Children, and Disability," "Start Your Own Parent to Parent Program," and "Learn About the Laws That Impact Your Family's Life" for 50 cents each.

■ CLEFT PALATE FOUNDATION

800-24-CLEFT (242-5338)
1829 E. Franklin St., Ste. 1022
Chapel Hill, NC 27514
Web site: www.cleft.com

One of every 700 newborns has some form of cleft lip or palate. The Cleft Palate Foundation distributes pamphlets on the genetics of cleft lips and palates, feeding an infant with a cleft, and a basic introduction to cleft lip and cleft palate, and will send a bibliography of other books and pamphlets available. The foundation makes referrals to medical specialists and parent support groups.

The foundation is affiliated with AboutFace, a support and information organization. Networking with pen pals and by telephone, videotapes, newsletters and an annual conference are part of

SPECIAL NEEDS

the support for families AboutFace offers. To contact AboutFace, call 800-225-FACE (3223) or e-mail: abtface@aol.com.

■ CYSTIC FIBROSIS FOUNDATION
800-FIGHT CF
6931 Arlington Rd., Rm. 200
Bethesda, MD 20814
Web site: www.cfs.org
Parent support, information and referrals to local centers and chapters are made by the Cystic Fibrosis Foundation. Brochures and other educational materials are mailed free of charge.

■ EASTER SEALS SOCIETY
(202) 387-4434
2800 13th St., N.W.
Washington, DC 20009
Through its local chapters, the Easter Seals Society offers a variety of programs for children with physical and mental disabilities. Some chapters offer therapeutic pools, respite programs, summer camps, and all offer referrals and written information on a variety of disabilities.

■ EXCEPTIONAL PARENT MAGAZINE
800-372-7368
555 Kinderkanack Rd.
Oradell, NJ 07649
Exceptional Parent is a monthly magazine devoted to parenting children and young adults with disabilities. Good articles on a variety of disabilities and how to deal with them are targeted to parents, professionals and educators. A resource guide is included in the magazine's January issue. Annual subscriptions are $32.

■ JUVENILE DIABETES FOUNDATION
800-223-1138
120 Wall St.
New York, NY 10005
Resources, brochures, and referrals for information and training are available through the national Juvenile Diabetes Foundation. The primary goal of this foundation is to raise funds for juvenile diabetes research. Informational pamphlets are available, as is the foundation's newsletter, "Countdown."

■ LEUKEMIA SOCIETY OF AMERICA, INC.
800-955-4572
600 3rd Ave., 4th Fl.
New York, NY 10016
This society has publications on most of the childhood leukemias. Financial assistance is also available to patients.

■ MARCH OF DIMES
888-MODIMES (663-4637)
TTY: (914) 997-4764
1275 Mamaroneck Ave.
White Plains, NY 10605
Web site: www.modimes.org
E-mail: Resourcecenter@modimes.org
March of Dimes' Resource Center offers free publications, brochures, and public health information sheets on general pregnancy issues and specific birth defects. The nonprofit organization, with 100-plus local chapters nationwide, can give referrals and information on pre-pregnancy, pregnancy, birth defects, genetics and drug and chemical exposure during pregnancy.

■ MEDIC ALERT

800-432-5378
2323 Colorado Ave.
Turlock, CA 95382

The MedicAlert emblem immediately identifies the wearer as needing special medical treatment during an emergency. A bracelet or necklace identifies the life-threatening allergy, critical medical condition, or impairment of 2.6 million Americans. The adjustable 6" stainless steel bracelet is suggested for children. For a $35 initial membership fee, and $15 each year thereafter, subscribers receive a bracelet with identifying information and MedicAlert's emergency response phone number.

■ MUMS NATIONAL PARENT-TO-PARENT NETWORK

(414) 336-5333
150 Custer Ct.
Green Bay, WI 54301
E-mail: MUMS@netnet.net

When a child is born with a medical condition or a child is diagnosed with a disorder, the family may have no one to turn to for support and sharing. MUMS matches families whose children have the same or similar conditions so they can provide mutual support, information, and education. Referrals are given, at your request, to local and national support groups, phone support, or matching with another family for phone and written contact. With one of the largest databases in the world (28 countries) of 8,600 families covering over 1,600 disorders, MUMS can match even the rarest conditions in many cases. A nonprofit organization, MUMS offers newsletter subscriptions for $10, and will send information about their orga-

nization at no charge (but donations are appreciated). If your child has a rare disorder or special need, it is well worth your while to contact MUMS.

■ MUSCULAR DYSTROPHY ASSOCIATION

800-572-1717
3300 E. Sunrise Dr.
Tucson, AZ 85718
Web site: www.mdusa.org

Clinics, physical and therapy evaluation and support groups are offered through local chapters of the Muscular Dystrophy Association. A wide variety of publications and videotapes are available.

■ NATIONAL ASSOCIATION FOR PARENTS OF THE VISUALLY IMPAIRED, INC. (NAPVI)

800-562-6265
P.O. Box 317
Watertown, MA 02272

NAPVI helps parents find information and resources for their blind and visually impaired children. The $20 yearly membership fee includes a quarterly newsletter, access to a national parent-to-parent network, information on legislation and conferences. NAPVI offers books, including *Children With Visual Impairments: A Parents Guide* at discounted prices to members.

SPECIAL NEEDS

■ **NATIONAL INFORMATION CENTER FOR CHILDREN AND YOUTH WITH DISABILITIES (NICHCY)**
800-695-0285
P.O. Box 1492
Washington, DC 20013
E-mail: nichcy@aed.org
Web site: www.aed.org/nichcy
NICHCY is a clearinghouse that provides information on disabilities and disability-related issues. Brochures such as "Parenting a Child With Special Needs: A Guide to Readings and Resources," "A Parent's Guide: Doctors, Disabilities, and the Family" and "Children With Disabilities: Understanding Sibling Issues" are available free or at nominal cost. In addition, NICHCY personally responds to disability questions, makes referrals to other organizations and agencies, and offers technical assistance to parent groups. NICHCY is a project of the Academy for Educational Development.

■ **NATIONAL INSTITUTE OF CHILD HEALTH AND HUMAN DEVELOPMENT (NICHD)**
(301) 496-5133
31 Center Dr.
Building 31, Rm. 2A32
Bethesda, MD 20892
Web site: www.nih.gov/nichd/
The Public Information and Communications Branch of the NICHD distributes research reports, fact sheets, and publications to health care providers and the general public on topics related to disease prevention in maternal and child health, congenital malformations, and vasectomy safety.

■ **NATIONAL ORGANIZATION FOR RARE DISORDERS (NORD)**
800-999-6673
P.O. Box 8923
New Fairfield, CT 06812
Web site: www.nord-rdb.com/~orphan
E-mail: orphan@nord-rdb.com
This is a clearinghouse for information on up to 5,000 rare disorders. NORD will send you information and articles and recommend other resources and networking possibilities. You may request articles for free; these contain files and medical literature. Reports are more in-depth, and include pertinent symptoms, causes, epidemiology, therapies, drugs, references and resources, all reviewed by a medical advisory board. The first report is free; there is a $5 fee for additional reports.

■ **NATIONAL ORGANIZATION OF PARENTS OF BLIND CHILDREN (NOPBC)**
(410) 659-9314
1800 Johnson St.
Baltimore, MD 21230
Web site: www.nfb.org
E-mail: nfb@acess.digex.net
Believing that, with proper training and opportunity, blindness can be reduced to a physical nuisance, NOPBC works to provide information and support to parents of blind children. An $8 annual membership entitles parents to *Future Reflections* magazine, informative literature, local resources, and a link to the National Federation of the Blind.

■ PATHWAYS AWARENESS FOUNDATION

800-955-2445
3633 West Lake Ave.
Glenview, IL 60025
Web site: www.pathwaysawareness.org
The goal of the Pathways Awareness Foundation is to assist families with concerns about their children's movement abilities. The foundation offers parents a free brochure regarding developmental milestones and early warning signs of physical, occupational and speech delays. If you have any questions about your baby's muscle control abilities, this brochure is an excellent first step towards answering your concerns. You can order other brochures and a video version of "Is My Baby Okay?" Pathways provides information and services for children with movement difficulties or physical challenges, with a strong commitment to early detection and intervention.

■ SHRINERS HOSPITAL

800-237-5055
International Shrine Headquarters
2900 Rocky Point Dr.
Tampa, FL 33607
Shriners Hospitals treat children ages 0 to 18 for orthopedic problems, burns, or plastic surgery (such as for cleft palate) in 19 orthopedic hospitals and burn institutes in the U.S., Mexico and Canada. A newly opened Sacramento, California, hospital treats both burn and orthopedic patients. Application forms, available by calling their national number, are reviewed for medical and financial eligibility. Since 1922, more than half a million children have been helped, completely free of charge, through the Shriners Hospitals.

■ SOCIAL SECURITY INCOME

800-772-1213
If your baby has a disability that is expected to last more than one year, you may be eligible for SSI. Eligibility and financial assistance depend upon income. Staffers can refer you to a local office, where you can set up an appointment. SSI will also make referrals to other assistance groups.

■ UNITED CEREBRAL PALSY ASSOCIATION

800-USA-5-UCP
1660 L St., Ste. 700
Washington, DC 20036
E-mail: ucpinfo@aol.com
Local branches of the United Cerebral Palsy Association offer families support, sibling workshops, activities, newsletters, information on funding and referrals, and respite care. The national group will get you in touch with one of the nation's 200-plus local affiliates, and provide cerebral palsy fact sheets and a publications catalog.

■ WOODBINE HOUSE PUBLISHERS

800-843-7323
6510 Bells Mill Rd.
Bethesda, MD 20817
Publisher Irv Shapell, who has a child with Down syndrome, offers more than 40 titles designed for parents of children with special needs. Considered a leader in disabilities publishing, Woodbine House aims to provide parents with a wide array of information. Book topics cover mental retardation, cerebral palsy, autism, deafness, epilepsy, Down syndrome, Tourette's and resource handbooks for parents of special needs kids.

SPECIAL NEEDS

"Yes, I'm Pregnant"

A Life Experience by Karen Bauman

All my life I have been perfectly healthy, or so I thought. At 35, I learned not everything in my body was in order.

My husband Tom and I had been trying for some time to have a baby, with no success. After two years of hoping and failing, I made an appointment with a specialist. More time passed, with tests and interminable waits, until the laparoscopy showed my tubes were badly scarred from an illness I hadn't even known I had. Our only hope to conceive was through in-vitro fertilization (IVF).

We interviewed three IVF clinics before deciding to use a well-known fertility center with a high success rate. Our chance of success was estimated to be 30% per try (cycle). We chose the "Option Three" plan, for three cycles (embryo implantations) to be performed within one year. Sometime during the coming year I would either conceive or be childless for life.

My first cycle (30 days) started with no exercise, no caffeine and no sex. Tom gave me daily intramuscular injections of fertility drugs, which were followed by two vaginal sonograms which monitored my egg follicle maturity and uterine lining. Three blood tests indicated my estradiol (hormone) level. According to the textbooks, I was a model case. Six egg follicles were surgically retrieved under general anesthesia. Eggs and sperm were then combined (in vitro) for two days. Four picture-perfect embryos were gently transferred vaginally into my uterus. I spent seven days in bed, waiting for the embryos to attach to my uterine lining.

I was filled with hope and fear. I pleaded, begged and bargained with God for a baby. Ten days after embryo transfer a blood draw indicates pregnancy. The results: no baby. But my embryos, estradiol levels, uterine lining, were all perfect. No complications. I was confused, angry and downright depressed. I felt I had lost control over my life. It seemed like a big broken promise. It just wasn't fair.

My driving sense of purpose escalated. I became single-minded, putting all my energy into making the dream of a baby a reality. I read every birthing, parenting and IVF book published. I was determined to do whatever it took. I tried again.

The staff at the fertility clinic was positive and supportive from start to finish. One of the three nurses always returned my call within the hour. They were there for me 100%.

Cycle Two—I knew what to expect from the physical procedures from the first cycle, the shots and surgery. The biggest challenge was the total loss of control. There was absolutely nothing I could do to ensure pregnancy. The wait was painfully exhausting.

The second cycle was another perfect cycle with quality embryos, uterine lining, estradiol level. Again seven days of bed rest was followed by a tenth-day blood draw—yes! I'm pregnant! Reproductive technology has blessed us with un-fathomable joy! We won! Sheer bliss!

I carried pictures of my six-week-old embryo and showed them to everyone, recounting my miracle to anyone who would listen. I welcomed with delight sore breasts and fatigue. I started buying maternity and baby clothing.

In my seventh week, I suddenly doubled over with severe cramps. Tom immediately rushed me to the hospital's emergency room. My IVF doctor diagnosed an ectopic pregnancy in my fallopian tube. He immediately removed both tubes. I recovered at home...waiting for seven days for a sonogram to see if the baby in my uterus was still alive. I had a one in 40,000 chance. Yes! Alive! This baby miracu-lously survived the ectopic pregnancy. The baby was the correct gestational size for eight weeks, with a normal heart beat. Two weeks later my IVF doctor released me to an obstetrician.

Three weeks later I woke up with an intuitive sickening feeling that something was seriously wrong. A sonogram that morning showed no heartbeat. There was no longer a miracle baby. I was in shock; I cried for days. This was the most horrible experience of my life, a heart-wrenching ordeal. I felt an unbearable loss, and was overwhelmed by

my grief. The worst part was how fast everything was erased. After imagining the baby, talking with new moms, planning the years ahead, my life suddenly collapsed in one second. My place in the world, my identity, was no longer the same.

My obstetrician explained it was just nature taking care of an abnormality. One in four women miscarry and it was "no big deal." Well, it was a very big deal to me! I searched out, and had every test done, to try to determine why I miscarried. Still no explanation. I'll never know why. It's an unsettling feeling.

Sometimes it seemed almost too painful to risk letting myself hope for a new pregnancy, and to risk being crushed again. But gradually the courage to try again grew. I had more hope than fear.

I joined a women's IVF group for eight weeks. That helped me immensely. Finally I found I wasn't alone. It was comforting talking with women who were having the same physical and emotional challenges. We gave each other hope and strength and confirmed the insanity of it all.

My friends were as supportive as they could be. They liked the happy, enthusiastic, positive Karen. (I prefer her also.) But with so many disappointments, coupled with massive amounts of hormones raging through my body, my energy was spent working overtime (IVF is very expensive).

Cycle Three—My last chance. The pressure was intense. I was hopeful, because I did get pregnant before. I tried to be realistic, understanding that getting pregnant is just the beginning of a very long process. There are many hurdles, and anything can happen.

Once again perfect embryos, estradiol, lining, bedrest, ten-day wait for a blood draw, then a five-week wait to see the heart beating. Pregnant! Fraternal twins! Two separate placentas, two beating hearts.

We are beaming with happiness. I am going to be a mother. We are going to be a family. I praise medicine. As my story goes to print, I am now one week to delivery ...waiting...and enjoying every minute. ❧

Editor's Note: Karen and Tom delivered two healthy boys shortly after this essay was written.

INFERTILITY

By Phillip Patton, M.D.

Raising a family is an expectation for most married couples. Unfortunately, 10% to 15% of all couples fail to conceive after one year and need to seek treatment from infertility specialists.

In the last decade the demand for infertility services has escalated tremendously, and the demand is expected to increase as more women enter the work force and delay childbearing. Most couples are shocked to learn that only one in four couples conceive each month of attempting pregnancy. Ultimately, 80% of young women (18-34) will conceive within one year, which is reassuring. Unfortunately, the prospects for older women are not as favorable. Less than 60% of women over 35 will conceive within the first year of attempting pregnancy. While only 4% of women in their early twenties suffer infertility problems, a staggering 30% of women over age 35 will have difficulties conceiving. A clear message emerges: women over 35 who want to have a baby cannot waste valuable time. Take charge, be assertive, and begin an aggressive program designed to start a family.

🖜

Most couples are shocked to learn that only one in four couples conceive each month of attempting pregnancy.

🖜

WHAT CAN WE DO TO IMPROVE OUR CHANCES?

It is imperative that women under 35 seek an infertility evaluation after one year of attempting pregnancy. Women over 35 must be even more vigilant. A logical first step begins with a consultation with your gynecologist. A thorough infertility evaluation takes about an hour, reviewing your general health, risk factors for infertility, and physical objectives. First, you should leave the consultation with a clear understanding about the causes of your infertility. Second, you should have a game plan that outlines your future evaluation and treatment that fits you. Be sure that these simple, but critical, objectives are met before you leave your physician's office. It is wise to limit any treatment plan to a short interval because nearly 60% of couples conceive within the first three to four months of directed therapy. Longer treatment plans are often frustrating and unproductive. The best results occur when there is an organized and evolving treatment plan. Some couples may require the services of a reproductive endocrinologist who has additional specialized training in infertility.

Take charge of your emotional needs as well. Fighting infertility may be one of the most stressful events in your life. Support groups such as Resolve may be tremendously helpful in putting you back on track. At times, couples may feel the need for counseling. Ask your physician about therapists who have experience in dealing with infertility issues.

The basic infertility investigation can be concluded within one month of seeing your physician. Disorders of ovulation, fallopian tube or sperm abnormalities are factors that can be easily reviewed. Infertile couples often have multiple problems which must be identified quickly to obtain the best results.

DISORDERS OF OVULATION

Ovulation problems can often be identified during your initial consultation. Unusually short or long menstrual cycles or irregular and unpredictable cycles are hallmarks of an ovulation disorder. Subtle ovulation problems can be diagnosed using a variety of tests, including blood tests for progesterone and pelvic ultrasonography used to monitor aberrant follicle development.

Both oral and intramuscular drugs are used to treat ovulation disorders. Make sure you know how these drugs work, their potential side effects, and their success rates. Serious ovulation disorders may not respond to treatment. For women with poorly functioning or absent ovaries, ovum donation is becoming a popular and highly successful option. Donor eggs can be fertilized with a male partner's sperm and the resulting embryos are transferred into the recipient's uterus. Both known and anonymous donors can be used.

SPERM DISORDERS

Sperm problems are one of the most common disorders identified. Even small irregularities in sperm may be associated with subfertility, and a delay in the diagnosis of a male-related problem can cost you valuable time.

A variety of therapies exist for sperm disorders. One of the most popular techniques is intrauterine insemination (IUI), a relatively simple procedure where sperm, washed free of the ejaculate, are placed into the uterine cavity with the aid of small plastic tubing.

For couples with a severe male-related problem, intracytoplasmic sperm injection (ICSI) offers new hope. ICSI refers to the injection of a single sperm into an egg in conjunction with in vitro fertilization (IVF). The resulting embryos are then transferred into the uterus after three days of culture.

An alternate treatment for male related problems is donor sperm. Donor sperm can be purchased from a sperm bank, and nearly all samples now have been frozen and quarantined for a minimum of six months to reduce the risk of infection. Pregnancy rates using donor sperm are highly variable and the results depend on many factors.

ABNORMALITIES OF THE FALLOPIAN TUBE

Damage to the fallopian tube may prevent sperm from reaching the egg at the time of ovulation. Obvious damage to the fallopian tubes can be determined by a radiologic procedure known as a hysterosalpingogram (HSG). An HSG involves the injection of a clear media which can be seen by X-ray. In women with open fallopian tubes, the X-ray media passes from the uterine cavity into the fallopian tubes and then out into the abdominal cavity. More subtle forms of tubal disease require laparoscopy for diagnosis. This is an outpatient surgical procedure where an incision is made into the area of the belly button and a small telescope is passed into the abdominal cavity under general anesthesia. Many forms of tubal injury can now be treated through laparoscope, avoiding the more expensive and risky abdominal surgery.

In vitro fertilization involves removing eggs by passing a needle through the vaginal tissues. The eggs are then fertilized in the laboratory and transferred into the uterus two to three days later.

KEY INFERTILITY TESTS

Most cases of infertility do not require "high tech" treatment. In fact, using a simple, low tech approach, nearly 70% of infertility causes can be diagnosed and treated effectively. A review of a simple but productive strategy is presented as follows:

- **Basal body temperature (BBT) records.** The BBT record is a simple method to evaluate whether ovulation occurs. Basal temperatures are taken orally immediately after waking before arising, and recorded on a special chart that plots the temperature record against the day of the menstrual cycle. Ideally, the basal temperature will rise slightly after ovulation, due to progesterone production, and remain elevated until a few days before menses.

- **Hysterosalpingraphy (HSG) and saline infusion sonohysterogram (SIS).** The HSG is considered the gold standard in the diagnosis of tubal blockage or uterine abnormalities, but the test is somewhat invasive and costly. A less expensive test with emerging promise, SIS uses ultrasonography combined with saline infusion to evaluate the uterus and the fallopian tubes. One to two teaspoons of fluid is used to distend the uterus. Pelvic ultrasonography used at the time of saline

FERTILITY TREATMENTS ON THE HORIZON

The progress of infertility treatment in the last decade has been staggering. While once thought of as experimental, in vitro fertilization is now a widely practiced technique. In addition, most high-tech infertility centers now offer donor egg and sperm programs, male factor treatment with intracytoplasmic sperm injection (ICSI), and some forms of surrogacy. Selected sites can perform preimplantation genetic diagnosis that can be used to detect genetic abnormalities in embryos before embryo transfer. The future promises to be exciting. The development of protocols for in vitro maturation of immature eggs could radically reduce the cost of IVF. Human egg cryopreservation, now a reality, may see widespread use in women requiring cancer chemotherapy, and potentially in women who desire "egg banking" for future use.

INFERTILITY

injection can trace the path of fluid into the uterus and diagnose abnormalities.

■ **Semen analysis.** A semen analysis should be performed early in the infertility investigation because 30%-40% of infertility is secondary to problems in sperm production or function.

■ **Post-coital testing.** Occasionally cervical mucus obtained at the mid-cycle after intercourse may identify mucus problems. However, the timing of the test is critical. Ovulatory or sperm problems are also factors that may cause a poor mucus test.

A FINAL WORD

Winning against infertility requires dedication to an organized plan which meets both your medical and emotional needs, and uses your resources wisely. Also, consider your personal value system when deciding your treatment. Infertility care is often an evolving process where one form of treatment is replaced by another form. Remember that a proactive plan coordinated with your caregiver is the best method to achieve your goals.

Contributing author Phillip Patton, M.D., is a Board Certified Reproductive Endocrinologist and Obstetrician-Gynecologist in Portland, Oregon.

🐾 RESOURCES 🐾

■ **INTERNATIONAL COUNCIL ON INFERTILITY INFORMATION DISSEMINATION (INCIID)**
(703) 379-9178
P.O. Box 6836
Arlington, VA 22206
Web site: www.inciid.org
This nonprofit group educates the public as to the prevention and treatment of infertility and pregnancy loss. Their web site is a filled with comprehensive infertility information that covers cutting-edge technologies and treatments. INCIID Interactive provides a place for you to discuss your questions and concerns with others. On tap: a set of fertility drug fact sheets which explain fertility drug options in detail.

■ **RESOLVE**
(617) 623-0744
1310 Broadway
Somerville, MA 02144-1731
Resolve offers information and support for those touched by difficulties with infertility. Send a self-addressed stamped envelope to the national headquarters for an information packet, including referrals to the nearest local chapter. Local Resolve services include monthly support group meetings, information on fertility specialists, resources and help with adoption agencies.

COPING WITH GRIEF

Losing a baby can be the most painful and challenging event most parents will ever have to face. No parent can anticipate this type of loss and is usually unprepared for the psychological, social, and even physical turmoil that accompanies the death of a child.

A PARENT'S FIRST REACTION

Though everyone's course through bereavement is different and there is no particular "right" way to grieve, for most parents the period directly following the infant's death is the most distressing. Initial grief is typically marked by shock, a feeling of numbness or bewilderment, and difficulty in comprehending events surrounding the loss. This is followed by the profound and intense emotions associated with grief. In the beginning, parents may experience all or some of the following:

❧

For most parents, feelings of depression and even despair will remain for varying lengths of time. This is normal.

❧

- Uncontrollable tearfulness, depression, or problems with work and concentration.
- Physical weakness, weight loss, loss of appetite, and difficulty breathing and talking.
- Problems getting to sleep and staying asleep. Parents may need to see their doctor regarding sleep medications. But a doctor may hesitate to prescribe medications to numb feelings, since those who deny and avoid all expressions of loss tend to fare considerably worse later.
- A constant, seemingly uncontrollable preoccupation with the child, accompanied by the tendency to withdraw from interest in the outside world. This can be a particularly difficult time for young children who don't have the capacity to understand their parents' withdrawal.
- Powerful guilt and self-reproach as they seek to come to terms with the death. At the same time, they may direct anger and rage at God, caregivers, and—most painfully—spouses and surviving children.
- Symptoms may become severe enough that parents doubt their sanity. They may imagine that they hear the cries or voice of their infant and even feel that they have caught a fleeting glimpse of him or her. These are not atypical manifestations of this type of loss and not a sign that the parent is losing his or her mind.

COPING WITH GRIEF

As disturbing as these feelings are, the intensity of this initial period will pass and is followed by a transitional time of variable length marked by a generally less powerful sadness and attempts to cope with the loss.

MAKING PROGRESS

For most parents, feelings of depression and even despair will remain for varying lengths of time. This is normal. During this period, parents may feel isolated and frequently misunderstood. Previously supportive and caring friends and relatives may be uncomfortable talking about the infant, using his or her name, or reminiscing. There is a sense from them that it is now time to "get better and get on with life."

Parents should realize that mourning an infant can be lifelong in many ways and more acute feelings of depression may take a year or two to lessen significantly. Because of this, support groups can be useful for parents in giving them assurance that others know and have survived what they are going through.

Anniversaries such as birthdays, holidays and the date of death are powerful reminders of the lost infant. Parents will cope better when they discuss or plan for these events in some way rather than ignoring them.

SPOUSES GRIEVE IN DIFFERENT WAYS

Studies show that men and women grieve differently in our society. Men tend to be less expressive in their feelings of grief although they may feel them acutely. Women tend to be more open about the emotions they are experienc-ing and more easily find outlets to express them. Men also are more likely to concentrate on work as a way of getting through their feelings of loss. For instance, women may wish to talk about the loss and men may wish to completely avoid the subject. These and other individual differences can lead to considerable tension in relationships.

Generally, it is best not to be silent about these differences in coping. Couples who tolerate and accommodate them tend to manage their grief better.

SIBLING GRIEF

This can be a particularly difficult time for young children who don't have the capacity to understand their parents' mourning and possible withdrawal. Parents may wonder how to tell siblings about the death. The way a parent may approach this depends a great deal upon the parent's style and the age of the child. A reasonable rule of thumb, as in much of bereavement, is that excessive concealment is generally a poor approach. Parents should speak honestly in a language the child can understand.

RESOLVING THE LOSS

As time passes, both the vivid memories and the pain begin to fade. However, this dulling of memories can be frightening and sad for many since these memories are a way to keep alive connections with the infant. Nevertheless, this is just one way the mind has of healing itself over time.

Parents should not expect to be entirely without feelings of loss. It is not unusual for someone to return briefly to a support group after an extended period to talk about these feelings. Many parents who have been through the initial process of bereavement find it healing to help others through it.

COMPLICATED GRIEF

In rare instances grief is prolonged, and bereaved parents will find themselves unable to function as well as they might expect. They may continue to have very low self-esteem and significant physical symptoms of grief longer than the 12 months which can be expected. They may give up hope and have suicidal thoughts. Under these circumstances, professional help and medications for depression may be needed. A visit to a physician might help with this decision. Major depression can needlessly prolong suffering in those who are bereaved.

SUBSEQUENT CHILDREN

Though the next child is not—nor should ever be—a replacement for the lost infant, he or she can be a source of considerable hope and healing. However, parents who have lost an infant to SIDS generally raise a new infant with much apprehension, as the risk of SIDS for subsequent children is five to ten times greater than that of infants in the general population. Even so, the vast majority of subsequent children will not die of SIDS. Additionally, there are medical approaches that appear effective in reducing the SIDS risk in this group and provide some degree of control over the threat of another loss.

This article was provided by the American Sudden Infant Death Syndrome Institute from their brochure, "Coping With Infant Loss."

A MISCARRIAGE MEANS LOSING A BABY, TOO

By Troy Smith

Miscarriages are far more common than most people think. According to the American College of Obstetrics and Gynecology, 15%-20% of all pregnancies end in miscarriage. Yet each woman who is expecting a baby begins to plan and anticipate the birth of her child from the moment the pregnancy test comes back positive. Even a very early pregnancy loss can lead to feelings of grief and perhaps guilt.

The guidelines above for coping with the death of an infant hold true for dealing with loss from miscarriage. If it makes you feel better to talk about it with friends or relatives, do so. Your health care practitioner may be able to refer you to a local support group, or you can contact the MIDS Support Group, Pails of Hope, the Pregnancy and Infant Loss Center, or SHARE—national groups (resource listings follow) created to help couples through this difficult time. Most offer a newsletter, peer counseling, and brochures and other publications.

Most women who miscarry go on to carry subsequent babies to term. If you have any questions or concerns, don't hesitate to ask your practitioner.

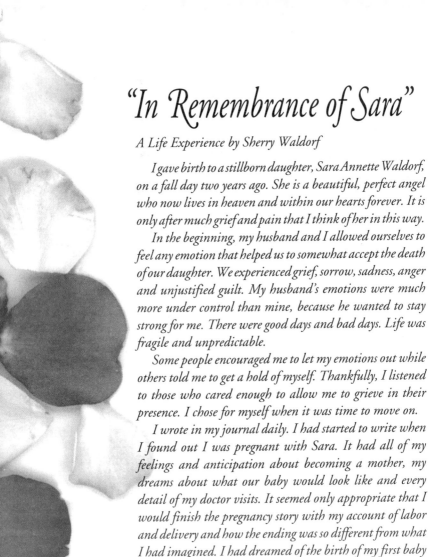

"In Remembrance of Sara"

A Life Experience by Sherry Waldorf

I gave birth to a stillborn daughter, Sara Annette Waldorf, on a fall day two years ago. She is a beautiful, perfect angel who now lives in heaven and within our hearts forever. It is only after much grief and pain that I think of her in this way.

In the beginning, my husband and I allowed ourselves to feel any emotion that helped us to somewhat accept the death of our daughter. We experienced grief, sorrow, sadness, anger and unjustified guilt. My husband's emotions were much more under control than mine, because he wanted to stay strong for me. There were good days and bad days. Life was fragile and unpredictable.

Some people encouraged me to let my emotions out while others told me to get a hold of myself. Thankfully, I listened to those who cared enough to allow me to grieve in their presence. I chose for myself when it was time to move on.

I wrote in my journal daily. I had started to write when I found out I was pregnant with Sara. It had all of my feelings and anticipation about becoming a mother, my dreams about what our baby would look like and every detail of my doctor visits. It seemed only appropriate that I would finish the pregnancy story with my account of labor and delivery and how the ending was so different from what I had imagined. I had dreamed of the birth of my first baby even as a little girl. I wrote lots of poetry. My journal was a tribute to Sara.

Sometimes, I wrote letters to people who had hurt my feelings by things they had said. I never mailed these letters— they are still in my journal. It helped just to put my feelings down on paper.

My mother-in-law made me a beautiful shadowbox to display my keepsakes of Sara—her ashes, footprints, pictures and crib card. I realized that I had kept everything and the grandparents had nothing. After all, they had lost a grandchild.

I wrote a special poem for Sara's grandparents. I had the poem done in calligraphy, included a photocopy of Sara's footprints and framed it. Our parents proudly display it in their homes.

I planted a flower garden around the beautiful marble headstone my Dad had engraved for me. I worked many hours in that garden. It was, and still is, great therapy. I decorated it with lots of angels, birdbaths and wind chimes. Family and friends gave us gifts for our garden. When I felt like crying, I would walk down to her garden and talk to Sara and pray to God for strength.

After only three months of grieving, writing and planting, I became pregnant again. One year after Sara's birth and death, I gave birth to another beautiful daughter, Payton Brooke Waldorf.

Now, Payton and I work in Sara's garden. I swing her in the yard swing. When she is old enough to understand, I will tell her about her big sister and they will, we will, celebrate their birthdays together. ❧

This article was first published in "Loving Arms," the quarterly newsletter of the Pregnancy and Infant Loss Center, Inc. in Wayzata, Minnesota.

⅋ RESOURCES ⅋

■ AMEND

(314) 487-7582
4324 Berrywick Terrace
St. Louis, MO 63128
AMEND (Aiding A Mother and Father Experiencing Neonatal Death) offers a free counseling service to parents who have experienced the loss of an infant. Volunteer counselors give neither medical advice nor information, but listen and share in order to help ease the pain of loss and suffering. A free brochure explains problems encountered by parents after the death of their baby.

■ AMERICAN SIDS INSTITUTE

(404) 843-1030
6065 Roswell Rd., Ste. 876
Atlanta, GA 30328
E-mail: prevent@sids.org
Web site: www.sids.org
The mission of the American SIDS Institute is to prevent and conquer SIDS and promote infant health through a national program of research, clinical services, professional education and family support. With regional offices in Washington, D.C. and El Paso, Texas, the Institute is an invaluable source of up-to-date information about SIDS. Their brochures provide advice for parents-to-be and parents concerned about SIDS. For those who have suffered a loss, the institute offers crisis phone counseling, literature and references. "Helping a Friend Cope with Infant Loss" is designed for friends who would like to know how to support a friend or relative experiencing a loss.

■ BEREAVEMENT SERVICES/ RTS

Gundersen Lutheran Medical Center
800-362-9567, ext. 4747
(608) 791-4747
1910 South Ave.
La Crosse, WI 54601
E-mail: berservs@lhl.gundluth.org
RTS is an international perinatal bereavement program which provides training and materials to professionals working with parents who have lost a baby. Parents who call will find compassionate staff who listen, provide written resources, and offer referrals to local support groups or RTS-trained health professionals. A free catalog includes materials for bereaved parents.

■ CENTER FOR LOSS IN MULTIPLE BIRTHS (CLIMB)

(907) 746-6123
Jean Kollantai
P.O. Box 1064
Palmer, AK 99645
CLIMB publishes a quarterly publication called "Our Newsletter" for families who have experienced the death of one or more, or all, of their children during a twin or higher multiple pregnancy. Several parents share their stories, poems and ideas to help with this unique kind of grief. Special issues feature parents who have lost a multiple to SIDS, and material for parents who learn during a pregnancy that one multiple will not live past birth. CLIMB keeps a list of national and international contacts for parents suffering similar losses.

SIDS PREVENTION STRATEGIES

Sudden Infant Death Syndrome is a terrifying thing to consider. New parents want nothing more than to protect their infant any way they can. For most families, that means taking all the precautions usually covered in infant care books:

■ Pregnant moms should not smoke, nor should anyone smoke around a newborn.

■ Babies should be put to sleep on their back or side, not on their stomachs, to lessen the risk of SIDS. "Back sleeping" is now considered the safest position for infants. Check with your doctor or call the national Back to Sleep campaign at 800-505-2742 for information on sleeping positions.

■ When sleeping, newborns should not be overdressed, nor should their room be overheated.

■ Avoid the use of sheepskin products in infant beds, which may lead to suffocation.

■ Don't put your baby to sleep in a water bed or a beanbag-type chair.

■ Don't use pillows in infant beds.

Premature and low birth weight babies are at higher risk for SIDS, as are those born to young mothers. SIDS may occur for no known reason. What it all boils down to is that it simply is not known exactly what causes SIDS. One possibility includes immature neural development. Another theory gaining respect is that SIDS babies do not rouse themselves when they stop breathing during sleep.

Some believe that one way to lessen the incidence of SIDS is co-sleeping, a traditional pattern of bed sharing between infant and mother, which causes a pattern of rousing and sleeping throughout the night.

Babies from two to four months old are beginning to experiment with both automatic and controlled breathing ("planned" breaths which enable humans to speak). Some babies may have difficulty with the transition. At this critical stage, having a parent close by, breathing rhythmically, may help the infant to keep on breathing when rousing.

By U.S. standards, neither parents nor infants "sleep well" in a shared bed. Both rouse more often, and movements of one affect the other. Yet the sleep may be better because a nursing mother can feed her baby during the night without fully waking up.

Some caveats do apply:

■ Make sure there is no possibility of the child falling off the bed, or being caught between mattress, headboard or wall.

■ Do not use a pillow, featherbed or heavy blankets near an infant.

■ No shared sleeping in waterbeds.

■ Never share a bed if you smoke, use drugs, or drink heavily.

One alternative is an "attached bed," which is similar to a crib pulled up to your bed. For special moments, there's no reason why a baby can't sometimes sleep in his own room.

GRIEF RESOURCES

■ CENTERING CORPORATION

(402) 553-1200
1531 N. Saddle Creek Rd.
Omaha, NE 68104
Web site: uikpage.com/C/centering
E-mail: j1200@aol.com
This company publishes a free "Creative Care Package" catalog that features several books and pamphlets on bereavement issues that deal with each facet of the death of a child. They also offer some of the best children's grief literature available.

■ COMPASSIONATE FRIENDS

(630) 990-0010
P.O. Box 3696
Oak Brook, IL 60522-3696
Compassionate Friends is a self-help organization offering friendship and understanding to bereaved parents. The group's purpose is to support and aid parents in the positive resolution of the grief experienced upon the death of a child. In all its literature and philosophy, Compassionate Friends promotes healing and fosters the physical and emotional health of parents and siblings. Upon your request, an information packet will be mailed which includes referrals to local support groups and information about joining. A subscription to the "We Need Not Walk Alone" quarterly newsletter for parents and grandparents is $20, and the group also publishes the quarterly *Stages*, written by and for siblings, for $10 per year.

■ MIDS SUPPORT GROUP INC.

(973) 263-6730
16 Crescent Dr.
Parsippany, NJ 07054
MIDS, which stands for miscarriage, infant death, and stillbirth, is a support group for parents suffering from all types of pregnancy or infant loss. Begun by Janet Tischler in New Jersey in 1982, the group has expanded to locations in many states. Besides offering understanding and support, group members are provided "telephone friends" who seek to provide a positive resolution to their loss. A quarterly newsletter is provided with the $18 annual membership fee to this helpful nonprofit group.

■ NATIONAL SUDDEN INFANT DEATH SYNDROME RESOURCE CENTER (NSRC)

(703) 821-8955, ext. 249
2070 Chain Bridge Rd., Ste. 450
Vienna, VA 22182
Part of the National Maternal and Child Health Clearinghouse, the NSRC produces and provides resources, referrals, and consumer education materials for families and medical professionals. A variety of materials are available free from NSRC on topics ranging from "What is SIDS?" to statistical research, bibliographies, and a variety of brochures. "Facing Anniversaries, Holidays and Special Events," "Parents and the Grieving Process," and "The Grief of Children After the Loss of a Sibling" are designed to help families deal with their loss.

■ PEN PARENTS

(702) 826-7332
P.O. Box 8738
Reno, NV 89507
E-mail: penparents@prodigy.com
Pen-Parents is an international referral network for parents, grandparents and siblings who have suffered the tragedy of pregnancy loss or the death of a child. Many bereaved parents find it healing to express their feelings through writing. Pen-Parents fills the need for support and validation through correspondence with others in similar situations.

Pails of Hope is a bimonthly publication, sponsored by Pen Parents, for parents who have battled infertility and/or experienced pregnancy or infant loss and are contemplating pregnancy, are pregnant or have given birth and/or adopted a baby subsequent to loss or infertility. A bimonthly newsletter (subscriptions, $15) includes articles, stories and poems.

■ PREGNANCY AND INFANT LOSS CENTER

(612) 473-9372
1421 E. Wayzata Blvd., Ste. 30
Wayzata, MN 55391
The Pregnancy and Infant Loss Center recognizes that the death of a baby can be one of life's greatest heartaches. The center provides information, education, and consultation services to both parents and professional caregivers. They can refer you to a support group in your local area. When you call, the center will send you a packet that includes Loving Arms, a quarterly newsletter filled with stories both sad and inspirational, poetry, and upcoming events nationwide. A descriptive order form lists a wide variety of books for parents, siblings and care providers, as well as books to guide families through subsequent pregnancies, and special remembrance items like birth certificates and memory books. Yearly membership in support of this nonprofit organization is $20 per year.

■ SHARE

800-821-6819
St. Joseph's Health Center
300 First Capitol Dr.
St. Charles, MO 63301
Web site: www.NationalSHAREOffice. com
The mission of SHARE (Pregnancy and Infant Loss Support Inc.) is to serve those who are troubled by a tragic death of a baby. Six times a year, they publish a newsletter with information and ideas from parents and professionals to support and provide a sense of friendship for bereaved parents. Subscriptions are free for one year, and $15 for each additional year.

■ SUDDEN INFANT DEATH SYNDROME ALLIANCE

800-221-7437
1314 Bedford Ave., Ste. 210
Baltimore, MD 21208
The National SIDS Alliance offers emotional and informational support to those who have experienced a baby's death due to SIDS. Publications, newsletters, and brochures are available from the national group. The alliance's 50-plus chapters offer peer counseling, personal visits, regular phone contact and assistance in funeral planning. They also offer support in future pregnancies and after the baby is born.

"My Baby's Premature Birth"

A Life Experience by Diane Hughes Valente

My first two children were born using natural childbirth and the guidance of a wonderful midwife. The thought of number three was a little sad because we had moved and felt the birth might not be quite the same. I investigated birth centers and midwives in the area and settled on one. Trying to help our little girls understand what was happening inside of me, I brought them to my ultrasound. With very little compassion I was told I had a complete placenta previa and would have to leave the birth center program. I would be seeing their affiliated doctors. I sat, wishing my husband was with me, and that my 2- and 3-year-olds were not. I switched practices the next day.

Approximately five weeks later, I felt something. I thought my water had broken, but it was not amniotic fluid; it was blood. There was no time for crying. Phone calls were made and we rushed to the hospital. The details are endless but they stopped the bleeding and sent me home a couple of days later. I was on bedrest with a husband who traveled, my own company to run in the height of the season, and two toddlers.

Life became surreal. I questioned everything—working, family relationships, my marriage and my friends. All of a sudden this third little baby was no longer a happy event but something that made me question all that I had.

One day I started to bleed again. I drove myself to the hospital. My blood count was very low and I was told my baby was going to be born then, in my seventh month. As we waited for the results of an amniocentesis to find out if the baby's lungs were developed, I felt like my life was at a standstill. We got the word that her lungs were good. My doctor was off-duty that weekend, and his partner had a dinner party to attend, but they both agreed that they would much rather be present for my daughter's birthday party.

They performed an emergency Cesarean section an hour later. Robin was born weighing three pounds, 12 ounces. Thank God we were where we were, with excellent doctors and emergency care.

Robin was placed in the special care nursery. I had to go home four days after her birth. Leaving her that day was the most painful experience of my life. The guilt on days I couldn't visit was unbearable. I pumped breast milk for Robin. She was tube-fed for a while until she was strong enough to bottle feed and nurse for short periods. We took her home the day she reached four pounds, around three weeks after her birth.

For me, having a premature baby was like having a first child all over again. I was not sure what to expect from her and I questioned my ability to care for this tiny little person. Looking back, I must say that I was just in shock all those months, both before she came and for a time after. I felt very alone and tired. It was very hard on my girls. I did everything I was not supposed to do with siblings—I would not let the other children touch her, I made them be quiet so she could sleep. It was not the ordinary beginning for a third child.

I realized a lot of things that I had planned would not now be possible. For instance, I was not going to be able to put this little girl in the home day care where her sisters spent three days a week. But we needed my income, so we decided to open a small photography studio near our home. Donald took two months off through the Family Medical Leave Act. Robin had made us realize that one moment can change your life forever. We found a wonderful nanny, and I was close enough to come home and nurse Robin at lunchtime.

Donald has left his job and joined our photography business full-time. Here we are, 13 months after our little one was born. She is behind other children her age physically but is catching up. She still is facing open heart surgery, but we feel very lucky to have her.

I must say I feel a bit like Dorothy in "The Wizard of Oz" for it was not the trip I intended to take. The experience has changed me forever, and I am glad to be home. ❧

QUESTIONS AND ANSWERS
Premature Infants

Neonatologist Charles F. Simmons, Jr., M.D., and Sharon D. Simmons, R.N., B.S.N., of Children's Hospital in Boston, Massachusetts, share current information on prevention and treatment of premature babies.

Q. *What are the reasons that babies are born prematurely?*

A. Approximately half of preterm deliveries result from maternal conditions such as congenital anomalies of the female reproductive tract, anemia, pregnancy induced hypertension (also known as preeclampsia or toxemia), premature rupture of the fetal membranes, or infection of the fetal membranes and uterine environment. However, a significant fraction of women begin premature labor for unidentifiable reasons. The risk of premature delivery is severalfold higher in women who have previously delivered a premature infant.

Q. *Is there anything that can be done to lessen the risk of having a premature infant?*

A. Preconception counseling may reduce the risk of preterm delivery in selected instances. Timely prenatal care in the hands of a qualified professional will assure that all the modern approaches to monitoring the pregnancy will be appropriately considered and utilized. If premature labor occurs, certain therapies may decrease the frequency of premature contractions and, if indicated, accelerate maturity of the fetal lungs.

Q. *What are the current statistics with regard to premature births and premature babies?*

A. Modern advances in the practice of obstetrics and neonatology have resulted in steadily improving morbidity and mortality of premature infants. Up to 10% of pregnancies in the United States result in preterm delivery (less than 37 weeks gestation), accounting for up to 450,000 births per year. As one would expect, the smallest and most immature babies have the most significant challenge for survival and normal outcome. Despite this, in 1997, greater than 90% of infants weighing more than two pounds survive, and the majority experience good long-term outcomes. However, individual pregnancies vary greatly. A woman should consult a trained specialist in maternal fetal and/or newborn medicine to determine the likelihood of fetal survival and possible long-term problems in the case of threatened preterm delivery.

Q. What medical technologies are commonly used with premature infants?

A. Major improvements in medical tests, treatments and medical devices have significantly contributed to the improvement in premature infant survival statistics over the past two decades. Examples include:

- **Isolettes and warming tables:** these devices maintain a newborn infant in a warm, neutral thermal environment, thus conserving calories otherwise expended to generate heat.

- **Cardiorespiratory monitoring:** these electronic devices continuously monitor both newborn heart and respiratory rates, and are equipped with alarms that alert nursing and medical staff to the presence of apnea (temporary cessation of breathing) or abnormalities of heart rate or rhythm;

- **Oximeters:** these monitors measure the oxygen saturation of hemoglobin in red blood cells in the bloodstream of the newborn infant. This relatively new approach allows noninvasive measurement of the efficiency of oxygen uptake in the lungs and delivery of oxygen to the baby's tissues.

- **Mechanical ventilators:** some premature infants experience temporary respiratory failure, and therefore require mechanical breaths administered via a ventilator or respirator. Conventional and high-frequency (or hi fi) ventilators increase the efficiency of oxygen exchange and carbon dioxide elimination by the lungs.

- **Arterial and venous catheterization:** the unstable mineral, fluid, and blood gas status of the extremely premature infant requires frequent tests performed on blood samples, which can be obtained through these catheters with minimal disturbance.

- **Laboratory micromethods:** the advent of new laboratory measurement technologies has resulted in drastic reductions in the amount of blood required for routine monitoring. An amazing number of tests can be performed on just a few drops of blood.

Q. What medical therapies are commonly used?

A. Several effective new medical therapies have markedly improved the outcomes of premature infants. Examples include:

- **Prenatal glucocorticoid therapy:** steroid treatment of the mother can accelerate maturity of the fetal lungs. The combination of prenatal steroids and effective mechanical ventilation has reduced premature infant morbidity and mortality.

- **Surfactant therapy:** premature babies with immature lungs temporarily lack a natural substance called surfactant. Surfactant is composed of lipid and protein molecules that reduce the surface tension and thus the collapsibility of the air sacs that promote gas exchange in the lung. Adequate surfactant production allows easy inflation and deflation of the air sacs and thus promotes adequate

PREMATURE INFANTS

gas exchange and oxygenation. Up to four doses of surfactant are usually given at six to eight hour intervals to infants with persistent lung immaturity.

- **Phototherapy:** phototherapy lights can promote the excretion of the waste product bilirubin from the bloodstream into the urine. Since the formation of the yellow pigment bilirubin occurs at an accelerated rate in premature babies, and since the liver is relatively immature, serum bilirubin concentrations can rise to dangerous concentrations in the extremely premature infant. Phototherapy alters the bilirubin molecule in the skin and reduces the risk of neurologic damage.

- **Intravenous therapy:** major advances in understanding the nutritional requirements of the premature infant have resulted in the design of intravenous solutions that can provide sufficient quality and quantity of calories to promote growth of the premature infant. Intravenous nutrition is a temporary measure in most infants, followed by a transition to feedings with breast milk or formula.

Q. *What is apnea and how does it affect the premature infant?*

A. Apnea is the temporary cessation of breathing. In the premature infant, apnea can either be central or obstructive.

- **Central apnea:** the immature brain of the premature infant may not send regular breathing signals to the diaphragm and other respiratory muscles. This temporary immaturity of brain signalling to the respiratory muscles can be overcome through treatment with aminophylline or caffeine, two well-studied medications that increase the regularity of brain cell respiratory signals.

- **Obstructive apnea:** extremely immature infants frequently lack muscle tone of the upper airways that conduct air to the lungs. Obstructive apnea often requires extra positive airway pressure through a tube placed in the nose. This continuous positive airway pressure is administered by a ventilator, and may, in selected instances, need to be accompanied by actual intubation of the trachea and mechanical ventilation.

Q. *What about breastfeeding the premature baby?*

A. Breast milk is almost always the best form of nutrition for any baby, whether term or premature. Premature infants who are not able to coordinate their suck-and-swallow reflexes will need to ingest breast milk collected by their mothers via mechanical or electric breast pumps. Infants who can digest breast milk but cannot yet suck and swallow will require feeding through a soft plastic tube placed through the nose or mouth into the stomach.

Because of the special needs of premature infants, it may be necessary to supplement breast milk with mineral and vitamin additives that optimize the nutritional status of the preterm baby. In addition to the beneficial nutritional aspects, breastfeeding may improve the immune status of preterm infants and reduce the incidence of certain types of infection. In addition, the routine of expressing breast milk and later, actual nursing, offers many emotional benefits to both the mother and the premature infant.

Q. When can premature babies be released from the hospital?

A. Former premature infants may be ready for discharge anywhere after the equivalent of 35 weeks gestation period. Rather than a specific age or weight, the discharge is related to when important developmental milestones are achieved. The infant must demonstrate:

- **Adequate thermal regulation:** the former preterm infant must maintain body temperature with minimal wrapping.
- **Adequate nutrition:** good weight gain on a reasonable feeding regimen every three to four hours will ensure the family's ability to cope with the infant's feeding needs.
- **Adequate respiratory control:** former premature infants must demonstrate regular respirations with no episodes of apnea or heart rate slowing. Absence of such episodes for a period of up to five days prior to discharge is the standard of care in many institutions across the country.
- **Adequate parental education:** ongoing parental education regarding any special infant needs,

cardiopulmonary resuscitation, and home resources are all part of routine discharge planning sessions that will precede discharge.

Q. Do you have any advice for parents of premature babies with regard to coping strategies?

A. "Hope for the best, but emotionally prepare for stressful times." This adage is useful for many parents and families who will experience euphoric highs and depressing lows during what can be a prolonged hospitalization. It is important to remember the support available from extended family, friends, and clergy in order to help cope with the uncertainties of hospital care and outcomes of premature infants.

Q. Do you have any advice for parents of premature babies with regard to working with insurance companies?

A. Although the value of a successful outcome for a premature infant is beyond measure, the associated financial costs of hospital care of the premature infant can be staggering. Several months of hospitalization can easily exceed $100,000. Families fortunate enough to have insurance should inform the insurance company of the birth of the premature infant as soon as feasible after delivery.

Irrespective of insurance, the financial aid office at your hospital should be contacted in order to determine whether any applicable local, state, or federal programs may help defray hospitalization expenses.

⅍ RESOURCES ⅍

■ INTENSIVE CARING UNLIMITED

(215) 629-0449
910 Bent Ln.
Philadelphia, PA 19118
Services to parents with a baby in intensive care are offered, including over-the-phone advice from parents who have had similar experiences with their babies. Volunteers are trained as counselors to help with crises. They publish a bimonthly newsletter on prematurity, developmental delays, grieving, and other parental issues.

■ IVH PARENTS

(305) 232-0381
P.O. Box 56-1111
Miami, FL 33156
IVH Parents offers support to parents whose babies have had an intraventricular hemorrhage—bleeding in the brain—that frequently occurs in babies born weighing less than three pounds. They provide caring counseling by phone and publish a newsletter.

■ LITTLE ANGEL FOUNDATION

(516) 736-2512
P.O. Box 510
Seldon, NY 11784
Founded to help parents of premature and seriously ill infants, the foundation offers support during and after neonatal intensive care. The group's information packet includes a telephone referral network, parent-to-parent listening program, high risk pregnancy and bereavement packages, video and book library and biannual newsletter.

■ PARENTCARE

800-808-2224
7910 Woodmont Ave., Ste. 300
Bethesda, MD 20814
Web site: www.look.net/acch
E-mail: acch@clark.net
Parentcare is part of the Association for the Care of Children's Health (ACCH), an international organization of parents and health professionals focusing on the unique needs of infants in health care settings. Parentcare provides information through publications, videos and conferences. Individual memberships range from $35-$65. ACCH's annual conference and twice-annual regional conferences address high-risk neonatal care issues.

■ SIDELINES

(714) 497-2265
P.O. Box 1808
Laguna Beach, CA 92652
Web site: www.earthlink. net\~sidelines
E-mail: sidelines@earthlink.net
Sidelines is a network of support groups across the country for women with complicated pregnancies and their families. Over 5,000 trained peer counselors can be matched to those who have had similar experiences. There is a lending library and an annual magazine covering a variety of issues such as how to cope with bedrest and dealing with various issues of difficult pregnancies.

"Bedrest Blues . . . and Triumphs"

A Life Experience by Krista Minard

Seven months along, my pregnancy had been a breeze so far. I had escaped morning sickness and major weight gain, and knew I was having a girl sometime in September. I expected to work at my job as a magazine editor right up until I had the baby.

The breezy part of my pregnancy ended on the way home from a seaside vacation with my husband, Mike, when I began having contractions every three minutes. A stop at the hospital landed me on a gurney with a fetal monitor and a comment from the nurse: "You're 26 weeks along? Oh, we've delivered them smaller than that...not much smaller, though."

The labor turned out to be false, but didn't stop until I'd received muscle relaxants and a syringe full of terbutaline (a contraction stopper). I was sent home with orders to rest quietly on my left side for the rest of the weekend, drink plenty of water and see my physician as soon as possible.

That Monday, my first day back at work after vacation, I left to see my obstetrician who examined me, discovered cervical effacement and ordered me to bedrest for at least the next six weeks. "We've got to get to at least 32 weeks," she said. No working at the office, no housework, no cooking, no walks, no gardening, no grocery shopping...the list of don'ts was endless. I could get up to use the bathroom, shower and drive to her office once a week for a checkup. She gave me a list of red flags that would require me to call no matter what time of day—contractions that are too frequent, too long, too strong or too different; bleeding; a gush of amniotic fluid. She also prescribed nifedipene, a medication that works on uterine contractions. The drug's side effects—light-headedness, vessel dilation, increased heart rate—were little compared to the risks of premature delivery.

When I got back in the car to drive the few blocks to the office, the contractions started up again. As my baby arched and kicked, I started crying—I knew I had to obey doctor's orders if I wanted my girl to be born healthy, but I wasn't prepared to quit work and lie around. I didn't have anything ready for the baby to arrive. Magazine deadline was looming. I was supposed to be a guest of honor at an out-of-town baby shower. The more I thought about it all, the more panicked I felt.

I got to the office and told my boss that I had to go home right away and lie down for the next two months. He offered me the use of the company laptop computer, and we concocted an arrangement that would allow me to continue to work from home, via e-mail, fax and phone. I called Mike and broke the news; he immediately pledged his willingness to pick up any household slack.

And so it went. Propped up on pillows, I had my computer, my files and my telephone within reach. A tremendously long cord stretched through the house from the laptop to the phone jack for modem access. The phone rang every five minutes—co-workers asking questions and expressing concern; friends and family members nagging me to take care of myself. I canceled the baby shower, a trip to my parents', a haircut appointment. I counted contractions. I drank my water. Mike fixed meals, fed the animals, ran errands, waited on me and kept the house clean—in addition to working 40 hours a week.

Every day at 6:00 p.m., I e-mailed to the office a contingency plan of what to do if I became unavailable. Then I unplugged the phone and broke the rules long enough to walk to the couch, where I watched reruns on TV. In July, I avidly followed the Summer Olympics, even the events I'd always hated, like heavyweight lifting and wrestling. I even endured the Dream Team and their squeaky shoes.

Friends and family visited. My sister brought a foot-high stack of books and magazines. Sisters-in-law Jody and Carrie transported the already-purchased baby shower gifts and set up my living room with so much pink, frilly stuff that my girl's arrival began to seem real.

I never thought I could look so forward to seeing the doctor. Once a week, I got to put on shoes and drive to her office. It felt strange to be out of the house, sort of like coming out of a dark, cool theater on a hot summer day. Each week, the prognosis was worse: cervix more effaced, baby further engaged. The 32-week mark came and went. "We've got to get to 36 weeks," the doctor said then. "Anything after that is gravy."

At 35 weeks, she stopped the nifedipene because my heart rate was too fast. She told me she expected I'd go into labor within a week. The contractions continued at about the same rate they had for the past two months. At 36 weeks, the baby was getting to be a good-sized girl, according to the doctor, but I might take it easy for another week. At 37 weeks she shrugged and said I could get up and go back to work. She also suggested that we schedule a labor induction. She was a little worried that my labor would proceed extremely fast, and she estimated that the baby was at least six pounds—the size limit she felt I could deliver.

I returned to work for two weeks, and felt better than I had in months. I wore the same denim jumper almost every day—just put a different shirt beneath it. I prepared for my maternity leave. At home, I sewed crib bumpers and curtains. I washed all the newborn drawstring gowns in special soap, burying my nose in them because they smelled so sweet. In a burst of energy, I assembled the crib and changing table, despite Mike's protests that he'd do it over the weekend. I went out to dinner with friends, shopped for diapers, took phone calls from people who said, "Still pregnant?" I patted my daughter on the behind, felt her feet flex against my ribs, and gave thanks that she'd stayed indoors.

Then, one morning, I woke up with crampy contractions and an unrelenting urge to clean up the garage. Instead, we went to the hospital, where our daughter, Anna Marie, was born that evening at 7:50 p.m. She weighed seven pounds, 13 ounces and was 21 inches long.

We'd made it to 39 weeks. ❧

BEDREST: A PRESCRIPTION, NOT A SENTENCE

You're at a routine obstetrical appointment. Expressing concern, your doctor recommends bedrest. "I can't be on bedrest!" you immediately think. But if you're like thousands of women each year, you won't have a choice. For the safety of your unborn child, a period of bedrest will decrease the chance of premature labor.

You will survive bedrest. We suggest calling Sidelines, a group dedicated to helping women through bedrest and complicated pregnancies, at (714) 497-2265. They will send you information to make this time easier for you and your family.

It is important to be equipped to cope with the stresses of bedrest. Be prepared to be totally dependent on others, and expect feelings of inadequacy. You can fight feelings of isolation by calling friends and relatives, and having people come and visit. People may tell you how "lucky" you are to "lay around all day." Know that bedrest is serious work for a confined mother, and the focus is on keeping you and the baby healthy through your pregnancy. Find friends who will be supportive and caring, and let them help you! Some suggestions:

- Be sure phone, phone book, television remote control, reading and writing materials and projects are within reach on the bed or next to it. Put everything into a laundry basket to set up your "nest."

- Have a small ice chest within reach, packed with the day's supply of drinks and snacks.

- Open your window—weather permitting—to let the outdoors in and get some fresh air.

- Make a list of things people can do for you, so that when they ask, you can easily respond and even give them a choice.

- Work on long-put-off projects: update photo albums, write letters, finish stitchery projects, mend clothes, update your phone book and holiday card list, reorganize files.

- Consider renting a sliding side table (similar to the ones used in hospitals) to make it easier to eat or write while in bed.

- Have a "date" with your husband—gourmet take-out food and candles.

- Invite another couple for a game of cards or trivia or to watch a video movie on Saturday night.

If you have other children in your household, find creative ways to interact with them. Play bed-basketball with rolled-up socks and a laundry basket. Keep building blocks, board games, coloring books and crayons, puzzles, play dough, children's books, paper, scissors, paste and old magazines in a laundry basket near your bed. Include paper towels for spills.

Sidelines provided information for this article.

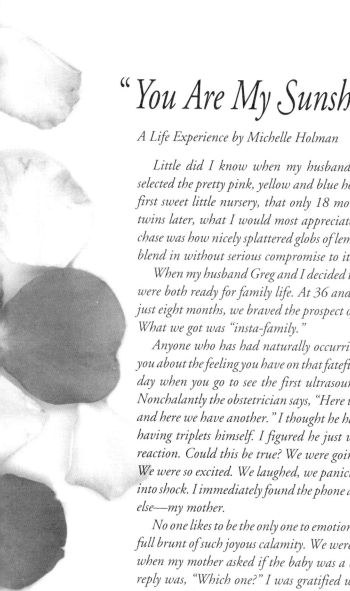

"*You Are My Sunshine*"

A Life Experience by Michelle Holman

Little did I know when my husband and I carefully selected the pretty pink, yellow and blue hooked rug for our first sweet little nursery, that only 18 months and a set of twins later, what I would most appreciate about our purchase was how nicely splattered globs of lemon yogurt would blend in without serious compromise to its beauty.

When my husband Greg and I decided to get married we were both ready for family life. At 36 and 31, married for just eight months, we braved the prospect of having a child. What we got was "insta-family."

Anyone who has had naturally occurring twins can tell you about the feeling you have on that fateful, albeit routine, day when you go to see the first ultrasound of your baby. Nonchalantly the obstetrician says, "Here we have one baby and here we have another." I thought he had to be kidding, having triplets himself. I figured he just wanted to see my reaction. Could this be true? We were going to have twins. We were so excited. We laughed, we panicked and we went into shock. I immediately found the phone and called—who else—my mother.

No one likes to be the only one to emotionally shoulder the full brunt of such joyous calamity. We were no exception, so when my mother asked if the baby was a boy or a girl, my reply was, "Which one?" I was gratified when I heard her scream and cry all at once. I had never heard her so happy.

I know I'm not the first woman to have twins, or at least that is what they kept telling me. But I was the only one of my immediate acquaintances, family or friends to have twins, so from my point of view I was the only woman to have twins.

At first it was funny, but at 21 weeks reality struck. I was in premature labor and dangerously effaced to 70%. I had immediate surgery and full bedrest was prescribed for the next four months. Hardship overcome is one of the rites of

passage to motherhood, and my mother was there for all of it. She flew in for the surgery and did not leave until the diabetes, toxemia, magnesium, terbutaline pump, two bouts in the hospital, bedrest, home monitoring and carefully adjusted diet were through. She waited on me nonstop for 135 days, day in and day out. Hardship or no, she was determined that I was going to have two healthy babies. I delivered Jacob William and Jessica Lynn at 38 weeks and both were, as my mother had willed, healthy.

Of course now the real circus began! Being a first time mom of two, I needed to learn and learn fast. Even before I began I was exhausted. After the first ten weeks of feeding, diapers, and laundry I wasn't sure which way I was going. Any mother of multiples will tell you it's not like having a second child in diapers, it's like nothing else one has ever experienced. The only advice that actually made any practical sense I received from a newly found friend with twins. She said, "Listen to your instincts. You are the mother of your two children and you will know the right thing to do for your children when the time comes." This was good advice, and with a little less panic as a result of her pep talk, most everything went smoothly.

We certainly should not forget about dealing with the adoring public. With the twins about three months old I got my nerve up to take them out in public and selected—the mall! It was revenge of the peekers. In just over an hour I had strollered no more than 50 feet. Don't get me wrong, I really do enjoy talking to people about our twins and I realize that people are naturally curious. I just couldn't believe how many times I was asked if my little girl dressed in pink and my boy dressed in blue were identical twins. This in itself is not so bad, but just try answering it 15 times in a single morning after about six hours of sleep in three days.

One of the most common comments I received was, "Oh, a boy and a girl—so...you're done." I often wondered if people were "telling" me I was done having children or asking me. My all-time favorite was from those who yelled in passing, "I'm glad it's you and not me." I simply responded, "So...am...I."

In a local Twins Club—a social support group for mothers of multiples—I found a haven. Only mothers of multiples truly understand what you are going through.

Now my sweet angels are nearly 2 and life is their playground. They can destroy the house in 15 minutes flat, outflank me in strategy, energy and resolve. They even communicate in their own secret language. I hear them jabbering to one another, laugh and scream, then run off to their next adventure. Sometimes I even feel left out, but as long as they are having a good time, life is good.

I've been lucky enough to wander across a wonderful poem which helps me puts my life in perspective now. It reminds me how blessed I am:

The Little Shadows

I saw a young mother with eyes full of laughter,
and two little shadows came following after.
Wherever she moved, they were always right there,
holding on to her skirts, hanging onto her chair,
before her, behind her—an adhesive pair.
"Don't you ever get weary as, day after day,
your two little tagalongs get in your way?"
She smiled as she shook her pretty young head,
and I'll always remember the words that she said:
"It's good to have shadows that run when you run;
that laugh when you're happy, and hum when you hum.
For you only have shadows when your life's filled with sun."
                                        —Author Unknown

As life would have it, unfortunately, my mother passed away suddenly when Jacob and Jessica were only four months old. She will never know them the way I dreamed she would and they will know her only through my memories. So my twins are destined to have a guardian angel. It is comforting to me that I knew theirs so intimately. When Mom used to touch my stomach, singing her favorite song, "You Are My Sunshine," it seemed silly. It seems entirely perfect now that Jacob and Jessica are truly the sunshines of my life. ❧

❧ RESOURCES ❧

■ MOTHERS OF SUPERTWINS (M.O.S.T.)

(516) 434-MOST
P.O. Box 951
Brentwood, NY 11717
This nonprofit organization provides resources, information, empathy, and support to families with triplets, quadruplets and higher number multiple births. Information about pregnancy issues, prematurity, development and family life is available.

■ NATIONAL ORGANIZATION OF MOTHERS OF TWINS CLUBS (NOMTC)

P.O. Box 23188
Albuquerque, NM 87192-1188
This organization was the brainchild of several mothers dealing with the stress of raising twins, and is now a network of 450 clubs. Its mission is to provide information to parents of twins and/or multiple births. Write for a free brochure, "Your Twins and You." If you're interested in starting your own local chapter, NOMTC can send you that information as well.

■ TWINS MAGAZINE

800-328-3211
(303) 290-8500
5350 S. Roslyn St., Ste. 400
Englewood, CO 80111
This national magazine offers support and caring for parents of multiples with a wide variety of articles and essays. It is printed bimonthly (six issues a year). An annual subscription runs about $24.

■ TWINS WORLD MAGAZINE

(219) 627-5414
11220 St. Joe Rd.
Fort Wayne, IN 46835-9737
Dr. Brandt publishes *Twins World* magazine. This magazine is for twins, parents of twins, and twinless twins. The magazine has sections on twin research studies, entertainment, social functions, and twin loss. The cost for the magazine is $20 per year.

■ TRIPLET CONNECTION

(209) 474-0885
P.O. Box 99571
Stockton, CA 95209
Web site: www.inreach.com\triplets
E-mail: triplets@inreach.com
The Triplet Connection maintains what is perhaps the world's largest data base of multiple births. Information packets include a copy of the organization's newsletter, information about strollers for multiples, and networking opportunities are available for parents who are expecting or who have had three or more babies. Other offerings include a quarterly newsletter (subscriptions are $20) and a resource list ($20).

■ TWIN SERVICES

(510) 524-0863
P. O. Box 10066
Berkeley, CA 94709
Twin Services has a complete listing of services including multiple birth information and referral, parenting publications, and consultations with multiple birth experts. This group operates a 900 number with information about caring for twins.

"Life as a Teen Parent"

By Cinderella Constant, age 17

Being a teen parent isn't all that it is cracked up to be. The reaction you first feel when you realize you are pregnant is shock and fear. Shock because you didn't think it could happen to you. Fear of what your parents and what your boyfriend might say.

When you're pregnant, you're looked down upon by many people, including your friends. You think someone will be there to help you. But you're wrong (well, in my case I was). When your parents find out you're pregnant, the way they look at you changes. You're not their sweet little girl anymore; you're the girl who was stupid and doesn't have a mind of her own. People stare at you when they notice the bulge in your shirt that has a baby inside, and look at you in contempt, in a way that makes you think that they think that you don't know what you're getting yourself into (I did, though).

When the baby is born, everything changes, especially the way your parents treat you. My parents treated me like I never knew what I was doing. Until the day I left.

You now have more responsibilities than you ever had before. After your child is born, you should know that your child is your number one priority. He comes ahead of everything, including when you go to school. If he's sick, you must stay home.

Those were all the negatives. Here are the positives. You're able to watch your child grow. You observe them learn new things. They do funny things that will make you laugh. You get to see the funny expressions they make. You feel proud when they do something new and when people say they are cute and big. I, myself, love the way my son smiles. It's so big and bright. He's a strong little boy who is always happy, except when he's sick.

One hard thing to handle is when they are sick. Sometimes you have to spend hours at the hospital trying to figure

out what is wrong with your child. Not knowing, just worrying. They are constantly crying, while you feel helpless because there is nothing you can do to make them feel better except give them medicine and love. When they do get better, you forget they were sick, when they smile at you with the expression of love.

All that is written here is my life as a teen parent. If you think you can handle this with no regrets (only if you're pregnant already), then I think you should keep the baby. Even though things have been hard, I don't regret the day he was born and all that I have sacrificed for him. ❧

MATERNAL AGE FACTORS

THE "OLDER" MOM

With more women deciding to delay childbearing until their careers are well established, this country is seeing an unprecedented number of births to women over 35. While there are risks associated with older maternal age, giving birth at an "advanced" age has its benefits. Mothers are generally more emotionally mature and prepared for the life changes that motherhood brings.

Down syndrome is the highest risk factor associated with older mothers. According to the March of Dimes Birth Defects Foundation, approximately 1 of every 1,250 25-year-olds have children with Down syndrome. Three in 1,000 35-year-olds have children with the syndrome, and the risk increases to 1 in 100 for 40-year-olds. While theories abound, it is generally agreed that the aging of the ovaries contributes to the increased possibility of genetic defects.

Women over 35 are more likely to miscarry than their younger counterparts, and twice as likely to develop diabetes during pregnancy. In the same age group, there is an increased risk of placental problems and bleeding, and these women are more likely to deliver by Cesarean section. On a happy note, the incidence of twins is highest for mothers ages 35-39.

How to best lower the risks? By following the generally prescribed rules of pregnancy: no smoking, drinking, or drugs; following a healthy diet, and taking 0.4 mg. of folic acid daily, preferably beginning before conception. Regular prenatal care is a must to have a healthy baby.

TEEN MOTHERS

According to Shelby Pasarell of Advocates for Youth (AFY) in Washington D.C., "Public perception holds that too-early childbearing leads to increased welfare costs, hopeless futures and a continuing cycle of poverty for adolescent mothers and their children. Many young teen mothers can, however, achieve academic success, have rewarding careers and lead productive and fulfilling lives." The key factors for the success of young mothers are educational and economic opportunities, along with social support services, and help from their families.

&.

With more women deciding to delay childbearing, this country is seeing an unprecedented number of births to women over 35.

&.

MATERNAL AGE FACTORS

The Children's Defense Fund found that, regardless of ethnicity or race, teenage girls with poor basic skills were more than three times as likely to become mothers as those with average skills. Teen mothers have only a 60% chance of graduating from high school by age 25, 30% lower than their childless peers, according to AFY.

Many school districts offer programs for pregnant teens which allow them to continue their schooling, often including parenting courses and an on-site day care center. Education can make the difference between good and poor employment opportunities.

Teenagers are more likely to delay prenatal care, yet are more at risk than older moms for giving birth prematurely. They are also at higher risk for developing preeclampsia. Inadequate nutrition is often a factor. Finding a caring practitioner the pregnant teen can trust is of utmost importance.

Although more teens are keeping their babies than ever before, adoption is always an option. Over half the babies adopted today are placed through independent adoptions, usually through a private adoption attorney. Whether through independent or agency adoption, the adoptive parents pay for the birth mother's medical care through pregnancy, labor and delivery. Birth parents can review photos and letters from prospective adoptive families in order to make a placement choice. Adoption laws vary widely from state to state. Many areas have adoption counseling services that can make a referral.

❧ RESOURCES ❧

■ ADVOCACY FOR YOUTH
(202) 347-5700
1025 Vermont Ave., N.W., Ste. 200
Washington, DC 20005
Advocacy For Youth is a national advocacy program concerned mostly with the impact of teen sexuality. They can provide fact sheets and resources for teenagers and their families.

■ MARCH OF DIMES
888-MODIMES
1275 Mamaroneck Ave.
White Plains, NY 10605
E-mail: Resourcecenter@modimes.org
March of Dimes' Resource Center offers free publications, brochures, and public health information sheets on general pregnancy issues and specific birth defects, including "Pregnancy After Age 30," a public health education information sheet.

CHILD ABUSE

Child abuse is not something we like to think about, but it does happen—in all types of homes, with families from all ethnic groups and all income levels. Physical abuse and neglect hurt defenseless trusting children, and are most often caused by someone the child is familiar with: a relative, a child care provider or baby-sitter, a parent. If you see a child in imminent danger, contact law enforcement and your local child protective services agency, and explain the nature of the situation. Take action to make sure the child is in a safe environment.

PHYSICAL ABUSE

Physical abuse is any act which results in a non-accidental physical injury. This includes severe corporal punishment, including occasions where a person is frustrated or angry and strikes, shakes or throws a child. Other intentional forms of abuse may include burning, cutting, poking, twisting limbs, or otherwise torturing a child.

A disturbing form of physical abuse is shaken baby syndrome, which occurs mainly in children under 1 year of age, and seldom after age 2. A baby's brain and blood vessels are very fragile and vulnerable to whiplash motions, such as shaking, jerking and jolting. The neck muscles of an infant or small child are weak, so the child's head is relatively heavy and the neck cannot support the stress of shaking.

That means that vigorously shaking a very young child can cause irreversible brain damage, blindness, cerebral palsy, hearing loss, spinal cord injury, learning disabilities and even death. Shaking a baby can cause the brain to actually recoil against the skull, and since infants' brains are not well protected, shaking causes the brain to bleed and swell.

This is a partial list of neurological symptoms that might alert to a possible shaken baby:

- Unable to lift or turn head
- Pinpointed or dilated pupils
- Blood pooling in eyes
- Pupils unresponsive to light
- Semi-consciousness or lethargy
- Difficulty in breathing
- Seizures or spasms
- Swollen head (which may appear later)

🌢

No matter

how

impatient or

angry you

feel, never

shake a

baby—ever.

🌢

CHILD ABUSE

Approximately 75% to 90% of cases of shaken baby syndrome include retinal hemorrhages, a symptom almost never seen with accidental head injuries.

Be sure to tell others who are in contact with your child about the dangers of shaking a baby—baby-sitters, child care workers, siblings and other relatives. You can also protect your baby from head injury by making sure you don't shake your child when you play. Keep a baby's head well supported when holding, playing with or transporting.

It is not your responsibility to diagnose shaken baby syndrome or other physical abuse. If you suspect abuse, check with your pediatrician or a mental health professional.

NEGLECT

Babies' needs are few, but a small fraction of parents seem unaware of the necessity of adequate changing, bathing, feeding and loving. Neglect of a baby's nutritional intake is cruel, and the symptoms are quickly obvious: a baby who doesn't gain weight because of lower-than-necessary nutritional intake and who is at risk for dehydration. Diapers need changing whenever wet or soiled to avoid diaper rash and possible urinary tract infections. Just as important is simply spending time with your baby, talking to her, holding her gently and making her feel cherished.

Without a loving parent, a baby can learn to withdraw; crying will diminish as the baby learns not to expect attention from caretakers. This can lead to long-term attachment problems and difficulty in school. Babies do take a lot of time, but neglecting a baby's needs, even for a short while, can lead to disastrous consequences.

WHEN A BABY CRIES

Babies cry for a variety of reasons—when they're hungry or need to be changed—but sometimes babies cry because they are having a hard time adjusting to life. This is not unusual. If there is no medical reason for the crying, the best thing to do is let your baby cry and keep your frustration under control.

- No matter how impatient or angry you feel, never shake a baby—ever.
- Be patient. The baby is not crying to irritate you, but rather is just responding to an internal need to cry.
- If you've had all you can take, lay the baby on his or her back or side, making sure he or she is safe from harm, and take a break. Let the baby cry it out.
- Call a friend or relative to let them know how you're feeling. If a friend can spend an hour with the baby while you take a walk or spend some quiet time alone, you'll be better able to deal with a fussy infant.

Parenting classes and support groups are all excellent outlets to receive advice and input on your specific problem areas.

Have reasonable expectations for your child and yourself. Realize that not everything runs smoothly all the time, and that even the most difficult stages in your child's life will pass.

If you are facing a crisis situation, call your local Parents Anonymous office or the National Child Abuse Hotline (800-422-4453). Don't be afraid to reach out for help when needed.

Information provided by Anthony Urquiza, Ph.D., the California Department of Social Services and Children's Hospital in Seattle, Washington.

TAKING CARE OF YOURSELF AND YOUR FAMILY

CHAPTER SIX

KEEPING YOUR RELATIONSHIP ALIVE

By Kari E. Hazen

THE BALANCING ACT

Friday night arrives again. A week full of demands, deadlines and stress is coming to a close. I think I saw the father of my children about five hours this week if I was lucky. Now, another round of demands and duties arrive for the weekend...laundry, bills and picking up this house. My husband and I will take our daughters to the park, read stories and give them the love and encouragement they need. Balancing the day-to-day responsibilities of work, home and children, we search to find time for one another.

Having a good relationship, and children at the same time, may be difficult. Couples must come to terms with the conflicting feelings that say: "I want to be a good parent" and at the same time "I want our relationship to stay strong and intimate...and even a little spontaneous."

Some may laugh at the idea that there is even the slightest possibility the two roles are compatible. Others will cheer, pop the champagne bottle and say yes! I, too, believe this is possible—not only possible, but also extremely important. I think we all want a life filled with love from our significant other and love from our children. The real question lies in how to make it work for us.

PRIORITIZE YOUR RELATIONSHIP

Whether you are a working mom or a stay-at-home mom, it is clear you are giving a lot to your children. It is something instinctive that moms do well. Because we give so much to our families, it is much more challenging to give to the relationship that started the family. So, how do we make our relationship a priority again? By simply doing that...making it a priority. Pick it up from the bottom of your to-do list and move it to the top. Focus on the time, or lack of time, you're spending together and decide to make it better. To many, it may not sound too simple; yet there are some small steps that can be

❧

Having a

good

relationship,

and children

at the same

time, may be

difficult for

today's

parents.

❧

taken to get the relationship rekindled again. Here are some practical ideas that many parents suggest to help keep your relationship strong.

- Try to get a baby-sitter at least once a month. It doesn't matter what you do, just that you leave the house and spend time with one another.

- Take a walk. This may keep your children occupied and gives you a chance to talk with little interruption. Walking also releases stress and provides good exercise.

- Try a vacation alone. This one is difficult for most moms, especially the first trip. Yet once you enjoy a trip away and alone, you will find how good it is for your relationship. Nothing brings intimacy back better than complete and utter silence to enjoy with your partner.

- Celebrate! Celebrate your anniversary, your birthdays and even your small triumphs. It's the little things that keep a relationship growing strong.

- Surprise one another. Put a small note in a lunch bag, car or coat pocket, telling one another how important you are...and really mean it. It will make you smile all day.

- Take a nap or just be lazy together. Many times when you have the opportunity to be lazy together, it seems like the perfect time to do what really needs to be done. That usually means chores and household duties. Every once in a while ...don't do it. Just relax, watch a movie together, take a nap, snuggle, eat a bag of chips or candy, and forget the rest of the world.

- Take an individual time-out. Even if it is just an hour or two, do something you really want to do with a friend, or alone, and enjoy it. The happier you are, the better partner and parent you'll be. Leave the guilt behind.

- Talk to one another. Having children is stressful. When things build up or problems occur, talk about them. Don't hold your anger or thoughts inside. Chances are that before your children were born, it was easier to communicate (no crying to compete with). Make time to share your feelings.

- Before reacting in a stressful situation, try seeing it from your partner's viewpoint. Chances are he or she is trying just as hard, is just as tired as you are, and loves your kids just as much. You are both in this together with the same goals—a happy, fulfilling family life.

- Give yourself credit. Know you can't do it all without support from your family. The whole family structure doesn't have to revolve around one person. Remember, it took more than one of you to make a family, and it takes more than one of you to care for a family.

- Know that having a good relationship with children isn't easy. At times, your relationship may seem incredibly wonderful and other moments may seem bleak. It's just life. By committing to work on your relationship, you are one step ahead of many couples. In the long run, when your children are grown and gone, you'll have a relationship and the silence won't frighten you.

"Camaraderie Makes the Difference"

A Life Experience by Julie Hanson-Lynn, M.A.

"If only I had known it would be like this . . ." "Why didn't anyone tell me, really tell me, it could be this way?" These thoughts crossed my mind several times a day after I brought my first child home from the hospital. "Am I the only one who feels this way?"

Although people said life with a newborn is hard, I was still unprepared for the realities of their demanding care, the disappointment in my postpartum body; the experience of months of sleep deprivation, and the isolation and loneliness of suddenly staying home.

Reading parenting magazines did little to reassure me. Their pictures showed moms happily exercising with their babies, serenely breastfeeding, and intently (enthusiastically, even!) stimulating their one-month-olds with all the proper paraphernalia. What's more, these moms were showered, fully dressed in clothes other than sweats, and had make-up on. Where was a picture of an exhausted mom, still in her pajamas at one o'clock in the afternoon, with her hair a mess and a breast pad unintentionally abandoned on the arm of the couch? Why wasn't I like the moms in the pictures?

I finally realized that I needed to be around other new moms. One day I was at a park and met a woman whose son was a week older than my daughter and we immediately connected. We laughed so hard when she told me she had been nursing just before the doorbell rang, opened the door to a delivery person and only after she shut the door did she realized her shirt was still unbuttoned! She invited me to join a play group she was a part of and it saved my sanity. None of us looked like the moms in the magazine pictures and I learned how to laugh about it. There was nothing wrong with me and I was doing a great job!

The friends I made in that group have been my closest friends for four years now, and my daughter thinks of their children as her own siblings. We get together as often as we can (with and without our kids); we share baby-sitting, and we are only a phone call away from each other when we need help or a supportive ear.

New parent support should be a part of every expectant parent's postpartum recovery plan. So completely do I believe this that I started my own private practice running support groups and educating health care professionals. If you don't find anything, start one yourself. Different groups do different things and attract different people so shop around to get ideas. At least then you'll know what is available to you after you have your baby. The key is to get out and get connected to others in a similar situation.

It is important to have a place where you can express all the emotions and thoughts you are having as a new mom and be reassured that you are not the only one. Most importantly, you too will learn how to laugh even though you have only had a few hours of sleep, your baby just spit up all over the shoulder of the third clean shirt you put on today, and you are late to an appointment. ❧

SUPPORT GROUPS

The arrival of a baby can unleash many new emotions and demands. Sometimes just being with other new parents helps to remind you that you aren't alone in your new role.

Participating in a support group is a great idea, especially for first-time parents, who often have many questions and concerns. The arrival of a baby can unleash many new emotions and demands. Sometimes just being with other new parents helps to remind you that you aren't alone in your new role. It is also fun to share your child's accomplishments and gain other parents' insights and clues to success.

This section includes national parenting support groups. Do some research to find out which group is right for your family. The hospital where you deliver may also offer support groups to serve your family's needs.

■ **F.E.M.A.L.E. (FORMERLY EMPLOYED MOTHERS AT THE LEADING EDGE)**
(630) 941-3553
P.O. Box 31
Elmhurst, IL 60126
Web site: http:\\members.aol.com\femaleofc\home.htm
F.E.M.A.L.E. is a national nonprofit support and advocacy group for women who have left full-time employment to care for their children. If you send a self-addressed stamped envelope to the address listed above, they will provide you with the nearest chapter. Most chapters hold two evening meetings per month as well as play groups and other activities to share with children. The $24 annual membership fee includes a monthly newsletter from the national organization.

■ MOMS CLUB (MOMS OFFERING MOMS SUPPORT)

(805) 526-2725
25371 Rye Canyon
Valencia, CA 91355

There are 4,000 chapters of this national nonprofit organization for women who are staying at home with their children (and for those who work part-time). Goals of the group include mental and social stimulation for parents, involvement in outreach projects which focus on the family, and social interaction for the kids. The groups typically meet monthly during the day with varying activities and child care options. In addition to the monthly meetings, some groups also plan field trips, playgroups, educational speakers and moms' nights out. Send $2 to the address above for an informational brochure.

■ MOPS INTERNATIONAL (MOTHERS OF PRESCHOOLERS)

(303) 733-5353
1311 S. Clarkson St.
Denver, CO 80210

This is a 25-year-old national support group which has nearly 1,500 groups nationwide. Groups typically meet twice a month during the day, and are geared to mothers of young children. The emphasis is outreach to moms who feel they may need support. Crafts, food and fun are all part of this group.

■ NATIONAL ASSOCIATION OF MOTHERS' CENTERS

800-645-3828
64 Division Ave.
Levittown, NY 11756

Mothers' Centers create an environment where women become part of a national network for support and exploration of issues that concern mothers and families. Over 50 centers are presently operating nationwide. The activities of different centers vary, but usually include workshops, seminars and discussion groups. A Mothers' Center representative will assist you in finding a local center, or send information on how to start and organize a center.

■ SELF-HELP CLEARINGHOUSE, NORTHWEST COVENANT MEDICAL CENTER

(201) 625-7101
25 Pocono Rd.
Denville, NJ 07834
Web site: www.cmhc.com/selfhelp/
E-mail: ashc@bc.cybernex.net

This organization provides information and a directory of more than 800 self-help and support groups, including parenting groups and those for a wide variety of medical conditions. The organization can also give you information about self-help clearinghouses that may serve your area. They also will mail a free handout on ideas for starting your own self-help group.

■ **STEPFAMILY ASSOCIATION OF AMERICA**
800-735-0329
650 J St., Ste. 205
Lincoln, NE 68508
For parents dealing with stepfamily issues, the Stepfamily Association offers support groups and education by trained facilitators at 50 chapters throughout the country. They also offer stepfamily education, information, referrals, books and a newsletter for stepfamilies and blended families.

■ **THE STEPFAMILY FOUNDATION**
(212) 877-3244
333 West End Ave.
New York, NY 10023
Web site: www.stepfamily.org
Membership in the nonprofit Stepfamily Foundation nets you a videotape, two audiotapes, publications, and a quarterly newsletter—eight pounds of information in all. The initial membership fee is $70, and $20 each subsequent year. Individual and family counseling sessions are available over the telephone. Although the organization sends no free information by mail, the web site contains more than 250 pages of interest to stepfamilies.

PUBLICATIONS OFFERING SUPPORT

■ **AT-HOME DAD NEWSLETTER**
(508) 685-7931, Peter Baylies
61 Brightwood Ave.
North Andover, MA 01845
This quarterly newsletter promoting the home-based father publishes a list of local coordinators who help fathers meet, get parenting advice, and plan activities. A subscription costs $12 per year. There are listings for books, online services, and magazines such as *Modern Dad* and an America Online chat group called "Stay-At-Home/Primary Care Dads Chat."

■ **THE COMPLEAT MOTHER**
(701) 852-2822
Box 209
Minot, ND 58702
Always provocative and sometimes outrageous, *Compleat Mother* is a quarterly magazine ($12/year or $20/two years) which celebrates breastfeeding and the family bed, and comes out strongly against disposable diapers and circumcision. While not for everyone, many will appreciate the pro-mothering viewpoint of this magazine.

■ **THE MOTHER IS ME**
800-693-6852
3919 Woodlawn Ave.
Falls Church, VA 22042
E-mail: zoey455@aol.com
Web site: ww.members.aol.com/zoey455/index.html
In 1997 the highly acclaimed quarterly *The Doula* merged with *The Mother Is Me*, a quarterly magazine edited by Amy

Condra-Peters. The magazine "offers all mothers, particularly feminist mothers, a collection of thought-provoking essays, fiction, commentary and book reviews" (of both adult and children's books). A sample issue costs $3.95, and a one-year subscription is $15.95.

■ MOTHERING

800-984-8116
P.O. Box 1690
Santa Fe, NM 87504
E-mail: mother@ni.net

"We are the publication for natural family living," proclaims *Mothering* magazine. In 1998 the magazine will be produced bimonthly. Supscriptions are $18 annually, $32 for two years, and $45 for three years. Beautiful photography illustrates articles on topics such as breastfeeding, home birth, educational methods—in all, a wide variety of articles and essays of interest to parents interested in natural family living. *Mothering* also publishes books on vaccinations, circumcision, fathering, homeschooling, and other topics.

■ THE NURTURING PARENT JOURNAL

800-810-8401
303 E. Gurley, Ste. 260
Prescott, AZ 86301
Web site: www.thenurturingparent.com
E-mail: letters@the nurturingparent.com

Attachment parenting is the theme of the quarterly *Nurturing Parent*. Articles encourage birth bonding, the family bed, unrestricted breastfeeding, father involvement, spousal commitment, and gentle discipline. The 40-plus page magazine ($18.50/year) includes in-depth articles enhanced with lots of photos, letters, essays, and parenting news briefs.

■ WELCOME HOME

800-783-4666
8310-A Old Courthouse Rd.
Vienna, VA 22182

Welcome Home is the product of the nonprofit Mothers at Home. Subscriptions to the 32-page advertising-free journal are $18. Each issue includes stories about joys and challenges of raising children, mother-to-mother problem solving, humor, and inspiring accounts of struggles and successes of at-home moms.

MASS CIRCULATION PARENTING MAGAZINES

■ CHILD
800-777-0987

■ PARENTS
800-727-3682

■ PARENTING
800-234-0847

■ WORKING MOTHER
800-627-0690

These widely circulated magazines are extremely helpful to new parents. All contain articles geared to parents of children from birth to teenage years, with doses of humor, advice, recipes, and ideas for family fun. You'll need to thumb through copies of each to see which is best suited to your needs.

Working Mother (10 issues/year) adds information of interest to moms heading back into the work force.

PUBLICATIONS

ONLINE SUPPORT

With just a computer, modem and phone line, parents can access a world of support and information. From checking an online version of a parenting book to chatting with other parents, the virtual community can be a wonderful resource. Here are some ways to get online. Note that the online world is rapidly growing; the resources were current when this book was published.

■ ONLINE SERVICES

America Online: 800-827-6364
CompuServe: 800-848-8990
Microsoft Network: 800-386-5550
Prodigy: 800-776-3449

The major online services, as well as a multitude of local providers, connect people throughout the country and beyond. You'll need to install their software and sign up as a member. It's easy to get free software and a free trial period, after which the monthly cost varies by the usage plan you prefer.

The major services offer bulletin boards for exchanging messages and "chat rooms" for real-time communication. They also offer e-mail, software files you can download and resource information on many subjects.

Each provides one or more areas specifically for parents. America Online has "Parent Soup" with message boards, experts, chat areas, reviews, and much more. Prodigy has message boards on parenting and a parenting page on their Internet site. Microsoft Network offers both "Home and Family" and "People and Communities" areas, with message boards, chat rooms, and resources. CompuServe, well-known for its business-related features, now offers a parenting forum.

All of these services also provide a way for users to access the Internet, which offers a multitude of places where parents can share and receive information. Here we've highlighted some of these sites.

■ INTERNET/WWW

Parents can access the Internet and its graphically-rich World Wide Web (WWW) through online services or through a direct Internet provider. With a direct provider, you'll also need Web browser software such as Netscape Navigator, which many companies include for free. Here's a small sampling:

Baby Online:
www.babyonline.com
This interactive site hosts expert panels to answer baby-rearing questions, and includes a parents' chat group.

Baby Web: www.netaxs.com/~iris/ infoweb/baby.html
Contains baby-related resources.

Birth Stories:
www.childbirth.org/articles/stories/ birth.html
For parents who love to read about birth stories, or would like to share their own, this is a great site.

Family.com: www.family.com
Family.com is part of Disney Online, and includes information from parenting newspapers throughout the U.S., feature articles and resources for parents.

Family Planet:
www.family.starwave.com
Family Planet offers daily news on family-related topics, experts discussing family issues, reviews, the *Parent's Resource Almanac* book online, and calendars of family events from around the country.

Father Net:
www.fsci.umn.edu/cyfc/ FatherNet.htp
Especially for fathers, Father Net includes excerpts of "Modern Dad" newsletter and chat groups.

Moms-at-Home:
www.iquest.com/~jsm/moms/
An online support area for moms who have chosen to stay at home.

National Parenting Center:
www.tnpc.com
Offers a variety of parenting resources, including thrice-yearly evaluations of toys, games and books.

Pampers Parenting Institute:
www.pampers.com
Organized by ages, this web site is a great general-purpose information site for parents. T. Berry Brazelton, M.D., is featured in an advice area.

Parent Soup:
www.parentsoup.com
This web site is the Internet version of AOL's parenting area, with much of the same information. There are bulletin boards and chat areas here, too.

Parents Place: www.parentsplace.com
Includes online news, resources, and areas to communicate with other parents. Parents Place's Web Doctor section answers parents' child health questions.

Parenttime:
www.ParentTime.com
Information geared to your child's age, expert advice, and the chance to chat with other parents are the main focus of ParentTime.

Dr. Toy: www.drtoy.com
At this site you'll find the Institute for Childhood Resources' list of the 100 best children's products and toys.

WorldVillage:
www.worldvillage.com
This "family-safe" web site includes articles, cartoons, reviews and contests.

ONLINE

"Real Life With Baby"

A Life Experience by Allison Blackham

I waddled through nine months of pregnancy and watched my belly expand to massive size. I visited the doctor and listened to a heartbeat, felt internal kicks and wiggles at all hours of the day and night. I furnished the nursery and bought tiny, cute baby clothes. I sat through childbirth classes and learned comical breathing techniques with ten other serious moms-to-be and their bemused partners. After months of anticipation, contractions began and I panted and grouched my way through labor. At labor's culmination, a wonderful nurse handed my newborn daughter to me and I was . . . surprised! There really was a baby in there!

That early surprise was a foreshadowing of things to come. No matter how well prepared I thought I was, the reality was still enough to knock me for a loop. The baby did difficult things, like cry. There were days when I seemed to cry a lot, too, especially when I'd had less than two hours of sleep the night before. My husband spent a lot of time cuddling two damp, sniffling females, both large and small, and wondered whether the end result of sex was all it's cracked up to be. Five babies later, I still remember postpartum as a wild and crazy ride. We grow into the calm, competent parents we want to be, but it takes time.

For most parents, sleep deprivation is the single biggest crisis of the postpartum period. Babies need a lot of sleep, but never when you do. Feedings every two hours around the clock, with fussing and crying in between, can make even the most compassionate and emotionally stable parent start to twitch. Let the housework go. Eat soup and sandwiches on paper plates, accept help from family and friends if it's offered, and ask for it if it's not. Get a support group going. This can be as informal as whining to your mom on the phone, but it's often good to talk to other new moms, sharing a weep and a laugh with women who are right there in the trenches with you.

With all the new and exciting things that come with a baby, it seems odd to talk about losses, but that's a reality of having a baby, too. Parts of your life are changed forever. You can no longer just up and do something you want to do, and romantic evenings alone are a thing of the past. Selfish pleasures (like an uninterrupted meal) go by the wayside. For the rest of your life, you will always have a child to consider. The advantages of having a child far outweigh the things you've lost, but you're not going to see all of that right away. Give yourself a break and feel a little sad or angry occasionally. Feelings never hurt anybody.

Poor Dad often gets lost in this postpartum time. Last week you were a couple, you had a life, things were good. Now you're Mom and Dad. The time you used to spend alone together is taken up in feeding, diapering, burping or, if you're lucky, sleeping. Sex? Who has the time or energy? Setting aside a few minutes each day to talk, smile at each other, hug and remember why you decided to be together in the first place is enough to keep you going. As soon as you feel comfortable leaving the baby with a friend or relative, it's great to establish a regular date night. Our children will someday grow up and leave us. We hope our partners will not. And after all, one of the best gifts parents can give their children is to love each other.

I was unprepared when I first held my newborn daughter, and felt inadequate in the days that followed. I've done almost as much growing as my daughter has in those 17 years. My biggest growth spurts have come out of the most difficult situations. As I've paced the floor with a wailing baby, spent the night sitting by the side of a wretchedly unwell toddler, curbed my temper when I'd rather yell, comforted when I'd rather scold, I've learned about unselfishness, patience, compassion and unconditional love. Those are big lessons to learn from such tiny people. It's too bad that we can't be magically transformed into wonderful, wise parents as soon as our children are born, but the process happens anyway. It's through the difficult, stressful, sometimes awful experiences of postpartum that we begin to grow into the good parents we are meant to be. ❧

QUESTIONS AND ANSWERS
Postpartum Depression

Information on postpartum depression was provided by a host of experts: Marcia Kahn, M.D., and Ann Howard, M.D., of the Women's Psychiatric Resource Center in Beaverton, Oregon; Abby Myers, ARNP, and Dawn Gruen, ACSW, of Seattle, Washington; Kathe Pratt of Sacramento and Kerry Breeler of Antelope, California.

Q: What are postpartum mood disorders (PPMD)?

A: Pregnancy is a time of many changes. Reactions to these changes cannot be fully anticipated, and it is not uncommon for women to experience anxiety and/or depression during their pregnancies. The symptoms described below may also occur during pregnancy, or after a miscarriage or weaning.

Once your baby is born, many expect that the postpartum period will be the best time of your life. But instead of joy, you may feel sad, depressed, anxious, even angry. You are not alone. Many women experience significant postpartum symptoms. It is important to realize that these disorders are not self-induced. A woman cannot "pull herself together" any more than she could if she had the flu, diabetes, or any other physical illness.

The postpartum phase (up to one year) is one of the most vulnerable times for women and their partners. Giving birth is a physical, psychological, and emotional challenge, during which everything is in upheaval. Because of this it is difficult to know when normal transitional issues become problematic. In this culture, the turmoil surrounding childbirth is minimized so that many people ignore or deny any negative distress associated with it. The difficult emotions that many experience are often attributed to feelings of exhaustion, with the hope that they will just disappear. But if a woman or couple is experiencing problems, it is important to acknowledge even the mildest forms of distress. Awareness of these adjustment problems can alert the family to seek information and possible evaluation for a postpartum disorder. If the distress continues to be unrecognized, postpartum disorders may progress to more severe dysfunction.

Q. What causes postpartum illness?

A. Mechanisms involved in postpartum illness are not completely understood. Research indicates that these disorders are biochemical and hormonal. The brain's neurotransmitters are directly responsible for the way we feel. They are affected by heredity, hormonal changes and environmental stress. Unfortunately, psychological disorders are stigmatized. These illnesses are difficult to explain. Those closest to a distressed mother need to understand that while psychological and environmental stress may play a role, postpartum disorders are also physical and biochemical.

Q. What are symptoms of the various postpartum disorders?

A. *Baby blues.* Between 50% and 80% of women experience "baby blues." Feelings of depression, anxiety and irritability usually begin two to three days after birth and subside within a week or two.

Depression. Of women who give birth, 10%-20% develop postpartum depression. Postpartum depression can strike any time in the year postpartum or at the time of weaning from breastfeeding. Many women experience postpartum depression between the third and ninth month postpartum, whether or not they experienced the "baby blues." They experience intense feelings of sadness, anxiety and despair that do not go away within two weeks after onset. Instead, the feelings increase with each week and may last for a year or more.

Other symptoms include:
- Feelings of doubt, guilt, helplessness, hopelessness or worthlessness
- Trouble handling your usual responsibilities, feeling overwhelmed and unable to cope
- Insomnia or sleeping too much
- Marked changes in appetite
- Loss of interest in things that used to bring pleasure, including sex.

PPD: TIPS FOR COPING

- Learn and identify the symptoms of postpartum distress as early as possible.
- Understanding and awareness help alleviate guilt and confusion. Don't try to deal with this by yourself. Isolation only makes things worse. Talk to others, join a support group to know that you are not alone and are experiencing something that many other parents go through.
- Consult a health professional who is experienced in postpartum disorders.
- Get your thyroid checked.
- Explore with a health professional the possibility of using medicines that can reverse chemical changes in your body which may have contributed to the depression.
- Counseling can help you learn how to cope and care for yourself.
- Obtain help with domestic chores and care for the baby. This will help relieve pressure and increase the likelihood of a quicker recovery.
- Allow yourself to grieve about your feelings of loss.

DEPRESSION

- Trouble attaching to baby emotionally (or later loss of attachment)
- Extreme concern for your baby
- Fear of harming the baby
- Thoughts of harming yourself

Panic attacks. Women may experience severe anxiety attacks which include the following symptoms: shortness of breath, dizziness or faintness, increased heart rate or chest pain, sweating, nausea or choking, numbness and tingling, or fear of dying or "going crazy."

Obsessive-compulsive symptoms. Examples include recurrent, intrusive thoughts, urges or images that cause a distress, such as excessive concerns about the infant's health or of harming the infant. Another component is the need to perform repetitive behaviors, such as compulsive house cleaning or checking to make sure things are in order.

Postpartum psychosis. One in 1,000 women develops this severe reaction. Symptoms are severe and may include insomnia, hallucinations, agitation and bizarre feelings or behavior. Postpartum psychosis requires immediate medical help. Remember that postpartum psychosis is treatable and the sooner intervention occurs, the greater the likelihood for earlier recovery.

Q. How long do postpartum disorders last?

A. Depending on the degree of severity and type of treatment, postpartum depression may last only a few months or up to a year (with proper treatment). Long-term studies indicate, however, that without treatment, it may take up to four years to recover. If left untreated, children and the couple relationship may experience irrevocable impact.

Q: How do I get help?

A: If you think you are having symptoms (even mild ones) that have continued for more than two weeks, discuss them with your health care provider. Unfortunately, some providers are not trained to recognize signs and symptoms of PPD. They may minimize the problem, telling you to just get some exercise or take a break from the baby. This is good advice, but may not be enough. If your provider minimizes your symptoms and you still feel distressed, find another provider who has experience with postpartum disorders.

You should request a medical evaluation (including a thyroid exam). Low thyroid levels are a strong indicator of postpartum depression and physical symptoms including headaches, appetite and sleep disturbance, hair loss and dizziness. Often women's thyroid levels test at the "low-normal" range, and a more sensitive test, such as a TSH test, can identify subclinical hypothyroidism. Once medical causes are ruled out, a referral to a qualified mental health professional should be made.

For women with mild symptoms, information and strong emotional support from family or from a support group may be enough. Others may need individual or group psychotherapy to help understand the contributing factors to their postpartum difficulties, to learn more effective stress reduction and coping skills, and to rebuild self-esteem. Many women benefit from medication in addition to psychotherapy. There are antidepressants which have been researched and approved for use while breastfeeding. Medication should always be monitored under the supervision of a physician or nurse practitioner.

It is important to involve your partner in your treatment as emotional support is one of the main factors in an earlier recovery. Postpartum disorders are quite treatable and with early intervention, recovery and stability for you and your family will be forthcoming.

❧ RESOURCES ❧

■ **DEPRESSION AFTER DELIVERY (D.A.D.)**
800-944-4PPD (4773)
P.O. Box 278
Belle Mead, NJ 08502
Web site: www.behavenet.com/dadinc
This nonprofit group provides information on postpartum blues, depression and psychosis, including diagnostic information, available treatment methods, a local professional referral list, and a list of local support groups and volunteer telepone contacts. Annual membership is $30, and includes a quarterly newsletter. Enclosed in the basic mailing are items such as national meeting transcripts available for ordering.

■ **POSTPARTUM SUPPORT, INTERNATIONAL**
(805) 967-7636
927 N. Kellogg Ave.
Santa Barbara, CA 93111
This organization sends brochures on postpartum disorders, including symptoms, checklists and available services to women experiencing PPD. Sent free of charge, the self-assessment questionnaire can help you discover if it is truly PPD you are experiencing. Annual conferences have been held at locations across the country and in Toronto and London. Individual memberships in PSI are $30, and include a quarterly newsletter.

■ **WOMEN'S HEALTH CONNECTION**
800-366-6632
5708 Monona Dr.
Madison, WI 53716
For women with postpartum blues and depression, PMS and other hormone-related disorders, the Women's Health Connection staff pharmacists are available to answer your questions by phone. An educational division of Women's International Pharmacy, this group's information is unbiased and would be helpful for anyone suffering from PPD. They will send a packet with brochures and a free copy of the informative newsletter "Connection" on request.

DEPRESSION

"More Than Blues"

A Life Experience by Kerry Breeler

The joy, shock, elation, fear, excitement, anxiety . . . and all the doubting of whether or not we were "ready" for a baby, and if we'd be "good parents," are often common feelings shared by those expecting—even those who plan their pregnancy and greatly desire children, as we did.

Our pregnancy was planned, but poorly planned at that, for we were in the process of relocating to a new city far from friends and family, transitioning into new jobs, and closing escrow on our first home. It wasn't until we were in the midst of this tremendous balancing act that we realized that "having it all" shouldn't have required us to get it all at once.

When juggling my mixed emotions, all these positive stressors caught up with me, and all the positive emotions I'd felt suddenly vanished and those which remained began to heighten and multiply. Next came insomnia, along with nausea and an inability and lack of desire to eat. Then I began questioning my future capabilities as a parent and was convinced I'd never meet my expectations.

I couldn't dismiss it as "morning sickness" or major anxiety any longer, once the anxiousness was incessant and I was totally blinded by pessimism and controlled by excessive worry and rumination. Having always been high-functioning and able to handle tremendous stress, naturally I felt quite desperate as my normal coping skills failed me and the sleep deprivation continued.

Luckily, with the help of a mild sleeping aid and the couple weeks off work ordered by my obstetrician, the feelings of hopelessness and incompetence diminished and I regained my self-esteem. Learning to lessen expectations of myself and to quit trying to be such a perfectionist through some brief counseling also contributed to my recovery.

What both the counselor and obstetrician failed to do, however, was warn me about what might be to come. They didn't warn me that I was at risk, let alone a higher risk, for

postpartum depression, and that after the remainder of my uncomplicated pregnancy, another even darker episode of depression might follow.

My prepared childbirth classes didn't touch on the subject either. But postpartum depression did begin, far beyond six weeks postpartum—a slow, insidious development that gradually eroded away the love and happiness I'd had with my child and husband. Simple tasks became overwhelming, lethargy and lack of motivation set in, and every symptom I endured during my prenatal episode came back, only tenfold. Then emerged distressing thoughts that harm might come to my daughter (first at others' hands, later at my own), along with obsessive-compulsive behaviors to distract me from my own thoughts.

Denial, guilt and shame, along with mistaking my symptoms of depression as the cause of it, kept me from seeking help sooner. By the time I did, I had lost my sense of self and was vulnerable to everyone's interpretations and diagnosis. Co-dependent, child of divorce, unhappy marriage...? These and other "issues" handed out by both friends and professionals only complicated matters.

What would have helped was a diagnosis of PPD rather than that of "chronic depression." Also, therapy designed around the idea that "the fire has to be put out before the house is rewired." And finally, a support group where my feelings could be validated and normalized by others who had "walked the walk," and recovered! No such luck.

But the "fire" was eventually put out by a phalanx of medications. Gradually I improved as I went through the motions of daily life, and after a few months realized I'd fully recovered when enjoyment, spontaneity and a reconnection to my family all reemerged. It was then that I happened upon some excellent materials on PPD, and learned that both my illness and its mistreatment were all too common.

Now an advocate for heightened professional and public awareness of PPD, I facilitate a peer group and am a telephone support volunteer. I share the universal message "You are not alone, you are not to blame, and you will get better." It's a message I wish I had received. 🙥

GETTING TO KNOW YOUR BABY

By Troy Maslow Smith

In the first trying days of parenthood, it may be all you can do to keep up with your baby's feeding, diapering and bathing. But soon enough you and your baby will have a chance to spend time together as daily companions. These early months are crucial to your baby's development, and the best way to help your little one is to just be a guide to the world. With your guidance, you will help pass on to your baby the gifts of living and learning and loving. Each day is a new adventure for your child, and through her, you will see the world anew as well.

TEMPERAMENT

As you get acquainted with your newborn, you will notice right away what type of temperament she has. Some newborns sleep 23 hours out of the day, while others may be awake for 12, and want to be entertained each of those hours. Some babies crave stimulation while others shrink away from lights, loud sounds and too much handling. Parents must adjust their methods based on their child's preferences. Sometimes this comes naturally, but be prepared to be frustrated at times when you and your child seem incompatible. With a little patience and some experimenting, you will adjust.

WIDE-AWAKE BABIES

Wide-awake babies are both a joy and a frustration to their parents. Bright and interested in the world around them, they are the babies who kick themselves out of infant seats and prefer being held nonstop. These babies may be happiest in a front pack or sling, where they can go where you go and do what you do. They like motion and stimulation.

Sleeping will often be difficult for the wakeful baby. What you should be able to do, of course, is to put the baby in her bassinet or crib when you sense she is getting sleepy, and let her fuss before she falls asleep. This may work. Or it may not. You may need to rock her through each hard-earned nap and expect wakefulness every night for months on end.

&a.

These early months are crucial to your baby's development, and the best way to help your little one is to just be a guide to the world.

&a.

Wakeful babies are sometimes soothed by pacifiers, by nursing, or just by being jiggled and danced with. (They are the best help for losing extra pregnancy pounds!) If colic is suspected, try some of the suggestions mentioned in the box. The biggest problem is finding a balance between stimulating the baby and finding a way to help the baby calm down and get enough sleep. The wakeful baby considers each hour spent sleeping an hour lost in which she could be playing, learning, and having fun!

SLEEPY BABIES

With a sleepy baby, parents may worry that their infant is not getting enough stimulation. The typical "good baby" may nurse easily, fall asleep quickly and cry rarely. When awake, he may be quiet and move little, preferring to watch the action going on around him. There is no cause for alarm; you have a calm, cool and collected child who will best thrive in a quiet atmosphere without a lot of outside stimulation. You will need to watch that your baby is not lethargic,

COPING WITH COLIC

A colicky baby is one who cries excessively, often in the evenings; not just once, but daily for up to four months. If you have a baby who cries excessively, it is best to have the child seen by the doctor in order to rule out any physical cause. Unfortunately, the cause of colic is unknown. Parents may try to comfort the baby using a number of time-tested techniques, and beyond that, they must just be patient.

Some helpful techniques for a colicky baby:
- Go for a ride in the car.
- Take the baby for a walk in the stroller.
- Carry the baby in a front pack or sling.
- Sing to, and play music for, the baby.
- Use the "colic hold"—baby lying stomach-down across the parent's forearm, resting her head on the parent's hand.
- Turn on the vacuum, washing machine or dishwasher—anything with a rhythmic sound or vibration.

If you find that you need time away from a crying baby, ask for help. See if your spouse, partner, a friend or a relative whom you trust will watch your child so you can get away for a short period. Go for a walk around the block or to the grocery store. Take time to relax and reassure yourself that you are not doing anything to cause your baby's colic. You may find that even a few minutes of relaxation can make all the difference in the world.

If the colic persists for a long period of time, make sure you work with your doctor. Join a support network to surround yourself with others who understand what you're going through. Colic for even one day may make the most excited new mother or father weary.

which may be an indicator of dehydration, along with diapers being wet less than every six to eight hours, a sunken appearance in her soft spot and eyes, and lack of saliva in the mouth. If you feel anything is physically wrong with your baby, give your pediatrician a call.

Whatever their temperament, most babies do best with a parent who is attempting to be calm and consistent. Even if the thought of giving that first bath at home (and dealing with the umbilical cord stump) fills you with dread, relax! Speak soothingly to your baby, and explain as you go what you are doing. Consider hiring a postpartum doula, or have a friend or relative with children over to give you pointers on bathing, breastfeeding and appropriate dressing for the weather. Just be confident that many parents have been in the same situation you are in, and have survived and thrived.

TALK, TALK, TALK

One way to keep yourself calm is to talk to your baby. At first it will not matter what you are saying; just hearing Mom's or Dad's voice will soothe the baby. You can say, "Now I'm going to change your wet diaper," and tell baby the steps involved. You can explain to the baby how you put her into her car seat, what color her hat is, and what the weather is like that day. Babies learn to process verbal information faster if they are spoken to regularly. Make eye contact when you talk, and wait after speaking for the baby to respond. Your baby will "talk" to you, if only by movements or an intent gaze. Soon she will coo back, and your "conversations" will naturally grow from there. Baby talk has its place as "play" language, but don't speak regu-

larly to your child this way! You want him to learn to speak using real words.

By hearing your voice used in a warm and loving way, your child will know that you love him. Your voice becomes associated with good feelings. It's up to you to try not to yell, no matter what age your child is or what he has done! As Jane Healy, Ph.D., author of Your Child's Growing Mind, writes, "Children who have learned to 'tune out' adult voices because they were loud, bossy, or hurtful may start school with poor listening habits." Keep this in mind when choosing child care for your little one, as well.

Talking to your baby has real benefits for long-term learning. Recent research at the University of Chicago showed that at 20 months, children whose mothers frequently spoke to them knew 131 more words than those with less talkative mothers. By 24 months, children of talkative mothers knew 295 more words than the other children. You can think of an infant's brain as "hard-wired" to understand language, and early exposure just gets the circuitry going faster. By two or three years of age, your child will be the one who talks all the time!

SINGING AND DANCING

Singing is a great way to introduce music into your baby's life. You can sing lullabies, show tunes or rock ballads and—no matter how off-key you are—your baby will not criticize your singing voice. If you are inhibited, put a lullaby cassette in your tape player and sing along.

Dancing is great for both you and the baby. You can do ballroom, country-western or modern dance to your favorite music. Just hold on tight to your baby (sounds like a country tune!) and dance.

MUSICAL SELECTIONS

In the car or at home, music is a perfect accompaniment to your day. It's never too early to introduce your baby to music—both children's music and music in your family's own favorite style.

Lullaby tapes are a great start. The soothing melodies may even do the job they were originally designed to do—help your baby fall asleep. Record stores, baby retailers and discount stores generally have a good selection.

Children's tapes are usually more upbeat, encouraging sing-alongs. When your child gets to the toddler stage, he will probably have a favorite tape which he'll want played again and again. It may drive you batty to hear "The Wheels on the Bus" ten times a day, but that is just how kids are. Relax and try to enjoy it! Some favorite children's musicians are Raffi, Tom Chapin, Red Grammar, and Sharon, Lois, and Bram (from the TV show). Disney also has many recordings sure to please both the children and adults.

For a change of pace, you might try playing classical music for your baby as well. The complex arrangements and stirring melodies seem to be a foundation for music learning. Works of Vivaldi and Bach may be a little easier on baby's ears than Beethoven's "1812 Overture." Try a classical music station and you may learn to appreciate classical as well.

Think of other things you can do to music; for example, clapping hands or exercises such as "bicycling" baby's legs to a bouncy beat. You might like to find out more about infant massage and give your baby a soothing massage with a calming new-age CD playing. Music gives your child an introduction to rhythm and beat, early keys to both music and mathematics.

BABY'S PLAYTIME

A basic necessity for babies is a clean blanket on the floor. If a child is constantly being held, or in an infant seat or automatic swing, he misses the opportunity to explore. A tiny infant won't do much beside kick his legs when placed on the floor, but eventually he will enjoy feeling the blanket's texture, explore toys you have placed around him, and learn to roll or crawl to get at enticing toys just out of reach. One caveat: don't lay your baby down right after feedings, as a sitting-up posture is easier for digestion. Luckily, almost all babies like to sit in infant seats or bouncy chairs where they can watch you.

Mobiles entertain many small babies. You may want to put them in places other than over a crib. Many parents report great success with a mobile over a changing table, especially those which are designed to entertain the baby, not adults! Look for bright colors, or black and white designs, to capture and hold your baby's interest.

Your baby's first "toy" will be his own hands. By about six weeks he will be able to find his hands by touch, and will

KNOWING BABY

mouth them. By around two months, your baby will be able to grasp toys and will begin to enjoy toys that make noise as they are shaken. Some good toy ideas are rattles that strap on the wrist (you don't have to worry about them being dropped), and chewable toys with easily grasped handles. Never give an infant anything smaller than golf ball size to play with in order to avoid choking.

In the following month or two, your child will begin to grasp objects on his own. This is the time that an activity gym becomes a worthwhile plaything for many babies. Designed like a miniature swing set, with colorful objects hanging from straps, activity gyms allow children to lie beneath them and swing at and grasp the dangling toys.

When handing a three-month-old a toy, show the object, describe it ("here is your soft blue rattle") and let your baby reach out for it. Don't rush him. Once he makes the attempt to grab for it, put it in his hand. This will reward the reaching impulse. Over the next month he will be refining this technique, and will soon be able to grab just about anything he sets his mind to—including hair, earrings, and coffee cups. The danger time has begun! If you have not yet child-proofed your house, you must do so now.

THE GREAT OUTDOORS

When the weather is nice, a favorite activity of most babies is a stroller ride. The gentle breeze on the face, new sights and sounds, and the pleasant vibration from the wheels on pavement will often soothe a child. You may be able to park the stroller under a tree and let the baby watch the movement of leaves above while you catch up on some reading. Stroller rides, or walking with the baby in a sling or pack, get you out in the "real world" when the four walls of your home may be closing in on you. It's not too early to check out neighborhood parks to get acquainted with other moms.

The joys of nature are there for you to introduce to your child—the caress of wind on the cheek, the tickle of grass on bare feet, the scent of flowers, and the feel of rain on a bare head. You can introduce these things to your baby as soon as she's ready. Sand is great, but not when her first impulse is to eat it. But a six-month-old will enjoy splashing in a sprinkler set very low, and a three-month-old will like feeling the texture of leaves or grass.

What other experiences should be part of a baby's daily life? Not many. A baby's needs are simple—a quiet place to sleep, regular feedings, diaper changes when necessary, and the firm guidance of a loving caregiver. All the rest will fall into place. Remember, your baby is part of an already-existing family. Although it may prove difficult, try not to let your life be turned upside-down.

The best advice is to read a lot about baby and child care. Take your pediatrician's advice. Ask friends who are experienced mothers and whose parenting style you admire for guidance. And trust your own feelings and intuitions. To be a good parent, you don't have to buy every gadget that is available, dress your baby to the nines every day, or fuss over your baby unnecessarily. Use common sense and you and your baby will grow more in tune with each other as the months (and years) go by.

INFANT MASSAGE

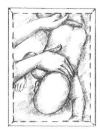

By Adrienne Disbrow, CIMI, Doula, CMT, ICCE

Touch . . . it is your baby's first sense and first means of communication. At six weeks gestation an embryo, less than an inch long, responds to touch. Many studies indicate that touch is an essential part of normal human development and that it is one of the basic necessities of life. With infant massage you will learn your baby's first language. You will also meet his basic needs and express your love and affection all at once.

In many cultures infant massage is an ancient skill passed down from generation to generation as a basic parenting tool. In our culture we are rediscovering the power of this ancient art. We can learn how to massage (touch) our infants and at the same time improve our confidence and competence in our ability to take care of our baby. With our complete attention during a massage, our baby learns about us as we discover him. Through massage, babies learn our smell, our voice, our touch, and how much we love them. We are learning our baby's nonverbal communication cues, likes and dislikes, and how he expresses himself. We are building a bond which will last a lifetime.

> *Touch is an essential part of normal human development and it is one of the basic necessities of life.*

PHYSICAL AND EMOTIONAL BENEFITS

As modern science studies this ancient art, we are discovering infant massage induces many physiological benefits.

- Both the giver and receiver of the massage experience a wonderful, warm feeling of relaxation and closeness.
- Dad or Mom (the massage giver) releases the hormone prolactin. Called the "nurturing hormone," it creates that warm, fuzzy, "I love you forever" feeling in the parents.
- Massage improves circulation, digestion, and increases neurological organization in the infant.
- It reduces muscle tension and helps baby relieve stress in a way other than crying.
- Babies who are massaged get into a deeper sleep. Deep sleep is where children do a lot of growing and repair work their bodies need.
- By strengthening the development of the gastrointestinal and respiratory tracts, massage can help reduce the symptoms of gas and colic.

WHEN TO BEGIN

Massage can start at any age, including newborns and even preemies still in the hospital. With adaptations for each developmental stage, massage can be shared as a family tradition through the teen years and beyond. As an infant becomes more mobile, we urge parents to be flexible and adapt the massage to their child's needs. When a child learns to roll, just allow them to roll and massage whatever part appears available.

Crawling and walking are challenging because the child is often more interested in moving. Parents may find massages become quite a bit shorter. Inventing games, songs, and rhymes to go along with the massage may capture a newly mobile baby's interest.

Toddlers often go through a stage of independence vs. dependence and may decide that massage represents dependence and reject it for a while. Have no fear: as they work through this stage they will return to massage. From 3 years on it is fun to test your own creative abilities and invent massages and games that suit your child.

Older children might appreciate a massage after a soccer game or dance class. And, finally, when your children have children, they will pass the massage tradition and all its benefits down as they lovingly massage their own babies.

Anyone can learn infant massage: parents, grandparents, siblings or child care workers. Working parents especially find it a wonderful tool to reconnect and bond with baby after being away.

CHOOSING AN INSTRUCTOR

Courses are available ranging from group classes in one session to private classes, to several group sessions over a period of time. The International Association of Infant Massage's certified instructors have been through specialized training and receive updates in research and techniques quarterly. Some Certified Massage Therapists and other specialists who work with new parents and babies may also have special training in infant massage. Videos and books are also available for those who prefer to learn on their own.

🐾 RESOURCES 🐾

■ **INTERNATIONAL ASSOCIATION OF INFANT MASSAGE (IAIM)**
800-248-5432
1720 Willow Creek Cir., Ste. 516
Eugene, OR 97402
The purpose of IAIM is to promote nurturing touch and communication through training, education and research

so that parents, caregivers, and children are loved, valued and respected through the world community. The association makes referrals to IAIM-certified infant massage instructors nationwide. IAIM also provides training and certification, a Gentle Touch warehouse for supplies and books, and a quarterly newsletter for association members.

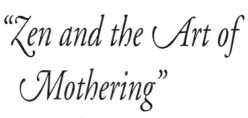

"Zen and the Art of Mothering"

A Life Experience by Felice Lopez

Zoe Rosalie is our little wild one who we are teaching to be a gentle human being. She is a ball of energy—walking, running and talking, often all at the same time. She enjoys being read to; playing with blocks; rearranging our house; finding and greeting cats, dogs and squirrels; singing; dancing, and speaking her own language. As we have nurtured her, she has become a loving, observant, curious and eager child. In turn, Zoe has transformed us into more patient, thoughtful and resilient human beings. As we have grown to recognize how much our words, actions and moods shape her overall development, we begin to be aware of ourselves, so that she receives the best part of who we are and who we are becoming.

We have trained our ears and eyes to understand Zoe's questions and to recognize what, and how, she is learning from us and the world around her. When she was around nine months old, she began to sing along with her evening lullabies. She'd be nursing and when I'd get to "up above the world so high," she'd turn away from my breast and sing all three syllables: "up above." Her participation was subtle, yet unmistakable, and made me realize how closely she'd been listening to all my hours of singing.

By 14 months she had mastered all the little utterances we had taught her—hi, bye, yeah, yes, no, uh-oh, and some we hadn't taught her. Apparently we often ask "why?" around our house because Zoe started asking "why?" in response to our statements, and she'd wait for our answer, however incomprehensible to her.

Lately she's noticed that we begin to talk by saying "umm." One day she took great delight in playfully mocking me. As she was nursing I chatted with my husband, Scott,

and when I spoke I began with "umm..." She stopped nursing, looked up at me, and said "umm..." and laughed. Scott and I continued our conversation, and Zoe proceeded to mimic me each time I said "umm," each time laughing harder, until all three of us were roaring with laughter.

Scott and I realized that just as we are her mirror to the world—reflecting our values back to her—she is a mirror to us, reflecting back who we are and what we do and say. I can observe her watching me, and catch fleeting parts of myself that can't be captured on film or tape. I can only see these parts of myself through Zoe's eyes.

We spend so much time planning what we want to impart to our children that we often don't pay attention to their teaching us. Although by nature we're able as mothers to nurse and as fathers to give tender care, we must learn how to do it. This learning is on a different curve than any other skill because, even though there are parenting books to read, the learning must be done by submitting to the child's timetable and personality. If we allow the mood, crying, or cooing of our babies to come forth and try to understand it without immediately quieting or recording it, then we can compassionately enter their reality. By listening to and learning about our babies as little people, we begin to go with their flow, start to teach them and in turn learn more about who we really are. Ultimately we realize that we are all children in the eyes of God.

As I've given and listened to Mother's Day greetings for the first time, I am reminded of the importance of savoring and reflecting upon each day's events—good and bad—that pass so quickly, yet add up to a child's lifetime of memories and experiences that mold their world view and personality. These are our experiences too, that can mold us if we let them. No matter how trying our tasks as parents may be, our job is made easier if we allow the days event's to wash over us— enveloping and becoming us—instead of resisting them, thinking they should be better, faster, less noisy. I submit myself fully to the role of parent, knowing I have much to offer and that I also have so much to learn that only Zoe can teach. ❧

THE VAST ADVANTAGES OF PARENTHOOD

By Joyce Armor

In trying to explain the deep and lasting significance of our wedding anniversary to our almost five-year-old son, I said, "If we hadn't gotten married, we never would have had you." He thought about this for a moment, then replied, "You mean Judie and Stephen (our very married but childless next door neighbors) aren't married?" I had obviously painted myself into a corner and tried to paint myself back out by explaining the differences between married couples with children and married couples without. He interrupted my riveting explanation to ask where lightning comes from, and I gave him my sage answer to such questions: "Go ask Daddy."

That was the end of the children vs. childless comparison for him, but not for me. My first thought was that Judie and Stephen have things that we don't. A new car, for one. Light (and clean) carpeting, for another. Time. But we have things they don't have, too. Toys, for instance. A refrigerator art gallery. Fruit by the Foot. Then again, they don't have to drag a bar stool outside, pry the screen off their bedroom window and somersault onto the bed, all in full view of passing traffic, because some little guttersnipe thinks it's funny to lock Mommy's bedroom door with the key inside at least once a week. They haven't changed enough diapers to cover the planet or broken up fistfights over a grain of sand. On a chilly, drizzling day, my son ran out of a friend's house into her front yard and sat on a huge pile of wet poop that had obviously been left by an elephant. I made the mistake of exclaiming, "Oh no! Look what you just sat in!" So he, naturally, scraped both hands across his backside and came up with handfuls of said elephant droppings. Horrified, he wiped the offending hands all over his brand new jacket.

Let's face it. Childless couples don't have to deal with the mounds of elephant and other droppings that parents do. They probably stay reasonably dry on rainy days. I am forever standing in a puddle in the rain fastening seat belts and trying to wrestle the car keys out of the fat little fist of someone who thinks it's funny to see Mommy's hair get plastered to her face.

My mother talks about the time my brother, age two, locked her out of the house in her nightgown in a snowstorm. For me it was the torrential rainstorm of 1986. I mean, haven't we all, at one time or another, had our front doors kicked in by the police? It's a tradition in our family. I'll bet Stephen and Judie don't have a locksmith listed in their personal phone directory. I see them come and go at odd hours, sometimes many times a day, and a hazy memory forms of a time when I could be spontaneous without hurrying to put on six shoes instead of two, or worse yet, trying to coax the kids into putting on their own shoes. Or standing over two little tooth brushers like a drill sergeant.

Okay, so Judie and Stephen can go where they want, when they want, and they're not at the mercy of baby-sitters or someone else's bowel movements. For their added enjoyment they have furniture without gouges, a clean house,

a gorgeous boat and nice tans. Somewhere in our house are the missing pieces to 347 puzzles. We have a swing set with a lot of miles on it and an Aqua-Slide, slightly chewed by an Australian shepherd. But they don't have anybody to color with either, or play jacks or hopscotch or baseball with, or all the other joys of childhood that we're rediscovering.

There are no little arms reaching out over there, not only to get comfort, but to give it. And nobody lives at their house who believes they know everything. Maybe, just maybe, we have a small person living here who will one day make an important scientific or economic or ecological discovery or who will in some other way make this world a better place. As I tucked him into bed a few nights after our anniversary conversation, my son hugged me extra hard and said, "I'm happy you got married and had kids." Me too!

EASTSIDE AND GREATER SEATTLE RESOURCES

Edited by Karen Wilkinson and Andrea Rowe

ACKNOWLEDGEMENTS

We would like to thank our families for helping to make this book possible by sharing us with the project. Our husbands, Dave and Jonathan, offered their patience and encouragement. Steve and Andrew gave up some of Mom's time and energy, and a special thanks to our babies, Ari and Matthew, who gave up extra time being held and snuggled as we were connected to phones and computer keyboards.

Thank you also to the many people at the various agencies, groups, and retail establishments we spoke with or visited. You were all helpful and informative, making our jobs all that much easier. You make Seattle a great place to live and raise children.

We'd like to thank Kristen Howard, Nanci Newell and the nursing staff of Northwest Hospital for their support and guidance. Also helpful were the medical professionals who reviewed this book prior to publication: Dana Blackham, M.D.; Rick Edwards, R.N.; Rosa Johnson, R.N.; Barry Lawson, M.D., and Teresa Schlesinger, M.D.

Thank you goes to business community who participate in The Baby Pages. It is your support of the book that confirms for us that this guide is a valuable resource to parents in Seattle.

We have found this guide to be an invaluable asset, and we hope you will too!

Karen Wilkinson
Andrea Rowe

HAVING A BABY, SEATTLE STYLE

CHOICES, CHOICES

Pregnancy and childbirth in Seattle these days are all about choices. In some cases, the choices may begin far before a woman becomes pregnant. There are insurance carrier choices, health care provider choices and hospital choices. There are a wide spectrum of insurance plans available as well as choices of plans if you are eligible for the Medicaid Healthy Options program.

How you and your partner prepare for the birth experience brings forth more choices. Do you attend childbirth education classes? Read everything you can get your hands on? Participate in private instruction, listen to your mother-in-law, or just be surprised? You will discover even more decisions needed in the timing of this preparation. Some people prefer to let their health care providers and insurance company make plans and decisions for them, while others choose to be more proactive and take advantage of all the opportunities surrounding them to best meet their specific needs.

Your choices may seem simple when compared to the many decisions you will make concerning your body and that of your growing baby. You must choose what you will and will not eat, how much you will work or not work, what type of exercise and activities you will or will not take part in, and even how you will relax. And, where will you live with this little bundle of joy? Do you need to move to a larger household or rearrange the sleeping arrangements of your current dwelling? Will your current set of wheels accommodate your new family?

Choices, choices, and more choices are to be made. Seattle is a place of choices as it comes with many different types of health care providers, excellent hospitals and a vast array of resources available for the expectant parent. Fortunately, here in Seattle, parents have the opportunity to create an individualized pregnancy to welcome their baby.

❧

Pregnancy

and

childbirth in

Seattle these

days are all

about

choices.

❧

CHOOSING YOUR PRACTITIONER

■ **COMMUNITY HEALTH ACCESS PROGRAM**
(206) 284-0331 or (206) 284-5291 or 800-756-5437
Expectant moms can call this free referral service that specializes in locating health care and community resources for low income, DSHS, and uninsured families. It serves both King and Snohomish counties. As part of the community health access program, this is a community based and supported non-profit agency that can refer you to an Ob/Gyn or pediatrician in King and Snohomish counties. They can also help you find certain health care providers who accept your specific insurance or help identify public programs you may be eligible for and facilitate the application process.

■ **DIRECT DOCTORS PLUS FOR AUBURN REGIONAL MEDICAL CENTER**
800-370-8640
As a resident of the greater Auburn area, Direct Doctors Plus can provide you with the names of physicians in the community. Referrals to all physician specialties are available through the program and appointments with a doctor can be made for you through one phone call to the service. Another benefit of the service is a health information library that contains more than 1,100 health-related topics. Just let the Direct Doctors Plus representative know what you are interested in and the information can be read to you over the phone or mailed to your home.

■ **HIGHLINE RESOURCE LINE**
(206) 439-5576
For help in selecting a health care provider or for a personal appointment to tour the Highline Family Childbirth Center, call this resource line. They also have information about childbirth classes.

■ **NORTHWEST HOSPITAL CHILDBIRTH INFORMATION HOTLINE**
(206) 364-BABY
Sponsored by Northwest Hospital, this informative service for patients of Northwest Hospital or residents of North Seattle and South Snohomish counties has a consulting nurse who can answer questions about pregnancy, childbirth, and the newborn. Also available are referrals to physicians or nurse midwives who deliver babies at Northwest Hospital.

■ **OVERLAKE MEDICAL CENTER**
(425) 688-5211
You can call this 24-hour service if you are looking for a physician referral from Overlake Hospital. They also make referrals for midwives who have admitting privileges at Overlake Hospital.

■ **PACIFIC ASSOCIATION FOR LABOR SUPPORT (PALS)**
(206) 325-1419
PALS provides expectant parents with a list of local labor support persons (doulas). Members of the association have completed a training program offered by either the Seattle Midwifery School or other certifying organizations. Many of the support people are childbirth educators; many have given birth; many also work in health-related fields.

Support is available before, during, and after labor. Fees for this service vary with most charging on a sliding scale.

■ PROVIDENCE MEDICAL CENTER

(206) 554-7768

Give this 24-hour referral number a call if you are looking for a Providence physician, including an Ob/Gyn or pediatrician. Registered nurses answer the phone and can give you general health advice or referrals.

■ PROVIDENCE RESOURCE LINE-EVERETT

800-554-6660

This is your toll-free connection to information and services that affect your health and well-being. You may call for a physician referral, register for an upcoming class, or ask for advice from a registered nurse. You can also access the Health Information Library where you will find useful and valuable information to increase your awareness and knowledge of specific health issues. There are more than 1,000 prerecorded messages to choose from.

■ SEATTLE MIDWIFERY SCHOOL

(206) 322-8834
2524 16th Ave. S., Rm. 300
Seattle, WA 98144

By calling this accredited midwifery school, you can receive the names and phone numbers of all licensed and certified nurse midwives in the greater Seattle area. This school also trains midwives and doulas.

■ STEVENS HEALTH SOURCE

(425) 640-4066

Calling this service links you with a health care provider employed by Stevens Memorial Hospital.

■ SWEDISH MEDLINK

(206) 386-6066 or 800-443-2762

Registered nurses are available to answer general medical questions. They can also help you find a health care provider who practices through the Swedish system.

■ VALLEY MEDICAL CENTER INFORMATION LINE

(425) 656-4636

Call this information line for a physician or other health care provider referral and press #1. You can also get information about classes available to the community by pressing #2 and talk to a consulting nurse by pressing #3. In addition, if you press #5 you can get information about children's immunizations.

❧

HOSPITAL CHOICES

Deciding where to deliver your baby may be one of the most involved decisions you will ever need to make when it comes to being parents. Some parents choose the place first, and seek a health care provider who will provide services at the place they have chosen. Others will choose a practitioner first and then plan together where the birth will take place. Whether you choose a hospital, birth center or home birth you can plan together with your health care provider to make it the special, once-in-a-lifetime experience that it will be.

If you choose to deliver at a hospital, this section provides data and a hospital chart to compare the different facilities. When comparing Seattle area hospitals, one can see that there are many similarities, but also that the facilities can vary greatly. Hospitals continue to constantly change and improve to better meet the expectations of Seattle parents. Most recently in the area Swedish Medical Center has opened its newly remodeled Women and Infants Center with all LDRP rooms, and Highline Community Hospital is currently undergoing a remodeling to offer LDRPs for 1998 births as well. Virginia Mason Hospital and Group Health Cooperative Central have undergone a remodel to offer 14 beautiful LDRPs and ten overflow mother-baby private rooms as both hospitals now use birthing facilities at the Group Health Central campus for deliveries.

ᨀ

Hospitals continue to constantly change and improve to better meet the expectations of Seattle parents.

ᨀ

PRE-BIRTH PLANNING

Many of the hospitals offer services from pre-pregnancy through postpartum. A few hospitals offer free seminars for couples who are just beginning to think about having children such as "Baby??? Maybe" offered by the Childbirth Center at Northwest Hospital and Evergreen's "Pondering Parenthood." Swedish Medical Center Seattle and Ballard even offer free pregnancy testing to get you off to the right start. All of the hospitals offer tours of the birthing facilities in some form or another. You can even tour via computer—Evergreen's web site includes a picture of one of their 36 LDRPs. Ballard Family Childbirth Center officers a monthly Tea and Tour—their special way of introducing their services. An informational video and a packet of printed information are also available at your request. Providence Family Childbirth Center in Seattle also offers afternoon teas at which a registered nurse and anesthesiologist will answer your questions and let you view their birthing facilities. Regardless of how and when you tour a facility, it is helpful for most prospective parents to see where they will be when they are in labor. This preview may help decrease some of the stress that comes with a new situation, such as childbirth, if the environment is not new to you and one you are comfortable with.

All of the hospitals will do their best to provide you with leading-edge obstetrical and nursing care and an individualized experience to meet your needs. It is up to you to decide what your needs are and how the services of the hospital fit these needs. As hospital stays are short, Seattle area hospitals have recognized that parents need to receive education and support both prior to and after returning home with their infants. All of the hospitals surveyed offer some form of prenatal and postpartum education. Many also go beyond postpartum to include many different parenting classes and support groups. You can find these later in this chapter and in chapter 6.

POSTPARTUM ASSISTANCE

In Washington, there is presently no law requiring insurance companies to pay for a 48-hour hospital stay after a normal vaginal delivery unless it is deemed medically necessary by your physician or midwife and falls within specific guidelines established by the health insurance plan. The federal law requiring insurance companies to pay for a 48-hour length of stay does not

apply in this state. This has led to postpartum services becoming a highly utilized service at all hospitals in the Seattle area.

Northwest Hospital offers 24-hour telephone access to a hospital nurse as well as a free private appointment with a nurse in their Postpartum Follow-up Clinic to help with any questions or concerns you may be having about yourself or your baby after returning home. Some facilities also offer the services of registered nurses to visit you in your home. Swedish Medical Center offers the choice of bringing your baby into their Mother-Baby Follow-up Clinic or having a registered nurse visit you at your home. Group Health provides a postpartum clinic that includes a visit with a neonatal nurse practitioner to physically assess your baby. The Family Maternity Center at Evergreen also offers a visit to their Postpartum Care Center, where a nurse specialist will assess you and your baby's well-being as well as encourage you to attend their weekly baby-parent support groups for helpful advice and companionship. Overlake's Childbirth Center continues to support new parents with a call at home from a mother/baby nurse 24 to 48 hours after your discharge, with the option of an individual appointment at their Postpartum Follow-up Program as well as sending you their Stork Club newsletter packed full of information about classes, parenting advice and special events for families.

Area hospitals continue to work toward ways to ensure the health of you and your baby with postpartum services, and look for creative ways to ease your transition into parenthood. The

HOSPITAL PHONE LIST

Auburn Regional Medical Center	(253) 833-7711
Evergreen Hospital Medical Center	(425) 899-3500
Group Health Hospital Central	(206) 326-3000
Group Health Hospital Eastside	(425) 883-5151
Highline Community Hospital	(206) 244-9970
Northwest Hospital	(206) 364-0500
Overlake Hospital Medical Center	(425) 688-5326
Providence General Medical Center (Colby)	(425) 261-2000
Providence Medical Center (Seattle)	(206) 320-2190
St. Francis Community Hospital	(253) 927-9700
Stevens Memorial Hospital	(425) 640-4000
Swedish Medical Center (Ballard)	(206) 781-6344
Swedish Medical Center (Seattle)	(206) 386-6000
University of Washington Medical Center	(206) 548-3300
Valley Medical Center	(425) 228-3450
Virginia Mason Hospital	(206) 624-1144

Women's Hospital and Childbirth Center at Overlake is the first hospital in the Northwest to offer you in-home doula support after the birth of your baby. The service is being provided on a cost-sharing basis for which you receive 12 hours of care over a four-day period. The Women and Infants Center of Swedish Medical Center also recognizes that after you bring a new baby home, there is not always a lot of time for doing errands and housework. They offer Swedish Home Helpers who cook meals, clean, do laundry, shop for groceries, or provide child care for a reasonable fee.

SPECIAL EXTRAS

Many of the hospitals offer some unique benefits which add that special touch to your birthing experience. Auburn Regional Medical Center provides departing parents with a complimentary dinner basket and a rocking-horse patterned carryall bag. Northwest Hospital's Childbirth Center gives each baby a hand-knit hat lovingly handmade by volunteers at the Hearthstone Retirement Home in Seattle and gives a handmade quilt donated by the Needle and I sewing group to all babies who spend time in their Level II Special Care Nursery. You can log onto Northwest Hospital's web site any time at www. babyhospital.org to find an extensive section about pregnancy and childbirth. Another nice benefit that comes from Ballard Family Childbirth Center is a gourmet picnic basket containing dinner for four so that you and your family may give your undivided attention to settling in with your new baby.

With so many choices of facilities and so many services and options offered, it is important to take time and evaluate your needs and desires before selecting a birthing facility. The birth of your baby is one of life's most memorable experiences. Start early and take your time to discover how and where you will bring new life into your family.

NEWBORN SCREENING

Before you and your baby are discharged from the hospital, a few drops of blood will be taken from your baby's heel and sent to the State Public Health Laboratory in Seattle for newborn screening. This testing identifies disorders that, if not detected and treated in the newborn period, can result in severe illness or mental retardation. The disorders currently screened in Washington State are phenylketonuria (PKU), congenital hypothyroidism (CH), congenital adrenal hyperplasia (CAH), sickle cell disease and other hemoglobin disorders.

The testing is very accurate; however, it is strongly recommended that a second specimen be collected at your baby's first check-up (ideally between seven and 14 days of age). This is to ensure that later developing or milder forms of the disorders screened for are detected. State law requires that your baby have a "heel poke" for newborn screening (unless it conflicts with your religious beliefs), but the best reason to have it done is to prevent the life-threatening and disabling health problems that can result when the disorders are not detected early.

If you have any questions about newborn screening, please call the State Newborn Screening Program in Seattle at (206) 361-2902.

HOSPITAL COMPARISONS	Annual Births	Nursery Level	% C-Sections
Auburn Regional Medical Center	577	I	20
Evergreen Hospital Medical Center	2900	II	16.7
Group Health Hospital Central	1201	II	11
Group Health Cooperative—Eastside Hospital	1000	I	15
Highline Community Hospital	800	I	17
Northwest Hospital	1200	II	19.8
Overlake Hospital Medical Center	3075	II	20
Providence General Medical Center—Colby	3217	II	less than 15
Providence Medical Center—Seattle	1950	II	16
St. Francis Community Hospital	1770	I	15.2
Stevens Memorial Hospital	1610	II	16
Swedish Medical Center—Ballard	545	I	17
Swedish Medical Center—Seattle	3800	III	21
University of Washington Medical Center	1700	III	21
Valley Medical Center	2940	II	16
Virgina Mason at Group Health Central	820	II	9

Midwifery Services	Beds in OB Unit	LDRs	LDRPs	Postpartum Program
Yes	11	5	0	Yes
Yes	36	0	36	Yes
Yes	22	0	14	Yes
Yes	20	5	15	Yes
Yes	11 17 (Fall '98)	5 0 (Fall '98)	0 14 (Fall '98)	Yes
Yes	20	0	20	Yes
Yes	28	10	0	Yes
Yes	48	12	0	Yes
No	22	6	0	Yes
Yes	22	8	0	Yes
Yes	16	0	13	Yes
No	12	0	8	Yes
No	34	0	17	Yes
Yes	40	5	0	Yes
No	21	10	0	Yes
Yes	22	0	14	Yes

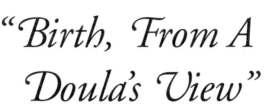

"Birth, From A Doula's View"

By Donna Hudson-Bryant, C.D. (DONA)

"What was going through your mind during that last contraction?" I know by her stillness, with eyes closed, breathing deeply and silently, that Jean is still in an early part of her labor. She has rushed to the hospital, thinking her labor was far along because contractions felt different. Contractions are four to five minutes apart, lasting 45 seconds. The midwife checks her and finds that she is only two centimeters dilated, though fully effaced. I know she is disappointed. "I'm trying to imagine what the baby is doing now, how he is moving down and my cervix is opening." Jean isn't letting these numbers hold her back from the work she must do.

She looks tired to me; it is nearly midnight. Jean is having trouble relaxing; I see that happen when women make the car ride to the hospital. The adrenaline gets pumping in that "this is it" moment and inevitably slows the labor progress, while making the pain seem worse. I suggest a warm bath, and the midwife agrees this would be a nice idea. We all go down to the tub room and get the water running. Water can be so relaxing. The warmth, the buoyancy, and the sound of it running washes the tension away.

Jean climbs into the tub. Bill, her partner, has been right with her throughout her labor. When she felt so different and wanted to come to the hospital, he felt as though he might be at his limit for helping her. But he is not afraid to be with her, to stay with her and accept her pain. Though he may doubt it, he is nowhere near his limit to help her.

Contractions come. "Let your body be heavy in the water. Let your shoulders drop, your bottom go loose, your legs be heavy. Yes, just like that; you're doing so well. Your baby is moving down; let that pressure be there. It's going away, so let it go...use your breath to blow the last of it away. Take a

deep breath when it's gone and let everything go. Now, slow deep breaths, shut your eyes and rest. You're so beautiful; so strong." Within half an hour, she is dozing between contractions which are maintaining a nice pace, every five minutes, but now lasting a solid minute.

"What was going through your mind during that last contraction?" Jean is now only focused on the work of the labor. There is no outside conversation. "I'm so tired. I'm not sure I can keep doing this for as long as it will take." I know she's turned the corner, that her labor is progressing more quickly now. Women say these things as they near the end. It's only been two hours since we got to the hospital and one hour since Jean got into the tub, so I am pleased.

By now, Bill has found a ritual of words and is pouring water over her belly, which helps Jean. "You guys are doing so well," I say. "That's it, just like that." His confidence has resurfaced. The nurse and the midwife check the well-being of mother and baby, and we take turns running errands, bringing Bill and Jean ice, juice, face cloths, music, etc., so that Bill doesn't need to leave. When he looks tired, I suggest that he change positions, and I massage his shoulders while Jean dozes. He's no good to her if he wears himself out. When Bill needs to leave, I am there to pick up the ritual. Jean is never alone.

Now Jean periodically belches and trembles. I can tell by the way she moans during these contractions that the pressure is very great; the baby is very low. "I'm trying to imagine where the baby is now, but it's hard...it hurts so much." The contractions are coming every three minutes now and are lasting well over a minute. "I want to get out of the tub." We wrap Jean in warm blankets. We walk towards her room but must stop every so often for the contractions. "The pressure doesn't go away," she says, looking at me with pleading eyes. With each contraction Jean sways her hips, hanging from Bill's neck. She moans and looks out at me with very wide eyes. The midwife suggests we check how far along Jean has gotten; we both sense that it is time to push.

Sure enough, Jean's cervix is completely open and her baby's head is moving lower. Jean pushes with each contrac-

tion now, moving herself into positions which feel right for her. The baby's progress slows at a point. "I'm tired. What should I do?" I suggest she try kneeling, hanging from the back of the bed with the head of the bed up high. She tries this, and it works right away. I get the camera ready. Jean doesn't want birth shots, but wants pictures of the baby immediately. Her beautiful little boy is born moments later, and he is vigorous from the start. I snap away.

The time after the birth is a whirlwind which winds down after an hour or so. During this time, I help baby Peter nurse for the first time. I bring food and drink to mother and father, and take lots of pictures. I stay with Bill and the baby while Jean showers; he is nervous about being alone with his son. When things become quiet, and we have all talked ourselves out, I leave the family to savor this special time.

As I drive home, I relive the labor, and think about the other women whose births my doula friends and I have attended. These families have told us many wonderful things: "You spoke at length with us about our previous birth, validating our concerns and giving us hope that we would have a better experience this time." "You encouraged me when labor got slow and coached me through the very intense contractions when I had to hold still for the epidural." "When the baby's heart rate dropped, you supported me while the medical staff took care of the baby, making sure that I knew what was going on and reassuring me so that I wouldn't get too frightened." "Throughout the labor, you let my partner coach me as much as he wanted, and took over when he needed a break or when things got over his head." "I loved the written birth report you kept; now we know just how the labor went."

It's a privilege to serve women as they become mothers. As a doula, I can offer women many things, but we never know how birth will go. At the very last, I will stay with her until her baby is born, accepting her pain and sharing her joys, supporting her wishes to the end. ❧

CORD BLOOD OPTIONS

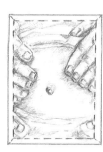

By Allison Aley

Until recently, umbilical cords from newborns were typically discarded after being cut. But doctors have discovered that umbilical cord blood can be used to treat certain cancers and blood diseases that, prior to this discovery, could only be treated by bone marrow transplants. Expectant parents have the option of donating the blood from their newborn's umbilical cord to a public bank where it can be used to save another child's life or of having it collected and stored privately for potential future use. The procedure takes one to three minutes, poses no risk to the mother or infant, and does not interfere with the normal delivery process. The decision to do either, however, must be made before birth so that appropriate arrangements can be made.

Growing medical evidence indicates that blood from a newborn's umbilical cord is a rich and effective source of transplantable stem cells—the building blocks of a new blood and immune system. Cord blood is increasingly being used as an alternative to bone marrow to treat a number of life-threatening diseases including leukemia, certain anemias, and other blood disorders. Cord blood collection is simple, painless, risk-free and cost effective when compared to a bone marrow harvest. Approximately 500 cord blood transplants have been done since 1988, and the results have been comparable to, or more superior than bone marrow transplants. Obviously, as in normal donations of blood, the more cord blood donations that are made, the more likely it will be that the correct match will be found.

Privately storing a newborn's cord blood ensures an exact match for that child, and greatly increases the chance of a match for siblings and other immediate relatives. Transplants using allogenic (sibling) cord blood have been successful in treating the diseases mentioned above. Autologous (using one's own) cord blood has been successfully used in gene therapy. If you perceive that your offspring will be at increased risk for certain cancers or blood disorders, you should speak with a specialist about the possible benefits of privately storing your child's own cord blood.

The blood is drawn from the umbilical cord by your provider after it has been cut. Special supplies and collection

❧

Parents may want to consider donating their baby's cord blood so that someone's life may be saved.

❧

materials are provided in advance by both public and private blood banks. If you are delivering at a hospital that is a collection site for a donor bank, they should already have the necessary materials and procedures in place for you to make a donation. If the hospital is not a collection site or if you are going to have your baby's blood stored privately, all arrangements must be made in advance so that the materials are there when you deliver and your health care provider has been able to look them over.

If you choose to donate your baby's cord blood, there will be no cost to you, but you will need to sign a consent form and provide a medical history including ethnic background and genetic diseases. There are several donor cord blood banks in the country. Locally, you may contact the Puget Sound Blood bank at (206) 292-1896. The Puget Sound Blood Bank's program will accommodate directed donations for acute needs, but at present does not have a long-term storage program. For donor cord blood

banks in other areas, call the Caitlin Raymond International Registry at (508) 756-6444. This organization keeps track of donations and conducts cord blood searches when a donor is needed.

If you decide to privately store your baby's cord blood, the cost will vary depending upon which bank you choose. Most charge up front costs for enrollment, processing, banking and storage. Then there is an annual storage fee. There may be rush fees as well if you wait too long to make the decision. Many smaller regional banks and some ovum and sperm banks, as well as physicians' offices, offer cord blood storage. In making your decision, you should consider a bank's:

- experience—how many cord blood samples it is storing?
- specialization—does it store matter other than blood?
- processing procedures—does it store whole or separated blood?
- cost—are annual costs guaranteed?

NATIONAL PRIVATE CORD BLOOD BANKS

- **CRYO-CELL INTERNATIONAL, INC.**
800-786-7235
(813) 938-3114
604 Packard Ct.
Safety Harbor, FL 34695

- **CORD BLOOD REGISTRY**
800-588-6377
1200 Bayhill Dr., Suite 301
San Bruno, CA 94066

- **VIACORD**   Baby Pages
800-998-4226
551 Boylston St., Ste. 40
Boston, MA 02116

- **NEW ENGLAND**
CORD BLOOD BANK
888-700-2673
(617) 262-5612
665 Beacon St., Suite 302
Boston, MA 02215

BIRTH CENTERS AND MIDWIFERY SERVICES

■ SALLY AVENSON, ARNP, CNM

(206) 527-8773
7602 6th Ave. N.E.
Seattle, WA 98105

Sally Avenson attends births at Group Health Central and Northwest Hospital accounting for 60% of the births she attends. Water births are available at Group Health Central in LDRPs with jacuzzi tubs. The other 40% take place in clients' homes. Her services are covered by most insurances, including Blue Shield (preferred), Blue Cross (preferred), and Medicaid.

■ CENTER FOR WOMEN'S HEALTH AT EVERGREEN

Debra Monson, ARNP, CNM
Lisa Greenburg, CNM
(425) 899-4455
12303 N.E. 130th Lane, Ste. 500
Kirkland, WA 98034

Both of these midwives attend births at Evergreen Hospital Medical Center which has large, beautiful LDRPs with jacuzzis, sound systems, and beds for a support person. They are covered by almost all types of insurance plans.

■ COMMUNITY MIDWIFERY SERVICES

Leslie Schear, L.M., L.C.
Bridget Albright, L.M.
(206) 324-0838
1802 12th Ave., Ste. A
Seattle, WA 98122

Almost all of the births attended by these midwives occur at home with a few clients delivering at Providence where they refer to. Many insurance compa-

nies cover their services including Ethix, Nyilcare, King County Medical, Blue Shield, and Group Health. Also available are lactation consultations. Community Midwifery Services provides postpartum visits in the first week after birth.

■ EASTSIDE MIDWIVES

Heike Doyle, L.M.
Janine Walker, L.M, C.P.M.
(425) 482-6264
13515 N.E. 175th St., Ste. D
Woodinville, WA 98072

Your home, or the Puget Sound Birth Center, are options for places to deliver with this midwifery service. Labor in water or water births are welcomed. Most insurance plans, including Group Health, DSHS and Healthy Options, will cover their services. They offer parents informed choices including modern medicine, homeopathy, and herbs, while honoring the deeper process of body, mind, and spirit.

■ EVERGREEN WOMEN'S CARE

Jeri Ann Ross, ARNP, CNM
(425) 899-6400
12303 N.E. 130th Lane, Ste. 420
Kirkland, WA 98034

This midwifery practice is in collaboration with four board-certified obstetricians and one other ARNP. All deliveries take place at Evergreen Hospital Medical Center, which is the first hospital in the U.S. to receive the UNICEF "Baby Friendly" award.

■ FRA NA READY, CNM
(206) 545-4181
2116 N. 42nd St.
Seattle, WA 98103
Fra Na Ready has been in private practice in the Seattle area since 1981, and has attended over 2,000 births. She attends women delivering at Northwest Hospital and Group Health Central. A "get acquainted" first consultation is free. Fra Na Ready is certified by and a member of the American College of Nurse-Midwives, and licensed as an Advanced Registered Nurse Practitioner in the state of Washington.

■ GREENBANK WOMEN'S CLINIC AND BIRTH CENTER
Cynthia Jaffee, L.M.
(360) 678-3594
3455 Old Country Rd.
Greenbank, WA 98353
Cynthia Jaffee attends 70% of deliveries at this state-licensed, freestanding birth center that is covered by all insurance companies. The other 30% of deliveries she attends are at either Whidbey General Hospital or Swedish Medical Center.

■ GROUP HEALTH CENTRAL AND EASTSIDE MIDWIFERY SERVICES
Linda Driskell, L.M.
Lorraine Hansen, L.M.
Leah Lambert, L.M.
Robin Ozerkis, L.M.
Jana Swett, L.M.
(206) 326-3500 (Central)
300 15th Ave. E. CNB 2
Seattle, WA 98112

Kathleen Britton, L.M.
MaryBeth Canaven, L.M.
Karen Chaunce, L.M.
Roberta Crosby, L.M.
Kathy Kernan, L.M.
Karen McConnell, L.M.
(425) 883-5577 (Eastside)
2700 152nd Ave. N.E.
Redmond, WA 98052
These groups emphasize client education, shared decision-making and individualized plans of care. Deliveries take place at either Group Health Central or Eastside. Both have large LDRP rooms complete with jacuzzis or soaking tubs. Group Health, Options, or Alliant Virginia Mason cover their services.

■ HIGHLINE MIDWIFERY SERVICE
Laura Leigh Brakke, ARNP, CNM
Gigi Jurich, ARNP, CNM
Laura Denman, ARNP, CNM
Caron Campbell, ARNP, CNM
Heidi Klammer, CNM
Claire Englander, CNM
(206) 242-0680
13030 Military Rd. S., Ste. 106
Tukwila, WA 98168
All births attended by this midwifery group take place at Highline Community Hospital. They are covered by most insurance plans and are a Healthy Options primary care provider. This group of midwives guides and encourages clients to participate actively in decision-making and considers them to be responsible partners in their health-care planning.

■ MERIDIAN WOMEN'S HEALTH

Corry Venema-Weiss, CNM, ARNP, MSN

(206) 368-6644

10330 Meridian Ave. N., Ste. 300

Seattle, WA 98133

Call this midwife for a free interview if you plan to deliver at Northwest Hospital or Group Health Central. She works with two female board certified obstetrician/gynecologists and offers evening appointments and free pregnancy testing. Services are covered by most insurance plans.

■ THE PRENATAL CARE CENTER

Michelle Grandy, CNM

Rebecca Frevent, CNM

Emily Ghilarducci, CNM

Ardyth Hintzman, CNM

Julia Wiklof, CNM

Stacey Wilson, CNM

(425) 261-3760

1330 Rockefeller Ste. 200

Everett, WA 98206

At this center the nurse midwives help you deal with all the physical and emotional aspects of having a baby. They have a team approach which includes access to a social worker/counselor and dietician. They attend all deliveries at Providence General Medical Center in one of their 12 LDR rooms. Most insurance plans including DSHS will cover their services.

■ PUGET SOUND BIRTH CENTER

Lee Anne Shelley, L.M.

Lisa Boyd, L.M.

(425) 823-1919

13128 Totem Lake Blvd. N.E., Ste. 101

Kirkland, WA 98034

Web site: www.birthcenter.com

These two midwives attend 75% of deliveries at this birth center that features spacious birth suites with private jacuzzi tubs. Their services are covered by most insurance plans. The other 25% of deliveries take place at home. They assist parents in preparing socially and emotionally for a new family member, as well as providing medical care. They offer a free, no obligation interview if you want to stop in and ask them questions.

■ SEATTLE HOME MATERNITY SERVICE AND CHILDBIRTH CENTER

Suzy Myers, L.M., MPH

Marge Mansfield, L.M.

(206) 722-3426

3830 S. Ferdinand

Seattle, WA 98118

Seventy percent of the births attended by these midwives take place in the homes of their clients with the other 30% occurring at the spacious birth center facility that comes complete with a kitchen, living room, a deep soaking tub, and a large birthing room. These two midwives were cofounders of the Seattle Midwifery School and since 1975 have welcomed over 1500 babies! Most insurance companies cover their services and they also attend some deliveries at Swedish, Providence, or another hospital of client's choice.

■ SEATTLE NATUROPATHY, ACUPUNCTURE AND BIRTH CENTER

Rich Postmantur, N.D., L.M., C.A.
Felice Barnow, N.D., L.M., R.N.
(206) 328-7929
2705 E. Madison
Seattle, WA 98112

You can have a natural birth in your home or in this licensed birth center with these two licensed midwives and naturopathic doctors. Water births are available and they also offer pediatric and total family health care. Medicaid and many insurance plans are accepted. They also offer a free prenatal consultation.

■ SOUND WOMEN'S CARE

Lisa Easton-Hummel, ARNP, CNM
(425) 640-4810
216 76th Ave. W., Ste. 205
Edmonds, WA 98206

This midwife will provide a highly personal, caring approach and assist in the total preparation for labor, birth at Steven's Hospital, and developing parenthood in the family. She will bill all insurance plans.

■ UNIVERSITY OF WASHINGTON MEDICAL CENTER MIDWIFERY SERVICES

Bonnie Berstein, CNM
Kathy Naughton, CNM
Cindy Rogers, CNM
(206) 548-4070
1959 N.E. Pacific St.
Seattle, WA 98195

Office locations for these midwives are in University District and the Northgate area. These three certified nurse-mid-

wives have provided personalized care to hundreds of Northwest mothers and babies. Each midwife has 24-hour-a-day access to on-site University of Washington physicians in case problems do arise. They attend births at the University of Washington Medical Center in spacious and private LDRs. Most insurance plans, including King County Medical, Sound Health, Health Plus, Qual Med, and Healthy Options, cover their services.

■ VIRGINIA MASON NURSE-MIDWIFERY SERVICE

Ann Darlington, CNM
Liz Gadzdyl, CNM
Carol Jones, CNM
Judy Lazarus, CNM
Cora Merkle, CNM
(206) 583-6511
1100 9th Ave.
Seattle, WA 98111

This midwifery practice recently celebrated 17 years of practice and delivery of over 7500 babies! They deliver babies now at Group Health Central in beautiful LDRPs with jacuzzi or soaking tubs assisted by supportive consulting obstetricians and nursing staff as necessary.

ᐟᐟ

FIRST STEPS PROGRAM

Through the First Steps Program, Washington State's Department of Social and Health Services (DSHS) offers expanded Medicaid eligibility and other support services for pregnant women and their babies. First Steps helps pay for medical expenses and helps to locate health care. It also assists with personal problems, child care, and transportation.

Finding out about First Steps begins with a phone call to the Healthy Mothers, Healthy Babies toll-free bilingual number, 800-322-2588. When you call, you'll receive at no charge:

- Resources and referrals to link you with maternity care providers in your community
- A packet of written information about pregnancy and maternity care
- An incentive—a baby book—to make an appointment for your first prenatal checkup. Books are now available in English, Spanish, Korean, Vietnamese and Chinese.

They'll also give you current guidelines regarding the state medical financing options and the eligibility requirements. If you have any doubts about your ability to pay your prenatal and delivery costs, it's to your benefit to consider the First Steps program. The income guidelines may surprise you. Even if you have insurance, the program can pick up costs of deductibles and other non-covered expenses if you qualify.

A major difference between this and other public assistance programs is that your assets (home, car, etc.) are not considered when qualifying for aid, only your monthly income. And, once you've qualified, your medical benefits can't be terminated during your pregnancy, even if your income changes. While the eligibility levels change from time to time, here's a general idea of the cutoff point for First Steps medical assistance (based on 1997 figures):

If you have any doubts about your ability to pay your prenatal and delivery costs, it's to your benefit to consider the First Steps program.

Family Size	Yearly Income	Monthly Income
2*	$19,629	$1,636
3	$24,661	$2,056
4	$29,693	$2,475

*Note that a pregnant woman counts as two people for this program.

VISIT A FACILITY

To apply for medical financing, you'll need to visit a DSHS Community Service Office (CSO). The office you visit is determined by your zip code; offices are listed in the blue pages of the phone book, under Washington State, and in this chapter. You can call first and have an application mailed to you (this may add about a week to the process), or go to the office to complete the application. Along with the application you'll need to provide the following: written proof of pregnancy, verification of income, social security or alien registration card, and picture ID.

Once you've submitted the application, you'll be given an appointment to return within five days to meet with a financial counselor. The counselor will review your application and explain the programs you qualify for. You'll be informed of your rights and responsibilities and, if eligible for First Steps assistance, you can then receive your DSHS medical identification card (formerly called medical coupons). The counselor will also ensure that you make contact with the First Steps social worker, if you haven't done this already.

MEET WITH A SOCIAL WORKER

Each CSO has a social worker who will explain the specific First Steps program services available. If the social worker is available on your first visit, you can meet then, even before your application has been reviewed. Otherwise, you'll make an appointment to meet with the social worker either in the office or in your home.

WIC AND OTHER SERVICES

Besides medical financing, you may qualify for the Women, Infants & Children (WIC) Supplemental Food Program. This program provides nutritious foods, education and assessments, breast-feeding promotion, and referrals to health and social services. Income guidelines are similar to those listed, although pregnant women are counted as one person for WIC eligibility. In addition, you must have a nutrition health risk to be eligible. Some of these risk factors are anemia, underweight, obesity, and smoking during pregnancy. Call Healthy Mothers, Healthy Babies for the WIC clinic nearest you at 800-322-3498.

First Steps also offers:

- Transportation to medical appointments
- Child care
- Maternity support services
- Childbirth classes
- Drug/alcohol counseling and treatment
- Assistance in obtaining public assistance and food stamps
- Dental coverage
- Case management with home visits by a public health nurse
- Family planning services (includes medical costs, and prescription and non-prescription supplies) for one year after pregnancy ends
- Automatic medical coverage for your newborn for one year

HEALTHY OPTIONS PLAN

DSHS/First Steps provides prenatal care and delivery coverage by paying a premium to a health maintenance organization (HMO) called a Healthy Options Plan. Plans available vary depending on where you live. You must select a plan and a primary provider (physician or nurse practitioner) within the plan. All of your medical care must be provided by your primary provider, or specialists that your primary provider refers you to; otherwise, the care will not be covered. There are no deductibles or co-payments. Prescriptions, medical supplies, dental care, and maternity support services are provided outside of the Healthy Options Plan and paid directly by DSHS to the provider.

Your local CSO will give you enrollment forms and a list of medical plans available for your selection. If you don't select a plan or primary provider, one will be selected for you. You may change plans monthly and change providers within the plan on a daily basis. If you have other insurance, your Healthy Options plan will act as your secondary insurance plan. If you have already been receiving medical care for your pregnancy from a provider outside a plan, you may ask to be exempt from having to use an HMO if you wish to continue with the same provider. Instructions on how to do this are available from the CSO.

You'll receive a medical ID card from DSHS monthly. This is used for billing purposes so you will have to show it to your providers. It's very important to keep DSHS informed of any address changes to ensure that you receive your ID card monthly. Coverage continues under First Steps for two months after delivery.

FIRST STEPS RESOURCES

■ HEALTHY MOTHERS, HEALTHY BABIES

800-322-2588

This statewide referral number will link you to resources in your area that participate in the First Steps program. You can find out current guidelines regarding state medical financing options and eligibility requirements. They will also mail the application forms to your home if needed.

DSHS COMMUNITY SERVICE OFFICES (CSO)

■ BELLTOWN CSO

(206) 464-7060
2106 2nd Ave.
Seattle, WA 98104
Hours: M-F 8:00 a.m.-5:00 p.m.
Serves zip codes 98101, 98104, 98121

■ BURIEN CSO

(206) 433-1336
15811 Ambaum Blvd. S.W.
Burien, WA 98146
Hours: M-F 8:00 a.m.-5:00 p.m.
Serves zip codes 98062, 98146, 98148, 98158, 98166, 98168, 98188, 98198

■ **CAPITOL HILL CSO**
(206) 720-3170
1700 E. Cherry
Seattle, WA 98122
Hours: M,T   8:00 a.m.-11:00 a.m.
        M-F   1:00 p.m.-3:00 p.m.
Serves zip codes 98102, 98112, 98122

■ **FEDERAL WAY CSO**
(253) 872-2145
1617 S. 324th
Federal Way, WA 98023
Hours: M-F   8:00 a.m.-5:00 p.m.
Serves zip codes 98003, 98023, 98054,
98063, 98093

■ **KING EASTSIDE CSO**
(425) 649-4000
14360 Eastgate Way, #N40-1
Bellevue, WA 98006
Hours: M-F   8:00 a.m.-5:00 p.m.
Serves zip codes 98004, 98005, 98006,
98007, 98009, 98011, 98014, 98019,
98024, 98027, 98033, 98034, 98039,
98040, 98045, 98050, 98052, 98053,
98065, 98068, 98072

■ **KING NORTH/BALLARD CSO**
(206) 545-7607
907 N.W. Ballard Way
Seattle, WA 98107
Hours: M-F   8:00 a.m.-5:00 p.m.
Serves zip codes 98103, 98105, 98107,
98109, 98117, 98119, 98133, 98177,
98195, 98199

■ **KING NORTH/LAKE CITY
CSO**
(206) 368-7200
11536 Lake City Way N.E.
Seattle, WA 98125
Hours: M-F   8:00 a.m.-5:00 p.m.
Serves zip codes 98115, 98125, 98155

■ **KING SOUTH CSO**
(253) 872-2145
25316 74th Ave. S.
Kent, WA 98035
Hours: M-F   8:00 a.m.-5:00 p.m.
Serves zip codes 98001, 98002, 98010,
98015, 98022, 98025, 98031, 98032,
98035, 98038, 98042, 98047, 98048,
98051, 98055, 98057, 98058, 98064,
98071, 98092, King County Area only
98371

■ **RAINIER CSO**
(206) 721-2775
3600 S. Graham
Seattle, WA 98118
Hours: M-F   8:00 a.m.-5:00 p.m.
Serves zip codes 98108, 98118, 98134,
98144, 98178

■ **WEST SEATTLE CSO**
(206) 933-3300
4045 Delridge Way S.W.
Seattle, WA 98106
Hours: M-F   8:00 a.m.-5:00 p.m.
Serves zip codes 98013, 98018, 98070,
98106, 98116, 98126, 98136

⪦

STAYING IN SHAPE

EXERCISE PROGRAMS

There are several ongoing exercise programs offered by Seattle area hospitals that directly address physical fitness during pregnancy. Other programs are offered by individuals, health clubs, and park and recreation districts. Since programs are constantly changing, you should verify times and locations. Before beginning any exercise program, be sure to talk to your health care provider and follow his or her instructions.

■ **AUBURN REGIONAL MEDICAL CENTER**
(253) 804-2822
Plaza One
202 N. Division
Auburn, WA 98001
A prenatal water aerobics series is offered that is an instructor-led 30 minute workout in a heated pool, including five-minute warm-up, 20 minutes of aerobics and five-minute cool-down. Participation requires physician approval and costs $45 for six sessions, individual or in groups of four. After your six-week checkup, join the 30-minute water workout called Postpartum Shape-Up that provides abdominal toning and general conditioning. Fee is the same for prenatal water aerobics.

■ **EVERGREEN HOSPITAL MEDICAL CENTER**
(425) 899-3480
12040 N.E. 128th St.
Kirkland, WA 98034
Maternity Fitness and Education is an exercise and fitness program for pregnant and postpartum women. Emphasis has been placed on providing a safe, low-impact aerobic session that is self-pacing, allowing for different fitness levels, and accommodating the changing body during pregnancy. The aerobics are followed by strengthening and stretching exercises focused on readying the body for birth and ultimately helping with the recovery process. This pre/post pregnancy low-impact aerobics and exercise program is a fun and easy way to shape up before and after delivery. You'll improve muscle tone, relieve discomforts of pregnancy, ease tension, and make new friends. The cost is $36 per month for as many sessions as you want to attend.

■ **HOLISTIC CHILDBIRTH EDUCATION AND YOGA CENTER**
(206) 547-9882
4649 Sunnyside Ave. N., Rm. 300
Seattle, WA 98103
E-mail: yogaaiki@ix.netcom.com
The center is dedicated to families and individuals, providing programs that promote personal growth and body/mind awareness through yoga and holistic health education. In addition to a whole range of general classes, there are weekly prenatal yoga classes for women and also monthly prenatal partner yoga classes. These classes explore specific poses that strengthen and open women's bodies for labor and birth. A once-a-week series costs $80, twice a week is $128, and drop-in classes are $12. After delivering, bring your baby with you to postpartum yoga classes for toning and support. The cost ranges from $38 for four classes to $72 for eight classes, and $12 for drop-in. They also offer several workshops

and classes including Conscious Birthing, Birth Advocacy Forum, Facts of Labor, Infant/Child CPR, and Father Support.

■ **MOM'S ON THE MOVE: PRENATAL/POSTPARTUM FITNESS CLASSES**
(206) 789-3857
Swedish Medical Center/Ballard
5300 Tallman Ave. N.W.
Seattle, WA 98107
These classes, which are designed for pregnant women and new moms, include tailored non- and low-impact workouts. They are taught by trained aerobics instructor Verna Reynolds, who specializes in prenatal and postpartum exercise fitness. Participants are also encouraged to bring their babies since free, on-site child care services are included in the $44/month class fee.

■ **NORTH SEATTLE YMCA**
(206) 524-1400
5003 12th Ave. N.E.
Seattle, WA 98105
The "Y" offers a prenatal/postpartum aerobics class, which is geared toward preparation for and recovery from childbirth. The workout includes low impact aerobics for cardiovascular fitness, muscle conditioning with emphasis on abdominals and upper body, and stretching to relax and relieve tension. Babies are welcome and this is a great support group for new moms, too. Classes are free for members, $7 for a day pass for non-members. One hour classes are at 9:30 a.m on Mondays and Wednesdays and at 6:10 p.m. on Wednesdays and Fridays. You may want to become a member; cost is a $45 joining fee and $21 monthly dues thereafter.

■ **OLYMPIC ATHLETIC CLUB**
(206) 789-5010
5301 Leary Ave.
Seattle, WA 98107
OAC offers a safe, low-impact workout program that is modifiable for all levels of fitness. Floor and step aerobics are combined with upper and lower body strengthening to provide a well-rounded workout for women in all stages of their childbearing year, from pregnancy to postpartum. The class is designed to improve the strength of those muscles most challenged by the condition of pregnancy and the event of childbirth: the abdominal, back, and perineal muscles. OAC also offers monthly seminars on topics related to pregnancy and child care. Infants are welcome to attend class with their moms; child care for babies over four months is also available for $2 per hour. The class cost is $10 for nonmembers. Cost for members is $4 per class or $24 per month of unlimited classes.

■ **SWEDISH MEDICAL CENTER**
(206) 386-2035
747 Broadway
Seattle, WA 98114
Swedish Medical Center offers both a prenatal and postnatal exercise class as well as a bed-rest exercise class. You don't have to be a Swedish patient to access these classes. When calling the number listed, a staff person may connect you with a recorded message line regarding the programs. Here is what we found:

The Prenatal Fitness class meets in the aerobic room downtown and costs $80 for eight weeks (two classes per week) or $5 per class. This class also offers a lecture series and informal discussions on fitness, exercise, and general childbearing related topics. If you do not use all your sessions during your pregnancy, you may receive a credit for their Moms and Babies postpartum exercise class.

The Moms and Babies class costs the same as the prenatal fitness classes. Classes are offered twice a week on a drop-in basis and focus on aerobics, floor exercises, and posture awareness work with an emphasis on safe resumption of activity following pregnancy. Babies are incorporated into exercises to keep them happy and interactive. Both classes are taught by physical therapists.

The Bed-Rest Exercises class is available if you need to be on bedrest due to pre-term labor or other complications of pregnancy. If your health care provider allows you to do these type of exercises, Swedish Home Health Services will send out a physical therapist specially trained to teach you these gentle and safe exercises that may help prevent some of the stiffness, muscle weakness and discomfort that prolonged bedrest can cause.

⚓

CHILDBIRTH EDUCATION RESOURCES

■ BATES TECHNICAL COLLEGE
(253) 596-1760 or 800-562-7099
1101 South Yakima
Tacoma, WA 98405

Bates has a training center for childbirth educators, birth doulas, and postpartum doulas. They also offer childbirth classes to the general public designed to fit anyone's needs or choices. Classes for teens, adults, and Spanish-speaking persons are just a few offered during the day or evenings—there are even classes which include romantic weekend getaways. They want you to be prepared, and to have fun while getting ready. Birth partners can experience pregnancy by trying the "Empathy Belly" that is available for classes. Medical coupons are accepted for most classes.

■ BIRTH EDUCATION NORTHWEST
(206) 282-1729

This nonprofit organization (formally known as Preparation for Expectant Parents or PEP), offers support and education for childbearing families through a variety of classes and workshops, including Birth Preparation Workshop, Breastfeeding Support Program, Homebirth/Clinic Birth Classes, Early Pregnancy Class, New Parenting Course, Sibling Preparation Class, Previous Caesarean Class, and private instruction. Their instructors are certified by the International Childbirth Education Association (ICEA) and most are also available to help with labor support.

■ **CHILDBIRTH EDUCATION ASSOCIATION OF SEATTLE (CEAS)**
(206) 789-0883
10021 Holman Rd. N.W.
Seattle, WA 98177
The Childbirth Education Association of Seattle, a nonprofit organization, provides classes to families on a variety of subjects including Labor and Birth, Childbirth Preparation, Newborn Care, Fathering, Infant Safety and CPR, Breastfeeding, Sibling Preparation, and much more. Teachers are health professionals who have additional training in their specialty areas.

■ **CHILDBIRTH EDUCATION WEEKEND GETAWAY**
(253) 596-1760 or 800-562-7099
Bates Technical College's Home and Family Life Department combines childbirth preparation classes with a romantic weekend in Port Townsend. The package costs $320 per couple and in-

cludes classes, handbooks and handouts, two nights' lodging, most meals and snacks, plus surprise romantic accents.

■ **PENNY SIMKIN INC.**
(206) 325-1419
1100 23rd E.
Seattle, WA 98112
Instructors Penny Simkin, PT, and Sandra Szalay, ARNP, offer classes on home birth preparation and also contract with local hospitals to provide childbirth education. Also available is a 40-minute video made by Penny Simkin called "Comfort Measures for Childbirth." You may rent it for two weeks at a time for $10 if you pick it up, or for $14 if they mail it to you.

■ **PERINATAL SUPPORT RESOURCES AND CHILDBIRTH PREPARATION**
(206) 789-1924
Terri Skoda, RN, BSN, is a Childbirth Education Association certified instruc-

PUBLIC HEALTH CENTERS
Many of the local public health centers offer a basic childbirth series, with payment by donation or DSHS medical coupon. Call the center nearest you for schedules.
- **Auburn**: (206) 296-8400 or (253) 833-8400
- **Columbia (S. Seattle)**: (206) 296-4639
- **Downtown**: (206) 296-4755
- **Eastgate (Bellevue)**: (206) 296-4920 or 800-244-4512
- **Federal Way**: (253) 838-4557
- **North District (N. Seattle)**: (206) 296-4765
- **Northshore (Bothell)**: (206) 296-9787 or 800-562-2956
- **Renton**: (206) 296-4700
- **Southwest (Burien)**: (206) 296-4646

tor who offers personalized instruction privately in your home or in small group classes at your doctor's office. Class dates and times are prearranged to meet your schedule. She offers "first time" parent, refresher and sibling adjustment classes. You will receive a textbook and articles at your home prior to class and the classes are individualized, specific to you and your partner's needs. She also offers free community resources and phone consultations as well as home visits for breastfeeding support and newborn care after your baby is born.

🔊

HOSPITAL EDUCATION COURSES

■ AUBURN REGIONAL MEDICAL CENTER
(253) 833-7711
20 2nd St. N.E.
Auburn, WA 98002
• Prepared Childbirth (8-week series)
• Fast Finish (3-week series)
• Big Brother and Sister Class

■ EVERGREEN HOSPITAL MEDICAL CENTER
(425) 899-3000
12040 N.E. 128th St.
Kirkland, WA 98034
• Labor and Birth Series
• Christian Childbirth Classes
• Teen Labor and Birth Series
• Labor & Birth Refresher
• Prenatal & Infant Nutrition
• Preterm Birth Prevention
• Caesarean Birth
• Vaginal Birth After Caesarean (VBAC)
• Planning for the Newborn

• Breastfeeding and the Working Mom
• Breastfeeding Basics
• For Dads Only
• Sibling Preparation
• Grandparents Class
• Infant and Child CPR
• Infant Massage
• Baby-Parent Time
• Feeding Fundamentals: Starting Solid Food
• Breastfeeding the Older Baby

■ GROUP HEALTH CENTRAL & EASTSIDE
(206) 287-2527 or 800-462-5327
Courses are held at Group Health centers throughout the community and are open to non-enrollees.
• First, Second and Third Trimester Birth Preparation Classes
• Birth Preparation for Teens
• Refresher Workshop
• Vaginal Birth After Caesarean Refresher
• Introduction to Infant Feeding
• New Parents Class
• Our New Baby: Sibling Preparation
• Newborn Care
• Lactation Class
• Breastfeeding Support for Working Women

■ HIGHLINE COMMUNITY HOSPITAL
(206) 244-9970
16251 Sylvester Rd. S.W.
Seattle, WA 98166
• Prepared Childbirth Series
• Prepared Childbirth for Teens Series
• Prepared Childbirth Series Fast-Track
• Refresher Course
• Breastfeeding Preparation
• Kangaroo Kapers (sibling program)

■ NORTHWEST HOSPITAL
(206) 368-1784
1550 N. 115th St.
Seattle, WA 98133
- Baby??? Maybe
- Expecting Changes
- Breastfeeding
- Mother and Baby Care
- Preparation for Labor
- Infant CPR and Safety
- Grandparents Class
- Refresher Course
- Siblings Class
- Parenting Your Infant
- Parenting Your Toddler
- Positive Parenting

■ OVERLAKE HOSPITAL MEDICAL CENTER
(425)688-5259
1035 116th Ave. N.E.
Bellevue, WA 98004
- Early Pregnancy
- Preparation for Childbirth
- Refresher
- Siblings Are Special
- Vaginal Birth After C-Section (VBAC)
- Fitness and Health Options for the Childbearing Years
- You and Your New Baby
- You and Your Growing Baby
- Congratulations, You're Almost a Grandparent
- Breastfeeding
- Just for Dads: Post Partum
- Infant CPR and Safety Proofing
- Kid Safety + Workshop (infant/child CPR and first aid)

■ PROVIDENCE GENERAL MEDICAL CENTER (COLBY CAMPUS)
(425) 261-3247
1321 Colby
Everett, WA 98206
- Healthy Beginnings: Planning for Pregnancy
- Childbirth Preparation Series
- Preterm Birth Education
- Once Again With Style (Childbirth Refresher)
- Breastfeeding Basics Course
- Teens 'n Birthing Childbirth Preparation
- Bed Rest Moms class
- Sibling Preparation (for ages 5-9 years)
- Kangaroo Kapers (for 2-1/2 to 5 years)
- Living With Baby Weekly Support Class
- Infant Safety and CPR
- Systematic Training for Effective Parenting (STEP)
- Car Safe Kids
- Infant Massage

■ PROVIDENCE MEDICAL CENTER
(206) 554-7768
500 17th Ave.
Seattle, WA 98124
- Childbirth Preparation & Refresher
- Mother Care/Baby Care
- Baby Safe
- Breastfeeding
- Sibling Class
- Adoptive Parent Class

■ **ST. FRANCIS COMMUNITY HOSPITAL**
(253) 952-7957
34515 9th Ave. S.
Federal Way, WA 98003
• Childbirth Preparation Series
• Childbirth Preparation/Spanish
• Childbirth Preparation/Weekend
• Childbirth Preparation/Accelerated
• Childbirth Preparation Refresher
• "You and Me Babe" (pregnant teens)
• Breastfeeding Preparation
• Newborn/Preparation and Care
• Kangaroo Kapers (sibling)
• CPR/ Infant Safety
• Love and Logic Parenting

■ **STEVENS MEMORIAL HOSPITAL**
(425) 640-4066
21601 76th Ave. W.
Edmonds, WA 98026
• Childbirth Preparation Series
• Childbirth Refresher
• Breastfeeding
• Sibling Class
• Newborn Care
• Pediatric CPR
• Kid Safety Plus
• Infant Massage

■ **SWEDISH MEDICAL CENTER—BALLARD**
(206) 386-3606
5300 Tallman Ave. N.W.
Seattle, WA 98107
• Preparation for Parenthood
• Preparation for Parenthood Weekend Class
• Refresher Course—Preparation for Parenthood
• Big Kids and Babies
• Infant Safety and Cardiopulmonary Resuscitation

• Everything You Always Wanted to Know About Babies
• Breastfeeding Your Baby

■ **SWEDISH MEDICAL CENTER—SEATTLE**
(206) 386-3606
747 Broadway
Seattle, WA 98114
• Childbirth Preparation Series
• Childbirth Preparation Seminar
• Refresher Series
• Sibling Preparation
• Siblings at Birth Class
• Dads Only Class
• Grandparents Class
• Breastfeeding
• Newborn Care
• Infant CPR and Safety
• Newborn Preparation Seminar
• New Mother Seminar/Support Group
• Private Childbirth Preparation Class
• Babies and You (free seminar series)
Swedish also offers "Baby Club" membership which includes admission to the classes above as well as unlimited clinic visits with a registered nurse and certified lactation consultant after your baby is born. It's a great value for $120 for a one-year membership.

■ **UNIVERSITY OF WASHINGTON MEDICAL CENTER**
(206) 548-4003
1959 N.E. Pacific St.
Seattle, WA 98195
• Prepared Childbirth Series
• Breastfeeding Class
• Your Baby's Personality
• Preventing Preterm Birth
• Pregnancy Planning for Women With Diabetes
• Sibling Preparation

- Baby Safety and CPR
- Spanish Prepared Childbirth Series
- Expecting Multiples Series
- Back to Work and Breastfeeding Class
- Private Childbirth Instruction
- Private Breastfeeding Consultations

■ **VALLEY MEDICAL CENTER**
(206) 575-BABY
400 S. 43rd
Renton, WA 98055
- Planning for Pregnancy
- Care During Pregnancy
- Labor and Birth
- Planning, Packing, Parking, Pushing
- Refresher Course
- Teens: Pregnant and Prepared
- Expecting a Grandbaby
- Breastfeeding and the Working Mother
- Infant Feeding
- Infant Child CPR and Early Childhood Safety
- Postpartum Care/Infant Interaction

■ **VIRGINIA MASON MEDICAL CENTER**
(206) 623-8655
1100 Ninth Ave.
P.O. Box 900
Seattle, WA 98111
A variety of childbirth education classes are offered through Birth Education Northwest and CEAS as well as private instruction. These include:
- Early Pregnancy Class
- Childbirth Preparation Series
- Preparing for Childbirth at Home
- Preparing for Childbirth the Natural Way
- A Childbirth Refresher Class
- New Parent, New Baby Class
- Breastfeeding Class
- Sibling Preparation Class
- Buying for Baby

❧

MATERNITY LEAVE

❧

Your

employer's

leave and

benefit

policies for

pregnancy

should be

applied in

the same way

as leave for

other

temporary

disabilities.

❧

In 1989, the State of Washington enacted a Family Leave Act. Four years later, President Clinton signed the Family and Medical Leave Act of 1993 (FMLA). The provisions in the federal government's FMLA are more generous to employees in most cases than Washington State's, so employees will usually request an FMLA leave, although both laws must be followed. For more information on FMLA, see Chapter 2.

For employees who work for companies that are not required to follow the FMLA, you are protected under the Washington law against discrimination and Washington's maternity disability regulations (WAC 162-30-020) which consider pregnancy discrimination to be sex discrimination. This is a violation of state law, and companies with eight or more employees are subject to comply with this act.

In the "average" situation, a woman is disabled by pregnancy for at least two to four weeks before her due date and four to six weeks after a vaginal birth. The period is a bit longer for recovery from a Cesarean birth. Your health care provider will determine when and if you are considered "disabled" by pregnancy and childbirth. Your provider holds the answer to how long you are physically disabled. You are only entitled to the amount of leave your doctor certifies you to be disabled.

If you are medically able to return to work, but choose not to, you are not covered by the Pregnancy Disability Leave Regulation. Here is a summary of the state's maternity regulations:

- An employer may not refuse to hire you because you are pregnant.
- Your employer may not discharge or penalize you because you are pregnant.
- Your employer must give you a leave of absence for the period of time you are disabled because of pregnancy or childbirth.
- You must be allowed to return to the same or a similar job with the same pay.
- Your marital status does not matter.

In general, your employer's leave and benefit policies for pregnancy should be applied in the same way as leave for other temporary disabilities. There may be exceptions to the above based on an employer's business necessity.

■ **WASHINGTON STATE HUMAN RIGHTS COMMISSION**
(360) 753-6770
711 S. Capitol
402 Evergreen Plaza Building
Olympia, WA 98504-2490
This department has the information on the pregnancy discrimination regulations. If you have questions or would like a complete copy of the regulations, this is the department to call.

■ **U.S. DEPARTMENT OF LABOR WAGE-HOUR DISTRICT OFFICE**
(206) 553-4482
1111 Third Ave., Ste. 755
Seattle, WA 98101-9795
This department's staff are the experts on the Federal FMLA. They can send you a complete copy of the Act. They also are a good agency to call if you feel you are being discriminated against.

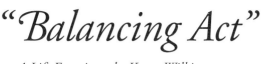

"*Balancing Act*"

A Life Experience by Karen Wilkinson

I found out I was pregnant with my first son, Stephen, just as I was putting the finishing editorial corrections on my Master's thesis after three years of graduate work in nursing. After four years of trying to become pregnant, I found myself to be at an awkward crossroads in life. I was ecstatic to soon become a mother but was equally as excited to continue my nursing career.

I found it difficult to enter the clinical nurse specialist market in pediatric nursing unless I was willing to work full-time. I chose the best option for my life at the time, and accepted a clinical faculty position in the School of Nursing while continuing to work as a staff nurse in a Level II nursery. After Stephen's birth, I was able to stay home with him for three months. Fall quarter came quickly, however, and I had to secure a child care situation and start teaching clinicals at the hospital. I was able to balance working at both of my positions and was happy with the large center where I left Stephen each afternoon for my husband to pick up after work. I always felt as if I was walking a balance beam, and it didn't take much to cause my balance to falter. I could walk the balance quite comfortably unassisted as long as we didn't have any illness or other pressing family needs.

Two and a half years later, when I had my second son, Andrew, I felt comfortable with my balancing act of motherhood and career and didn't have the same fears, hesitations, and concerns about returning to work. In fact, I felt confident enough to start a clinical nurse specialist position at the area's large children's medical center and keep my teaching position on the side since my clinical students were at the same site. Again, I was able to stay home with our new son for three months before leaving the boys with a nanny who came to the house while I went to work. I spent my days providing care and my expertise for toddlers with various medical conditions that brought them into the hospital as my

own children were growing up at home with someone else's care and expertise.

Slowly I began to lose my balance on that narrow line between being the mother I wanted to be and the clinician I wanted to, and was expected to, be. Only a short while later I found myself to be totally off balance and without any feet standing on that balance beam as I became a single mother. My career focus quickly changed from one of challenge and personal growth to one of survival and necessity. I hired a great live-in nanny and began to work many long hours. It took a long while before I felt like I was somewhat balanced again on that beam and could be the mother and often times the father that my boys needed. I would come home after a long day and have dinner with the boys and just be a mom until bedtime and save my professional life and worries until the adult hours of the night. Luckily, I can survive on minimal sleep and was blessed with many supportive friends, co-workers, church, and family to help spot me while walking that balance beam.

I never even imagined that three years later I would meet the most wonderful man and great father, Dave, who I now am married to. And even harder to imagine was the birth of our son Matthew four months ago. As I sit here at the keyboard with him sleeping on my lap, I realize that I'm not even thinking about climbing back onto that same old balance beam I spent so much time trying to conquer.

Matthew was born in July, and I enjoyed staying home with him and our other two sons until October. I have just returned to my faculty position half-time for this year. I have come to realize at this point in my life and career that this is where I belong. Dave works for a company that allows flexible working schedules so is able to stay home one day a week to be with the boys while I am at the University and hospital teaching. It is so much easier to go to work knowing your family is at home waking up just like any other morning with a parent there to make waffles, find lost homework and jackets, and take care of them. The other day of the week I go in to teach I have a baby-sitter with her own infant come to the house for the afternoon.

People ask me how can I work when I have three children and not feel overwhelmed and frustrated with so little time? I just do it because that is how I keep my life balanced. I have shifted my focus from not just being the best that I can be in the clinical setting but also to being the best that I can be at home with my family.

By teaching only half time, I can pick up different, fun, and challenging work such as research editing. I don't feel like a working mother when I can sit with my son at the keyboard and work on editing projects. We aren't always terribly productive when we take time out to giggle and make funny faces and baby chatter or wipe up the drool from the keyboard. There is no time clock to punch, however, only deadlines to meet that I can budget my time for as I choose without taking away time from my active sons and fun-loving husband.

I'm still trying to walk a balance required line but this time with a little different approach and purpose. It's a line that requires some balance but isn't suspended in the air with little room for error. I know the direction I need to go but have more flexibility to discover and experiment along the way. For example, I can take Andrew to swimming lessons and play with Matthew while he's awake on the pool deck. However, if he is sleeping then I can pull out a professional journal to enrich my nursing knowledge while I wait for swimming to finish. We are becoming quite organized in our household as with the boys' growing age come many more activities that require parental time and involvement—Cub Scouts, soccer and church activities, just to name a few. The time we save by our organizational ploys, such as planning our meals in two week periods and only grocery shopping twice a month, we can use as family time being adventurous, doing some of the many activities we share as a family. Yes, we are one of those two-working parent households, but I believe we are balanced in our work and our play. Our children are growing up appreciating the fact that Mom and Dad are professionals and go to work for their own enjoyment and challenge but also to provide for them. ❧

WASHINGTON CHILD CARE REGULATIONS

CHILD CARE CENTERS

Child care centers are facilities licensed to care for more than 12 children. Centers that care for infants have an adult-to-child ratio of 1:4. (One adult must be available to care for every four infants under the age of 12 months.) For toddlers from 12-29 months, the ratio is 1:7. Ratios for children 30 months to 5 years are 1:10; 5 years and older, 1:15. These ratios are established to make sure your child will receive ample care and attention.

A growing trend in recent years are on-site (or near-site) child-care centers that are provided by employers. Several local businesses and organizations offer this option in the Seattle area, including the City of Seattle and The Seattle Times. Hospitals and medical centers with child care centers for their employees include Fred Hutchinson, Group Health, Northwest, Providence, Swedish and Virginia Mason. The federal government has also been very supportive of this concept, with on-site centers at NOAA's Western Regional Center, EPA's regional headquarters, downtown Seattle, Federal Center South, GSA in Auburn, and several more on the way.

Specific arrangements with each on-site center and employer vary: employers may or may not subsidize care costs, some contract with child care companies to operate the centers while others hire their own employees, and some are overseen by a nonprofit board made up of parent-employees. Many allow children of non-employees to attend their center too, if space is available. While an on-site center is not necessarily less expensive than centers elsewhere, parents enjoy the convenience of having their children nearby and the opportunity to see them during the day. For working mothers of nursing infants, these centers provide an option to continue nursing during the workday.

According to Child Care Resources, the local child care referral agency, costs for full-time infant care at child care centers in King County range from $3,515 to $11,700 per year, with an average yearly cost of $7,224.

🍂

Before a license is issued, all child care centers and homes are checked for health and safety hazards.

🍂

FAMILY CHILD CARE HOMES

Family child care refers to child care in the private home of a licensed individual. The number of children a single provider can care for depends on the age range of the children and the experience of the caregiver. A new licensee can care for six children, with no more than two under the age of 2. With one year of experience, the caregiver can also choose to care for eight children, ages 2-11, or ten children ages 5-11. With an assistant caregiver and one year of experience, the home can care for nine children, with up to four under age 2.

To evaluate each licensed family child care provider, the licensing board visits each child care home before the initial licensing and is supposed to make annual inspections, too. Because of the large number of child care homes and the small number of licensors in King County, homes usually get visited once every two to three years. Licensors also visit homes when a complaint is made.

According to Child Care Resources, annual costs for family child care in King County range from $975 to $14,040 per year, with an average cost of $5,760.

ABOUT LICENSING

All child care centers and family child care homes in Washington state are licensed by the Department of Social and Health Services.

A child care license limits the number and ages of children in care. A license requires that all child care providers are checked for criminal and child abuse records. Before a license is issued, all child care centers and homes are checked for health and safety hazards.

If you have questions about the care your child is receiving at a center or home, talk to the teacher, director or home provider about your concerns or impressions.

If you think the children in care are at a risk of health and safety hazards and you have talked to the provider without any results, you can call the licensing authority and request an investigation of the care situation.

CHILD CARE

PROVIDER QUESTIONS OR CONCERNS?

LICENSING QUESTIONS OR COMPLAINTS:

- **DEPARTMENT OF SOCIAL AND HEALTH SERVICES**
  King County: (206) 721-4080
  (centers)
  (206) 721-4160
  (homes)
  Snohomish County: (425) 339-4780

REPORTING ABUSE OR NEGLECT:

- **DSHS CHILD PROTECTIVE SERVICES**
  Seattle: 721-4115
  South King County: (206) 872-2665
  East King County: (206) 649-4110

CHILD CARE REFERRAL AGENCIES

■ CHILD CARE RESOURCE AND REFERRAL NETWORK

(425) 258-4213

Hours: M-F   8:30 a.m.-3:30 p.m.
This referral line is operated by the Volunteers of America and provides referrals to child care homes and centers in Snohomish County. It is free for Snohomish County residents.

■ CHILD CARE RESOURCES

Seattle: (206) 461-3207
1265 South Main St., Ste. 210
Seattle, WA 98144

Bellevue: (425) 865-9350
15015 Main St., Ste. 206
Bellevue, WA 98007

S. King County: (206) 852-3080
841 N. Central Ave., Ste. 126
Kent, WA 98032
Hours: M-Th   9:00 a.m.-3:00 p.m.,
              5:30 p.m.-8:30 p.m.
       F   9:00 a.m.-1:00 p.m.
Telephone information and referral which connects parents seeking child care with licensed care providers is just one of Child Care Resources' services. Its data base can link you with a provider near your work or home. It also offers the "Needs 'n Kids" program which lists providers who care for children with various physical or developmental disabilities. Child Care Resources also provides employer programs, seminars, workshops and advocacy on child care-related topics. Operated as a nonprofit agency, Child Care Resources serves the Seattle/King, East King and South King counties. Costs are determined on a sliding scale basis.

■ DAYCARE FINDERS

(206) 932-3677

Hours: 24-hour voice mail
A business begun in 1995, Daycare Finders is run by a woman who previously owned a child care business for 20 years. The company helps individual parents, as well as corporations seeking child care referrals for employees. For a $29.95 fee, Daycare Finders will provide a list of all licensed day care openings meeting a client's specific needs, such as age of child, location of child care center, special schedules, etc. They will provide lists for up to a two-month period for the $29.95 fee and only list those with openings that fit the client's requirements. The client is responsible for interviewing caregivers and making the final decision.

■ KING COUNTY FAMILY CHILDCARE ASSOCIATION

(206) 467-1552

Hours: M-F   9:00 a.m.-4:00 p.m.
This nonprofit organization will send you a list of licensed child-care homes in King County, sorted by zip code. The roster is free and is updated continuously.

■ SEATTLE DEPARTMENT OF HOUSING AND HUMAN SERVICES

(206) 386-1050

If you're eligible, you may have 25%-90% of the cost of child care subsidized by the city. You must live within the Seattle city limits, be employed or in job training, and qualify based on income guidelines.

■ **WASHINGTON STATE CHILD CARE RESOURCE AND REFERRAL NETWORK**

(800) 446-1114

This is the number to call in Washington state if you live somewhere other than King or Snohomish County and need to find child care. The state line can put you in touch with your local child care resources agency.

OTHER RESOURCES

■ **OFFICE OF CHILD CARE POLICY**

State Department of Social and Health Services
P.O. Box 45710
Olympia, WA 98504-5710

You may order a free copy of "Choosing Child Care: A Consumer Guide for Parents" by sending a postcard to this address. The booklet was prepared by DSHS and the Seattle Department of Human Resources, and includes a checklist to complete as you visit potential child care sites.

IN-HOME CHILD CARE AGENCIES

■ **ANNIE'S NANNIES**

(206) 784-8462
5018 Greenwood Ave. N.
Seattle, WA 98103
Hours: M-F   9:00 a.m. - 5:00 p.m.

In business since 1984, Annie's Nannies is the Puget Sound area's original nanny service. Annie Davis and her partner (and daughter), Suzanne Royer McCone, personally interview all families and nannies. Families rely on the partners' skills in matching just the right nannies with parents and their children. The company's goal is to make sure that every family has the best nanny to share in the parenting of their children. Annie's Nannies' screening process includes a criminal background and driving record check in any state in which the nanny has lived. Also, all references are personally spoken to by the agency.

Salaries for nannies range from $1,200 to $1,800 per month for full-time live-out and $900 to $1,200 plus room and board for live-in, depending on the position and their experience. Part-time nannies make between $7 and $10 per hour. Annie's Nannies' placement fee is $1,600 with $150 of the fee as a deposit at the time they meet the family. The remainder is due after hiring the nanny. They give a one-year guarantee on all placements. This means that if the nanny does not work out for whatever reason, she/he will be replaced. Annie's Nannies is always available for a phone consultation as needed with the family or nanny for the duration of employment. Most of their nannies are with families for many years. Annie's will cover last minute calls, overnights and sick child care. All nannies are CPR certified.

■ AROUND THE CLOCK

(206) 367-2222

Full time and part time nannies are available. With 24 hours notice, temporary child care is also available. All nannies are double screened by the Washington State Patrol—for driving and criminal records. Then each nanny candidate is seen by a licensed counselor and has all her references checked. Around the Clock's nannies are all certified in CPR and first aid. By this point Around the Clock has a working knowledge of their prospective employees, so when they come to your home for the pre-selection interview they can better match your parenting philosophy and style with those of a nanny. Placement fees range from $1,000 for part-time to about $1,400 for full-time. Monthly salaries range from $1,000 to $1,800; live-in wages are slightly less.

■ CAREWORKS INNOVATIVE
   ## NANNY SOLUTIONS

(206) 325-7510 (24 hour voice mail)
(425) 641-9522 Eastside

Careworks is a nanny placement service dedicated to supporting families in finding child care solutions to suit their individual needs. The owner, Linda Stacey, started her business after seeking nannies for her own family and finding that the kind of service she had pictured wasn't being offered. Her service-oriented focus has been well received by her clients, as she was voted the Best Nanny Service for two years in a row by readers of *Seattle's Child* newsmagazine and given their Golden Bootie Award.

Careworks' first step in working with a family is an in-home interview to help define the family's parenting philosophy and to develop a clear picture of what a nanny's role can be. Both the family and prospective nannies are asked to complete two evaluations designed to assess compatibility in the areas of parenting, communication style and temperament. Careworks also does a complete screening of all nanny applicants, including criminal and traffic checks, and requires CPR and first aid certification. They personally interview the references of applicants, and select only applicants who receive "glowing" recommendations. The cost for the initial application is $100 and includes this in-home interview. The placement fee is $1,200 which includes a one-year guarantee. Full-time nannies are paid $1,200-$1,800 monthly for live-out and $1,000-$1,400 for live-in.

Because Careworks recognizes that different families have different needs, and because they want to make nanny services available to more people, they also offer a free nanny share network for parents who want to share the services of a nanny and reduce their costs. Names of families interested in sharing are kept in a data base and matched by needs.

■ DREAMBOAT NANNIES

(206) 232-2553

Hours: M-F   8:00 a.m.-6:00 p.m.

Dreamboat Nannies matches parents with live-in or live-out nannies. They require nanny applicants to provide between four and eight references, and besides verifying these, the agency also checks the criminal and traffic history and health of the nanny. Nannies also need to have CPR and first aid training.

The $75 application fee gets the process started and includes as many potential nanny interviews as needed to find a match. The placement fee is $950 and there is a nine-month guarantee. Nannies generally are paid from $6-$10/ hour for live-out and usually not less than $800/month for live-in.

■ JUDI JULIN, R.N., NANNYBROKER INC.
(206) 624-1213 or (425) 392-5681
25620 S.E. 157th Street
Issaquah, WA 98027
Hours: M-F   9:00 a.m.-9:00 p.m.
            Emergencies anytime

Nannybroker Inc. is owned by a registered nurse, Judi Julin, who has been interviewing nannies for 25 years and placing nannies for nearly nine. As the owner of her business, she strives to be as accessible as possible to her clients. Julin has also authored a book entitled "So You Want to Hire your Own Nanny."

Nannybroker Inc. offers live-in or live-out, permanent or part-time care. All applicants are fully screened and both personal and work references are thoroughly checked. You pay no up-front fees and only pay the agency once a child care provider is found. The fee for a permanent provider normally equals a monthly salary which runs about $1,300. For temporary help, the fee equals about $8-$10 daily and wages are between $8-$10 per hour. Overnight stays are also available with wages at $100 each 24-hour period and the agency fee of approximately $15 per day. For permanent placement, a 90-day guarantee is offered through this service which means if your nanny does not work out, Nannybroker should replace him or her at no additional cost.

■ A NANNY FOR U
(425) 745-9882
24-Hour Pager: (206) 969-1119

Rebecca Anderson-Vidmore, owner of A Nanny For U, brings five years of nanny experience to the nanny placement business. The philosophy of A Nanny For U is to provide a nurturing environment in which your child is both stimulated and secure. They also focus on providing ongoing support and communication to their clients and nannies in order to sustain long-term placements.

Offering 90-day and one-year guarantees, with fees ranging from $700-$1,100, A Nanny For U is unique in that no up-front or application fee is paid until a nanny is placed with the family. Rebecca personally meets the families in their homes to ensure a long-lasting nanny-parent relationship. A Nanny For U does not limit the number of nanny candidates that a family may consider. Each nanny is carefully screened after completing the application and interviewing with A Nanny For U. Criminal and driving records are checked, as well as three child care references. Upon being hired, nannies are sent to Kid Safety Plus, a CPR, first aid, and overall child safety class. Nanny salaries range from $8-$10 per hour for part-time, $1,200-$1,600 per month for full-time live-out, and $800-$1,400 for full-time live-in.

CHILD CARE AGENCIES

■ **FLYING COLORS**

(206) 298-9669

Flying Colors offers specialized and crisis child care for the preschool age child who may be too disruptive for a traditional child care setting. This service's pre-social curriculum with an effective behavior management program is of great help to families.

୬

TEMPORARY AND SICK CHILD CARE

■ **ANNIE'S NANNIES**

(206) 784-8462

5018 Greenwood Ave. N.

Seattle, WA 98103

Hours: M-F   9:00 a.m. - 5:00 p.m.

■ **AROUND THE CLOCK**

(206) 367-2222

With 24 hour notice temporary child care is available.

■ **BEST SITTERS**

(206) 682-2556

Best Sitters is one of the oldest temporary child care services. In business for more than 25 years, Best Sitters provides temporary child care in your home and at major hotels. There's a four-hour minimum and fees for one child begin at $41 (first four hours) and $8/hour after that. Rates vary depending on number of children, whether there is another adult on the premises, starting time for care, if child is ill, and if overnight care is needed. Baby-sitters must be at least 25 years old or have two or more years of nanny experience.

■ **HEALTHTEAM NORTHWEST TEMPORARY CHILDCARE SERVICES**

Affiliated with Children's Hospital and Medical Center

(425) 482-4000

(800) 888-4429

2525 220th S.E.

Bothell, WA 98021

Hours: M-F   7:00 a.m. -5:30 p.m.

Sat.-Sun. 7:00 a.m. -3:00 p.m.

If your child is mildly ill or injured and cannot attend regular school or child care, Temporary Childcare can help you secure appropriate child care; they can also provide this service if your child is well. Common illnesses or conditions appropriate to this program include, but are not limited to: chicken pox, ear infections, strep throat, tonsillitis, conjunctivitis (pinkeye), mumps, flu, mild injuries. You first must register with the service and complete a service agreement and preregistration form. If you are unable to preregister, you can get help the day you need service for a $5 fee. When you need the service, the staff may help find the right provider for you. Prices for the service are $12 per hour for one child and $5 per day for each additional child with a total limit of three children. The child care providers are nursing assistants who are experienced in sick child care needs and developmentally appropriate craft activities. They are also certified in CPR. There is also an on-call nurse available 24 hours a day.

୬

WHERE TO SHOP

So you are pregnant. Now what? The nursery? Selecting a car seat? You go to the store and...you feel sick. Not morning sickness but simply overwhelmed from the hundreds of decisions you now have to make. Which brand? What model? How do you figure out what you really need versus what is just cute or trendy? Shopping for a crib, car seat, and high chair are a necessity, but being an informed, prepared consumer gives you an advantage.

After the hard work of equipment shopping is done, the fun begins! You'll be lucky if you aren't given too many baby clothes, because this is the best part of shopping for baby. Finding a "style" for your baby that fits his personality, your budget and life's little surprises may be a challenge and a joy. I will never forget the look I gave my husband when he asked me, in all seriousness, why I needed to buy more clothes for the baby. He assured me that all the baby needed was three outfits—he would wear one, one would be in the wash and the other in the dryer. He has since rethought those words several times!

It is amazing how fast babies grow into infants, then into toddlers. It is even more amazing that something that fits one day will be way too small the next. This stage of constant growth spurts is when buying at resale shops can be the most helpful. Your baby is too young to have an opinion about being dressed in ducks, bunnies or in bright stars and stripes. They like warm and dry best!

Discovering a favorite store is like seeing an old friend. You can always find what you are looking for. Seattle is very shopper-friendly. With its booming economy, you'll find new retail stores beckoning at every turn. Parents and parents-to-be will find an amazing shopping selection which ranges from the basic to the truly unique. This chapter's store reviews include thumbnail descriptions which will give you a good idea of what to expect before you shop.

The creativity of Seattle entrepreneurs is found in the expanded local product pages, where you'll discover everything from the "original hooded towel" to where to get your baby's photo on a T-shirt to a snuggly fleece bed sack for your little bundle.

﹅

Parents and parents-to-be will find an amazing shopping selection, which ranges from the basic to the truly unique.

﹅

MALLS

There are many malls in the greater Seattle area and their locations are listed below with the mall hours. Information is not repeated for each store located in a mall in the following descriptions.

■ ALDERWOOD MALL

(425) 771-1121
3000 184th St. S.W.
(from Seattle going north on I-5 take the 181B exit. From the north, take the Alderwood Blvd. exit.)
Lynnwood, WA 98037
Hours: M-Sat.	10:00 a.m.-9:30 p.m.
       Sun.	11:00 a.m.-6:00 p.m.

■ BELLEVUE SQUARE

(425) 454-8096
231 Bellevue Square
Bellevue, WA 98004
Hours: M-Sat.	9:30 a.m.-9:30 p.m.
       Sun.	11:00 a.m.-6:00 p.m.

■ EVERETT MALL

(425) 743-2722
1402 S.E. Everett Mall Way
(from I-5 take the Mukeltio Spwy. exit)
Everett, WA 98204
Hours: M-Sat.	10:00 a.m.-9:00 p.m.
       Sun.	11:00 a.m.-6:00 p.m.

■ FACTORIA SQUARE MALL

(425) 747-7344
4092 Factoria Square Mall S.E.
(from 405 take the Coal Creek exit; from I-90 take the Richards Rd. exit)
Bellevue, WA 98006
Hours: M-Sat.	10:00 a.m.-9:00 p.m.
       Sun.	11:00 a.m.-6:00 p.m.

■ FACTORY STORES OF AMERICA OUTLET CENTER

(425) 888-4505
North Bend, WA 98045
Hours: M-Sat.	10:00 a.m.-7:00 p.m.
       Sun.	10:00 a.m.-6:00 p.m.

■ LAKE FOREST PARK TOWNE CENTER

(206) 367-7717
17171 Bothell Way N.E.
(from I-5 take the N.E. 205th St. exit)
Seattle, WA 98155
Hours: M-Sat.	10:00 a.m.-9:00 p.m.
       Sun.	11:00 a.m.-5:00 p.m.

■ NORTHGATE MALL

(206) 362-4777
758 Northgate Mall (exit 173 from I-5)
Seattle, WA 98125
Hours: M-Sat.	10:00 a.m.-9:30 p.m.
       Sun.	11:00 a.m.-6:00 p.m.

■ PACIFIC EDGE OUTLET CENTER

(360) 757-3549
Burlington, WA 98233
Hours: M-Sat.	10:00 a.m.-9:00 p.m.
       Sun.	10:00 a.m.-6:00 p.m.

■ REDMOND TOWN CENTER

(425) 867-0808
7730 Leary Way N.E.
(from 520 east take the Marymore exit)
Redmond, WA 98052
Hours: M-Sat.	10:00 a.m.-8:00 p.m.
       Sun.	11:00 a.m.-6:00 p.m.

■ **SEA TAC MALL**
(253) 839-6150
1901 S. Sea Tac Mall
(from I-5 take the 320th St. exit)
Federal Way, WA 98003
Hours: M-Sat. 10:00 a.m.-9:00 p.m.
       Sun. 11:00 a.m.-6:00 p.m.

■ **SOUTHCENTER SHOPPING**
   CENTER
(206) 246-7400
633 Southcenter Shopping Center
(Junction of I-5 and 405)
Tukwila, WA 98188
Hours: M-Sat. 10:00 a.m.-9:30 p.m.
       Sun. 11:00 a.m.-7:00 p.m.

■ **SUPERMALL OF THE GREAT**
   NORTHWEST
(800) SAY-VALU
Auburn, WA 98001
(I-5 to 405, exit 2 (SR167)
Southbound to Supermall exit)
Hours: M-Sat. 9:30 a.m.-9:30 p.m.
       Sun. 11:00 a.m.-7:00 p.m.

■ **UNIVERSITY VILLAGE MALL**
(206) 523-0622
2673 N.E. University Village Mall
(corner of 45th and 25th Ave. N.E.)
Seattle, WA 98105
Hours: M-Sat. 9:30 a.m.-9:00 p.m.
       Sun. 11:00 a.m.-6:00 p.m.

■ **WESTLAKE CENTER**
(206) 467-1600
400 Pine
(from I-5 north exit Seneca St.; from I-5 south exit Stewart St.)
Seattle, WA 98101
Hours: M-F 9:30 a.m.-9:30 p.m.
       Sat. 9:30 a.m.-8:00 p.m.
       Sun. 11:00 a.m.-6:00 p.m.

❧

FURNISHINGS/ EQUIPMENT

■ **BABY DEPOT—BURLINGTON**
   COAT FACTORY
(253) 735-9964
Supermall of the Great Northwest

(425) 776-2221
24111 Hwy. 99
Edmonds, WA 98020
Hours: M-Sat. 10:00 a.m.-9:30 p.m.
       Sun. 11:00 a.m.-6:00 p.m.
Cash, Checks, Visa, MC, AmEx

Who worries about coats when the Baby Depot is nearby? With everything from clothing and equipment to furniture at discounted prices, there is no reason to shop anywhere else. Their furniture department is one of the largest in the area, with many cribs and toddler beds on display, all featuring coordinated bedding and accessories in attractive themes. There are also plenty of strollers, car seats, playpens, swings, rocking chairs, lamps, and other furniture items. The Baby Depot carries major brands like Childcraft, Century, Simmons, Graco, Aprica, and Perego, and prices are discounted about 20%-30% from other retail outlets.

Besides furniture, a well-stocked accessories section includes nursing supplies, safety items, baby bottles, bibs, toys, books, car seat covers, diaper bags, bedding, and more. I have been here several times and have seen entire lines

FURNISHINGS

(such as Sassy) on a 25% off surprise sale.

The store has a large baby clothes' section where they carry popular brands in both casual and dressy styles, again at discounted prices. They have preemie sizes available, as well as some christening gowns. There's also a small maternity section with casual and career wear, nursing lingerie, and maternity hose.

The Baby Depot offers a 10% discount when you buy an identical item for a twin (or triplets!). Staff was very helpful and considerate, and quite knowledgeable about the wide range of products they carry. You may also sign up for the mother-to-be registry. One store policy to be aware of: Burlington doesn't give cash (or credit card) returns, only exchanges or in-store credits.

■ BELLINI JUVENILE DESIGNER FURNITURE

(425) 451-0126
201 Bellevue Way N.E.
Bellevue, WA 98004
Hours: M-Sat.   10:00 a.m.-6:00 p.m.
          Th   Open until 8:00 p.m.
Cash, Checks, Visa, MC, AmEx
Sigh. Bellini always reminds me of Beverly Hills, where I first knew of them. In Seattle it is located just a few blocks from Bellevue Square in the Park Row Shopping Center. Bellini presents a beautiful display of cribs, bedroom sets, and accessories. The products are high quality with a definite designer feel. You can think of Bellini as the kind of store that sells only the best. The store also carries Dutailer gliders as well as beautiful quilts and linens, both affordable and heirloom quality. Bellini is best known for their cribs. Every Bellini crib converts into a youth bed, saving parents the

extra expense of purchasing a toddler bed later. The furniture you purchase at Bellini will last for years and retain its quality. Prices are more affordable than you may think, with cribs in the $400 range.

Bellini carries birth announcements that can be custom ordered and offers numerous wallpaper and nursery accessories to help you design that very special room. They also offer free gift wrapping and a baby registry.

■ A CHILD'S ROOM
(425) 643-7050
15123 N.E. 24th St.
Redmond, WA 98052
Hours: M-Sat.   10:00 a.m.-6:00 p.m.
          Sun.   Noon-5:00 p.m.
Cash, Checks, Visa, MC, AmEx
Located off the 148th N.E. exit from the 520 freeway, A Child's Room is just east of the Overlake Sears store. There's a dreamy feel to this place as you walk in and notice the bedroom sets, attractively outfitted in themes from Winnie the Pooh to the Wild West. Although the store specializes in furniture for bigger kids, they do have a baby section that includes a selection of lamps, mobiles, wall hangings, night lights, and picture frames. A Child's Room also carries a nice assortment of books, rattles, stuffed animals and toys for baby, as well as baby books and family memory books. They have some clothing in infant and toddler sizes too, by such makers as Little Me and Gear Kids.

■ CRIBS ETC.

(253) 582-3320
9315 Gravelly Lake Dr. S.W.
Lakewood, WA 98499
Hours: M-F   10:00 a.m.-6:00 p.m.
      Sat.   10:00 a.m.-5:00 p.m.
Cash, Checks, Visa, MC
You want cribs—Cribs Etc. has got cribs! Ragazzi, Dutailier, Childcraft, Simmons and more can all be found here. They also carry the largest selection in the Northwest of "The Crib for Life" in five models starting at $298, including the youth bed kit. There is always a sale or mattress promotion going on to make their already good prices better!

■ GO TO YOUR ROOM

Baby Pages

(425) 453-2990
13000 Bel-Red Rd.
Bellevue, WA 98005

(206) 528-0711
6411 12th N.E. (Roosevelt Square)
Seattle, WA 98115
Hours: M-Sat.   10:00 a.m.-6:00 p.m.
      Sun.   Noon-5:00 p.m.
Cash, Checks, Visa, MC, AmEx
Go To Your Room has always been a dream store. It is owned by two mothers who know how to help you make a cozy, comfortable, friendly and colorful environment in which your baby will enjoy sweet dreams. Their philosophy is to meet the needs of parents. The Seattle store now features a huge inventory of Peg Perego strollers and high chairs, including the Prima Poppa, which is not only height adjustable but reclines as well so that you can use it from infant to toddler stages. It is the best-rated high chair on the market. The Bellevue store now carries a nice selection of the "kid approved" Aprica strollers.

Being the largest seller of Dutalier glider rockers has earned them Dutalier exclusive dealer status for their new line of gallery fabrics which makes the rocker not only comfortable but an object of beauty. Now you can bring that rocker out of the baby's room and into the living room!

Also new is a big selection of ready-to-hang framed artwork. Styles range from classic Pooh, fairytale and nursery rhyme characters to Anne Geddes. A real bargain for the quality at $20-$60, now there is a way to decorate your child's walls besides plastic stick-ups! There is still a large selection of cribs, tons of Ragazzi, cradles from Simmons, lamps, mobiles, strollers, wall hangings, posters and bedding—California Kids, Nojo, Baby Guess, Pine Creek—for babies and older children. The atmosphere is unrushed, informative and fun. Because of Go To Your Room's on-site furniture warehouse, you can drive away with your purchase or use their delivery/assembly service. Customer satisfaction is a goal, and it shows. The play area features a Duplo table. Gift registry is available.

■ KIDS CLUB

Baby Pages

(425) 643-5437
15600 N.E. 8th
Bellevue, WA 98008
Hours: M-Sat.   10:00 a.m.-9:00 p.m.
      Sun.   11:00 a.m.-6:00 p.m.

(206) 524-2553
University Village Mall
Cash, Checks, Visa, MC, AmEx
Located at the south end of Crossroads Mall, the Bellevue Kids Club store is a complete department store for kids. It's bright, clean, colorful, and very welcom-

ing—the kind of store that you'll want to walk through slowly, so you don't miss anything. There's a well-stocked shoe department, with Keds Prewalkers, Weeboks, and more, all affordably priced. There's lots and lots of cute clothing for infants and children, and plenty of hats, bows, and other items for accessorizing.

The toy section is quite complete too, with items for all ages from infants to school-age—toys, puzzles, Brio kits, stuffed animals, books, cassettes, and more. Near the toy section, the store offers a complete Medela nursing display, with nursing supplies and pillows. They also sell feeding products of the Avent line, including bottles and bottle sterilizers, a manual breast pump, and breastfeeding accessories.

Kids Club's furniture and equipment section takes up about half the store. There's a full selection of cribs (more than 20 on display when I visited) by such makers as Simmons, Ragazzi, and Childcraft. Prices were reasonable and some items were on sale. A rocking bassinet by Simmons caught my eye, as did the rows of strollers and high chairs. Cribs were adorned with attractive bedding options and accessories by Nojo, Cotton Tale Designs, and other manufacturers. Special orders are welcome too, and the sales associates here go out of their way to help you and to make you feel welcome. Kids Club has several play areas to keep your children occupied while you shop; they also offer a baby registry and from time to time they have free parenting classes and story hours.

The Kids Club at University Village is a smaller store, featuring the high-quality clothing and accessories that the Bellevue Kids Club is well-known for.

They also offer toys, breastfeeding supplies, and other baby items. Furniture is carried from time to time and can be ordered from the Bellevue store for delivery directly to your home. An added plus when shopping at this store are the new features of the upgraded University Village shopping center. There's an outdoor play area for kids ages 2-6 and some fun cow sculptures, as well as an assortment of new and remodeled restaurants and the Barnes and Noble superstore.

■ MERRY GO ROUND BABY NEWS
(425) 454-1610
11111 N.E. 8th St.
Bellevue, WA 98004
Hours: M-Sat. 10:00 a.m.-6:00 p.m.
       Th   10:00 a.m.- 8:00 p.m.
       Sun.   Noon-5:00 p.m.
Cash, Checks, Visa, MC, AmEx

Merry Go Round sells both clothing and baby products, making it convenient for parents to shop in one place. It offers a wide selection of cribs, strollers and car seats. Product lines include Simmons, Child Craft, Graco, Kolcraft, Aprica, Combi and more. Pricing is competitive—during my visit, several cribs were available in the $300 range.

Merry Go Round also carries a nice selection of infant and toddler clothing with many brand name designers to choose from. Plan on spending $13 and up for an infant's outfit. The store had one of the widest selections of preemie outfits and accessories we found. Along the front wall were clothing, hats, and even Pampers diapers. They also carry christening gowns for both boys and girls. Merry Go Round is located near Bellevue Square and has been in business since 1947.

■ THE RIGHT START
(425) 451-2445
Bellevue Square Mall
Cash, Checks, Visa, MC
If you have ever wished there was a product that could make life a little easier for you, The Right Start is the place to look first. Under one little roof you can find a multitude of problem-solving items. If you can't seem to keep Junior's socks on no matter what you do, Cutiecakes non-skid stretchy booties at $9 are "keepers" for your tot's tootsies! If Junior happens to go through a growth spurt right after you spend a small fortune on new clothes, a four-pack of extenders can be purchased for only $10. These small fabric swatches snap into a garment's existing crotch snaps, extend the length by 3 to 4 inches, and increase wear-time by about six months!

Developmental toys are an important part of the store's inventory. You can find the entire repertoire of Black and White toys, as well as activity bolsters, soft primary colored fabric teethers, and a wonderful activity globe pillow. At $23, the pillow has five soft animals with buckles and bows that move and squeak, to keep your baby happily entertained. The Italian line, Chicco, is one of the store's featured exclusives. Their great four-piece layette set in a drawstring bag sells for $50. Chicco's baby skin care line, Infinite Dolezze, is also available. I purchased a $16 "Baby Einstein" video for my son. It has nursery rhymes in seven languages and he absolutely loves it.

The Right Start is known for its emphasis on safety items for infants. From an illuminating ear scope at $27, to Britax car seats, to the newest stroller designs, the store works with manufacturers to assure that products meet the highest safety standards. They guarantee every product they sell. And, if you are lucky enough to get your hands on a catalogue, save it; they can be difficult to find. The Right Start is a great place for parents and kids of any age.

■ STARS CHILDREN'S WEAR
(425) 392-2900
55 N.E. Gilman Blvd.
Issaquah, WA 98027

Hours:	M-F	9:30 a.m.-9:00 p.m.
	Sat.	10:00 a.m.-7:00 p.m.
	Sun.	11:00 a.m.-6:00 p.m.

Cash, Checks, Visa, MC, AmEx
Stars not only carries a great selection of clothing, toys and Beanie Babies, but they now carry a nice selection of cribs and baby bedroom furniture featuring the Legacy by Child Craft series. Strollers are well represented by Graco, Century, Evenflo and Chicco, to name only a few. Bedding by Lambs and Ivy, Brandy Danielle and Nojo is also abundant. There are also playpens by Fisher Price and Graco and even Snugli and Baby Bjorn packs galore in the new layette section. Whew! You can find all your favorite brand names at Stars at 20% to 40% below retail everyday. There are also periodic sales which bring the bargains to an even greater level. Stars also makes shopping fun with weekend entertainment like clowns and magic acts. It's a day trip!

FURNISHINGS

■ **USA BABY**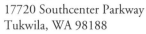
(206) 575-1016
17720 Southcenter Parkway
Tukwila, WA 98188
Hours: M-Fri. 10:00 a.m.-9:00 p.m.
     Sat Open until 6 p.m.
     Sun. Noon-5:00 p.m.
Cash, Checks, Visa, MC, Discover
Just past the Southcenter Mall behind Applebee's Restaurant is Seattle's newest baby furnishings retailer. USA Baby is set up in room-like areas so you can see how merchandise will look in your home. When I visited, I heard not one, but two customers praise the set-up and delivery staff! I was impressed at the knowledge and interest staff showed in the store's merchandise. There was so much "Pooh" at this store that my baby went nuts. The wall of comforter/bedding sets had brands like Lambs and Ivy and Spot. All were typically priced; however, the sale section featured about eight sets that were marked 20%-40% off! The "ultimate safety" Britax car seat is sold here for $169. I saw Baby Pedic mattresses for $99 and entire "Crib for Life" sets at $999 including both dressers.

As a national franchise, most stores carry similar items. I found the baby registry a valuable asset. They also offer free layaway with no time limit! I found a variety of interesting baby gifts such as: baby time capsules for $20; "It's a Boy/Girl" golf tees, $4 for 12; and four-piece baby silver sets at $30 with boxes for a child's first tooth and hair clippings.

~

MATERNITY STORES

■ **A PEA IN THE POD**
(206) 292-9200
Westlake Center
Cash, Checks, Visa, MC, AmEx
This elegant maternity boutique believes you don't have to compromise fashion during pregnancy. A Pea in The Pod has a dynamic selection of tailored business suits, career and casual dresses which range from $68 to $185. The casual selection ranges from conservative to trendy.

The selection of special occasion evening wear features everything from simple black dresses to beaded evening gowns—all of which are gorgeous. A Pea In The Pod offers its own label, as well as other designer labels, in petite to larger sizes. One- and two-piece maternity swimsuits are available year-round starting at $58. The store also carries a variety of maternity lingerie.

There is a nice sitting area with toys, so husbands and children are made to feel welcome. A Pea in the Pod also has a personal shopping service and overnight shipping. Watch this store for sales. Markdown merchandise may be discounted as much as 75%.

■ **BABY LOVE MATERNITY**
(206) 246-7111
Southcenter Shopping Center

(425) 776-1262
Alderwood Mall
Cash, Checks, Visa, MC, AmEx
Baby Love is a locally owned maternity clothing store. Baby Love opened its first doors in 1973 and has a loyal clientele. Conveniently located in two malls,

customers can shop seven days a week and evening hours. At Baby Love, you'll find a wide array of clothing and accessories. They offer clothing that is comfortable as well as career attire. Pricing is competitive with other large maternity stores. Career dresses start around $70. Most dresses are very fashionable and fun. Casual clothing costs about $25 on up. And, for the budget conscious, a clearance rack offers excellent buys. Baby Love also offers a huge selection of undergarments, including hose, bras, and nursing wear. Most of the undergarments are behind the counter, so you'll need to ask a sales person for the merchandise. Also, Baby Love now rents hospital-grade Medela breast pumps.

■ BIRTH AND BEYOND

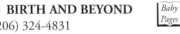

(206) 324-4831
2610 E. Madison St.
Seattle, WA 98112

(425) 402-9366
14450 Woodinville-Redmond Rd.
Woodinville, WA 98072
Hours: M-F   10:00 a.m.-6:00 p.m.
        Sat., Sun. 11:00 a.m.-6:00 p.m.
Cash, Checks, Visa, MC, AmEx, Disc.
Owned by Lyndsey Starkey, Birth and Beyond is truly a unique maternity store—unique in the fact that it does not carry maternity clothing, but instead just about anything else you may want during pregnancy and postpartum. You'll find a wide selection of nursing clothing, books, tapes, breast pumps, slings, music and much more at this sophisticated, yet friendly store. Birth and Beyond also has childbirth classes, a resource lending library and much-appreciated personal attention to its customers. We also found

many unique local products here. If you're pregnant, have a new baby or are just interested in learning more about childbirth, this store should be a definite stop. The new location gives Eastside moms the same great store and selections!

■ DESIGNER MATERNITY FACTORY AND KIDS RACK

(425) 451-1945
11010 N.E. 8th St.
Bellevue, WA 98004

Hours: M-Sat.   10:00 a.m.-6:00 p.m.
        Sun.   Noon -5:00 p.m.
Cash, Checks, Visa, MC
Only one block from the 405 and a few blocks from Bellevue Square Mall is a small "home"-like store that carries a wide variety of maternity wear. At first when you drive up to the store it seems a little unconventional, as the entrance is difficult to find. Once you enter the store, you'll find a nice variety of maternity clothing, with brands such as Hayley Michaels, and our favorite Japanese Weekend. Clothing ranges from the sophisticated to the fun and funky. Prices start at about $20 for most items and expect to find an average work dress starting at $50. There is always a special promo going on where you will find even better bargains on top name maternity wear that you will see at the quality chains stores, but at lower prices here. You'll also find one-on-one service as the owner, Denise, and her employees provide individual fashion coordinating for moms-to-be. During our visit, she offered many good suggestions from clothing to nursing bras. Best of all, they have a bathroom easily accessible for any pregnant woman—a definite plus in this book. Denise began her career as a de-

signer and she has gone back to those roots with a new line of her own nursing wear featuring the same invisible seamless zippers that many of the high fashion designers use. A top seller has been a heather two-piece pants set at $49.99. These do not look like nursing tops either, ladies! You can wear them without getting knowing looks or questions from passing La Leche League members. In addition, she still carries Carewear, Discreet Wear and Secrets dresses. And, if you're looking for children's or infant clothing, this store offers a variety of apparel 50%-70% below retail. You'll find name brands, party dresses (velveteens) and daily wear at very affordable prices. There is also a large selection of books, toys and accessories.

Designer Maternity is in the process of negotiating for a new larger location so CALL to check the location before you go!

■ MIMI MATERNITY
(425) 637-8785
Bellevue Square
Cash, Checks, Visa, MC, AmEx
Mimi Maternity is owned by the same company as A Pea in the Pod. The difference you'll find between the two stores is that Mimi is a little more contemporary and casual. The prices are also slightly lower. Quality, fun, and fashionable is the best way to describe this store. And, it is difficult to imagine the clothing in stock as maternity wear. It's like looking at all the most fashionable styles and realizing you don't have to miss out on the latest look even though you're pregnant. Items start at about $20. Mimi also has nursing bras, underwear, and lingerie. I found the staff at Bellevue Square very knowledgeable and helpful.

■ MOTHERHOOD
(425) 454-1355
Bellevue Square
Cash, Checks, Visa, MC, AmEx
Motherhood is conveniently located on the ground floor of Bellevue Square, two stores down from the Tugboat. As part of a national chain, it offers only the "Motherhood" label. There is a nice selection of casual and professional clothing mid-priced to upscale. Dresses range in price from $40 to $100, shorts and tops between $20 and $40, and pants and skirts from $20 to $50. The store also carries maternity undergarments including panty hose and nursing bras.

During my visit, many items were on sale at substantial savings. A mailing list is available to keep customers informed about upcoming sales. The sales staff is very friendly, helpful and upbeat.

■ VILLAGE MATERNITY   *Baby Pages*
(206) 523-5167
University Village Mall
Cash, Checks, Visa, MC
Voted as best maternity store by *Seattle's Child* readers, Village Maternity is conveniently located in the beautiful University Village. Village Maternity prides itself in offering primarily 100% cotton clothing for both children and expectant mothers. In maternity wear, mothers can find stylish, contemporary clothing. Many items have a natural and comfortable touch. Sweaters, jumpers and business suits all offer an original "Seattle" feel. I also found nursing tops and one of my favorite brands, Japanese Weekend, at Village Maternity. Formal wear rentals are available for your special occasion. Pricing is very competitive.

For children's wear, the selection is a little bit smaller, but complete. All children's clothing is 100% cotton with most of the name brands you would expect. A variety of play and dress clothing is available for infants and toddlers

❧

DEPARTMENT/ DISCOUNT STORES

■ THE BON MARCHE
(425) 455-2121
Bellevue Square

(206) 344-2121
Westlake Center

(425) 712-6000
Alderwood Mall

(253) 529-6000
Sea Tac Mall

(206) 440-6000
Northgate Mall

(206) 656-6000
Southcenter Shopping Center

(425) 710-6000
Everett Mall

The Bon Marche's infant and toddler clothing section offers the impression of pure class, quality and elegance. It carries delightful children's wear from manufacturers such as Carter's, Little Me, Dior and Baby b'Gosh. The Bon Marche also has a nice selection of pre-emie wear and christening gowns. And when shopping during one of their fantastic sales, prices are very competitive with even some of the discount stores.

The Bon Marche carries maternity clothes at their stores in downtown Seattle, Northgate, Everett, and Alderwood. The maternity department has a

nice selection of dresses, separates, swimsuits, sleepwear, rompers, and maternity hose. They carry both upscale and casual clothing, in a range of prices. A full price Hayley Michaels pant suit cost $114, and denim overalls and jumpers by J. Michele were in the $50-$60 range. There were some great bargains on the sales rack, though, with colorful sweaters originally priced at $43 discounted to $12, and a rayon romper by Oh! Mamma reduced from $98 to $24.

At the Downtown and Northgate Bon Marche, you can also visit Toytropolis or the "city of toys." And, this it is...stroll through the "zoo" for a look at the selection of stuffed animals—everything from the whimsical to wild! Whatever your desire, Toytropolis has much to offer. Some of the well known brands include Brio, Playmobil, Educational Insights, Parent's Magazine Developmental Toys and Ravensburger. Free gift wrapping, children's activities, and special events are also just a few of the unique features you'll find at Toytropolis.

■ COSTCO
(206) 622-1144
4401 4th St.
Seattle, WA 98105

(253) 874-0878
35100 Enchanted Pkwy.
Federal Way, WA 98023

(425) 828-6767
8629 120th N.E.
Kirkland, WA 98034

(425) 542-0494
Aurora Village
Hwy 99 & 205th N.E.
Edmonds, WA 98020

❧ *Call ahead to confirm hours and locations.*

DEPARTMENT/DISCOUNT

■ COSTCO . . .

(206) 575-3311
1160 Saxon Dr.
Tukwila, WA 98188

(425) 313-0964
1801 10th Ave. N.W.
Issaquah, WA 98027

Hours: M-F   11:00 a.m.-8:30 p.m.
       Sat.   9:30 a.m.-6:00 p.m.
       Sun.   10:00 a.m.-5:00 p.m.

This membership-only store is an excellent place to find bargains. Unfortunately, however, it does not always carry the same brands and so you never know what you'll find from one visit to the next. You also cannot depend on any sales help in making your baby product purchases. Costco usually does carry Huggies diapers in large packages of 160 in size medium and 120 in the large size. Also, Baby Fresh diaper wipes are often in stock. Products such as strollers and car seats usually can be found but the selection is limited to a few brands, including Baby Trend, Emmaljunga, Century and Gerry. There is also a good selection of clothing that includes the locally-made Cotton Caboodle, Osh Kosh b'Gosh, and Carter plush. Books are always a great bargain here. This section includes tape cassettes, and at times, crayons, paints, and markers. The toys are sometimes plentiful, especially during the summer and winter holiday seasons, but again, it is hit and miss.

Costco prices often beat any items you may find on sale at other stores. Check into a membership.

■ FRED MEYER

(253) 931-5550
801 Auburn Way N.
Auburn, WA 98002

(425) 865-8560
2041 148th N.E.
Bellevue, WA 98007

(206) 433-6411
14300 1st Ave. S.
Burien, WA 98168

(425) 348-8400
8530 Evergreen Way
Everett, WA 98208

(253) 952-0100
33702 21st Ave. S.W.
Federal Way, WA 98023

(253) 859-5500
10201 S.E. 240th
Kent, WA 98031

(425) 820-3200
12221 120th Ave. N.E.
Kirkland, WA 98034

(425) 670-0200
4615-A 196th S.W.
Lynnwood, WA 98036

(253) 840-8150
1100 N. Meridian St.
Puyallup, WA 98371

(425) 235-5350
17801 108th Ave. S.E.
Renton, WA 98055

(206) 328-6920
417 Broadway E.
Seattle, WA 98102

(206) 784-9600
100 N.W. 85th (Greenwood)
Seattle, WA 98117

ᨮ *Call ahead to confirm hours and locations.*

(206) 546-0720
18325 Aurora Ave. N.
Seattle, WA 98133

(206) 440-2400
13000 Lake City Way N.E.
Seattle, WA 98125
Hours: Most stores,
       M-Sun.   7:00 a.m.-11:00 p.m.
Fred Meyer is the local leader in "one-stop" shopping, since nearly all of their stores include a full grocery store. Fred Meyer have a full line of baby products, including furniture, strollers, car seats, swings, monitors, toys, books, and safety items. The infants' and children's clothing departments offer a good variety of affordable choices, from brand names like Gerber Babies to their own line, Fred Bear. Many of the larger stores also have a maternity department with a selection of apparel for expecting moms.

     Fred Meyer discounts prices in all of their departments and has frequent sales and temporary price reductions. While it's certainly possible to find an individual item at a lower price somewhere else in town, it's unlikely that you'll find such a range of choices and overall low prices at any other single store.

     Besides basic groceries, Fred Meyer was one of the first local grocery chains to offer a natural foods section—a trend that many other stores have followed. Seven of the stores—Auburn, Bellevue, Federal Way, Lynnwood, Puyallup, and both Renton—have a family-friendly feature called "Freddy's Playland." It's an in-store play area where you can drop off your preschoolers (2- to 6-year-olds) for up to one hour while you shop. There's no charge for this service and safety and health rules are strictly en-

forced. Parents and their kids get numbered ID bracelets and parents also get a pager so they can be contacted if needed.

■ KMART
(425) 228-5840
440 Rainier Ave. S.
Renton, WA 98055

(425) 747-4300
15015 Main St.
Bellevue, WA 98007

(425) 774-7726
22511 Hwy. 99
Edmonds, WA 98020

(425) 353-8103
8102 Evergreen Way
Everett, WA 98203

(253) 852-9071
24800 West Valley Hwy.
Kent, WA 98032

(206) 767-7004
7345 Delridge Way S.
Seattle, WA 98106

(206) 363-6319
13200 Aurora N.
Seattle, WA 98133
Hours: Daily   8:00 a.m.-9:00 p.m.
K-Mart is among the lowest priced local stores for maternity and infant wear. The maternity section has a few fashionable outfits (the New Edition line) under $20 with most tops and pants available for under $10. Nursing bras and maternity underwear are located in this section and priced at $6 each. Depending on which store you visit, the merchandise and store appearance differs.

     Infant attire ranges in price from $3 to $8. K-Mart has a nice selection of infant clothing and offers a large section containing bottles, rattles, bibs, cotton diapers, blankets and comforters.

The baby product selection equals that of other discount stores and is very well-priced. Evenflo, Fisher Price, Graco and Gerry were a few of the brands in stock. A Jenny Lind crib can be purchased for about $100 and many other popular products are available at close to the lowest prices in town.

■ LAMONTS

(425) 771-6497
3100 184th St. S.W.
Lynnwood, WA 98037
Hours: M-Sat.   9:30 a.m.-9:30 p.m.
      Sun.   11:00 a.m.-6:00 p.m.

(425) 644-2941
15600 N.E. 8th
Bellevue, WA 98008
Hours: M-Sat.   10:00 a.m.-9:00 p.m.
      Sun.   11:00 a.m-6:00 p.m.

(206) 433-0676
460 S.W. 152nd
Burien, WA 98166
Hours: M-Sat.   10:00 a.m.-9:00 p.m.
      Sun.   11:00 a.m.-5:00 p.m.

(425) 644-2921
4001 Factoria Square Mall
Bellevue, WA 98006
Hours: M-Sat.   10:00 a.m.-9:00 p.m.
      Sun.   11:00 a.m.-6:00 p.m.

(425) 367-7716
Lake Forest Park
17171 Bothell Way N.E.
Seattle, WA 98155
Hours: M-Sat.   10:00 a.m.-9:00 p.m.
      Sun.   11:00 a.m.-5:00 p.m.

(206) 367-7690
900 Northgate Plaza
Seattle, WA 98125
Hours: M-Sat.   9:30 a.m.-9:30 p.m.
      Sun.   11:00 a.m.-6:00 p.m.

(253) 839-8950
2001 S. 320th
Federal Way, WA 98003
Hours: M-Sat.   10:00 a.m.-9:00 p.m.
      Sun.   11:00 a.m.-5:00 p.m.

(425) 821-7788
12601 120th N.E.
Kirkland, WA 98034
Hours: M-Sat.   10:00 a.m.-9:00 p.m.
      Sun.   11:00 a.m.-6:00 p.m.

(206) 938-4116
2600 S.W. Barton
Seattle, WA 98126
Hours: M-Sat.   10:00 a.m.-9:00 p.m.
      Sun.   11:00 a.m.-5:00 p.m.

(425) 557-6550
775 N.W. Gilman Blvd.
Issaquah, WA 98027
Hours: M-Sat.   10:00 a.m.-9:00 p.m.
      Sun.   11:00 a.m.-6:00 p.m.

Lamonts offers one of the nicest and most affordable selections of children's clothing around. During several visits, I took advantage of sale items on infants' wear. When on sale, basic clothing such as leggings and T-shirts are about as affordable as anywhere else in the city. They carry name brands such as Hush Puppies, OshKosh b'Gosh and Carter's. In fact, they offer a huge display of Carter's wear that includes T-shirts, sleep wear and blankets. This is a good place to shop for babies and children as it offers everything from play clothes to dress wear and the prices are great. Lamonts also offers a small selection of Carter's preemie wear starting at $10.

■ **MARSHALL'S DEPARTMENT STORES**
(206) 575-0141
17900 Southcenter Pkwy, Ste. 154
Tukwila, WA 98188

(206) 367-8520
15801 Westminister Way N.
Seattle, WA 98155

(425) 771-6045
3205 Alderwood Mall Blvd.
Lynnwood, WA 98036

(425) 644-2429
2150 148th Ave. N.E.
Redmond, WA 98052-5534
Hours: M-Sat.   10:00 a.m.-9:00 p.m.
　　　　Sun.   11:00 a.m.-6:00 p.m.
Marshall's infant/toddler section is well-marked with signs which are easily noticeable. Although the selection is limited, the prices are excellent. You will find many name brands that elsewhere may cost at least 20% more. Marshall's also has a small maternity clothing selection. You can count on a bargain when shopping at Marshall's.

■ **MERVYN'S**
(253) 941-8800
2201 S. 320th
Federal Way, WA 98003

(425) 672-7765
3301 184th S.W.
Lynnwood, WA 98037

(425) 643-6554
4126 124th S.E.
Bellevue, WA 98006

(206) 439-1919
1100 Southcenter Shopping Center
Tukwila, WA 98188

☙ *Call ahead to confirm hours and locations.*

(425) 558-9500
17601 N.E. Union Hill Road
Redmond, WA 98052
Hours: M-F   10:00 a.m.-9:30 p.m.
　　　　Sat.   9:00 a.m.-9:30 p.m.
　　　　Sun.   10:00 a.m.-7:00 p.m.
Mervyn's is famous for its baby clothing sales. When a sale pops up, people line up outside the store's doors because of the quality of the merchandise that is discounted. OshKosh b'Gosh and Sprockets are just two of the lines Mervyn's carries. The Sprockets line is great for the necessary T-shirts, onesies, and jumpers. You can buy clothing at Mervyn's from $8 on up. The infant department also has crib coordinates, layette items, stuffed animals and infant shoes.

■ **NORDSTROM**
(206) 628-2111
1501 5th
Seattle, WA 98101
Hours: M-Sat.   9:30 a.m.-8:00 p.m.
　　　　Sun.   11:00 a.m.-6:00 p.m.

(206) 246-0400
Southcenter Shopping Center

(206) 364-8800
Northgate Mall

(425) 455-5800
Bellevue Square

(425) 771-5755
Alderwood Mall
At Nordstrom, service and presentation are as close to perfection as you can find in a large department store. Seattle natives know the excellent reputation Nordstrom has built and maintained. The children's department is no exception. The selection is ample and the

DEPARTMENT/DISCOUNT

quality very good. Nordstrom offers its own lines—Basically Nordstrom and Baby N Hand (along with other name brands.) It also offers everything from custom bedding to outerwear to toys. Voted by Seattle's Child as the best place to buy shoes, you'll find a wide array of styles in your favorite brands that should last, at competitive prices. I found Nordstrom a favorite place for special gift items. And, prices may surprise you. Even the most budget-conscious person can find something in their price range, such as soft and comfortable footed pajamas for only $9. Employees do a nice job of gift-wrapping at no extra cost, which is great when you're shopping for presents. A Seattle favorite, Nordstrom is a wonderful place to shop!

■ JC PENNEY CO., INC.

(425) 771-9555
18601 33rd Ave. W.
Lynnwood, WA 98037
Hours: M-Sat.   10:00 a.m.-9:30 p.m.
        Sun.   11:00 a.m.-6:00 p.m.

(425) 454-8599
Bellevue Square

(206) 361-2500
Northgate Mall

(206) 246-0850
Southcenter Shopping Center

(253) 852-3260
403 W. Meeker
Kent, WA 98031
Hours: M-F   10:00 a.m.-8:00 p.m.
        Sat.   10:00 a.m.-6:00 p.m.
        Sun.   11:00 a.m.-5:00 p.m.

Penney's has a nice selection of maternity and children's wear. Mid-priced maternity clothes are available with casual jumpers starting at $36 and career

dresses starting at $64. They also have name-brand jeans and other casual attire that start at $20. For summer, they carry several cute floral outfits and Cherokee-brand relaxing wear. In the fall, the store offers corduroy jumpers. Penney's also has its own line called Maternity Dividends. The maternity section has the basics and then some.

The infants' and toddlers' area features clothing, baby products, and gifts. The clothing includes name brands such as Sesame Street and Carter's, as well as Penney's own line, Toddletime. A few preemie and christening outfits are also offered. Books, toys, and stuffed animals can also be found in this department. Penny's offers a gift registry as well as their extensive catalog.

■ ROSS DRESS FOR LESS

(206) 575-0110
17672 Southcenter Pkwy.
Tukwila, WA 98188

(425) 644-2433
14327 N.E. 20th
Bellevue, WA 98007

(253) 941-2122
32075 Pacific Hwy S.
Federal Way, WA 98003

(206) 367-6030
13201-B Aurora Ave. N.
Seattle, WA 98133

(206) 623-6781
1418 3rd Ave.
Seattle, WA 98101

(425) 313-9616
975 N.E. Gilman Blvd. #D
Issaquah, WA 98027
Hours: M-Sat.   9:30 a.m.-9:00 p.m.
        Sun.   11:00 a.m.-6:00 p.m.

Ross carries brand-name clothing for a very reasonable price. You can find OshKosh b'Gosh, Levi's, Carter's and more at discounted prices. Girls' dresses can be found for under $10 and overalls are sold for about $15. The store also carries diaper bags, a few baby items, and infants' and children's shoes. Ross is one of the easier discount stores to shop at because each department is very organized and clearly labeled. Some Ross stores also carry a few reduced-priced maternity items.

■ T.J. MAXX
(206) 363-9511
11029 Roosevelt Way N.E.
Seattle, WA 98125

(253) 946-2887
1910 S. 320th
Federal Way, WA 98063
Hours: M-Sat.　9:30 a.m.-9:30 p.m.
　　　　Sun.　11:00 a.m.-7:00 p.m.
T.J. Maxx is a brand name discount store that offers an infants' and children's department located toward the back of the store. Prices here are very good, although their selection is limited to stock on hand. This is a good place to shop when you have the time to go through the racks. It is also the kind of store you'll want to visit frequently, since the merchandise is always changing. Sock bins have great, durable OshKosh b'Gosh socks for at least half price.

■ TARGET
(425) 670-1435
18305 Alderwood Mall Blvd.
Lynnwood, WA 98036

(206) 575-0682
301 S. Strander Blvd.
Tukwila, WA 98188
(206) 932-1153
2800 S.W. Barton
Seattle, WA 98126

(425) 562-0830
4053 Factoria Square Mall S.E.
Bellevue, WA 98006

(425) 353-3167
405 S.E. Everett Mall Way
Everett, WA 98208

(253) 850-9710
26301 104th Ave. S.E.
Kent, WA 98031

(425) 556-9533
17700 N.E. 76th St.
Redmond, WA 98052

(425) 392-3357
755 N.W. Gilman Blvd.
Issaquah, WA 98027
Hours: M-Sun.　8:00 a.m.-10:00 p.m.
A wide array of infants' and children's clothing and maternity wear await you at Target. In addition, you'll find a nice selection of baby products. As a discount store, Target's prices are reasonable, and the quality is good. Target carries a nice selection of casual maternity wear, focussing on big shirts and stretch pants. Most shirts are under $12 and you could put together an outfit for close to $20.

　　Target's baby department has an abundance of layette items, most between $3 and $14. Target also carries a large selection of bottles, rattles, cups

DEPARTMENT/DISCOUNT

and other baby necessities. The store has socks, shoes, tights, and booties as well. Prices on disposable diapers, wipes, and formula are close to the best in town. Cloth diapers, wraps and plastic pants are also available. Parenting and children's books are discounted by 10%.

Parents-to-be who register for Targets computerized gift registry are given a bar-code scanning tool so they can scan in to their wish list any items they need.

Target's mid-sized baby product department includes items by Fisher Price, Gerry, Cosco, Graco, Evenflo, Playskool, and Little Tikes. Most swings, strollers, cribs, and walkers are on overhead shelves, making it difficult to test them. Overall, Target has much to offer in quality, selection, and price.

🐾

CHILDREN'S CLOTHING STORES

■ BOSTON STREET BABY STORE
(206) 366-9802
Northgate Mall/Outlet

(206) 634-0580
Wallingford Center
1815 N. 45th
Seattle, WA 98103
Hours: M-F   10:00 a.m.-8:00 p.m.
       Sat.   9:30 a.m.-6:00 p.m.
       Sun.   10:00 a.m.-5:00 p.m.

(425) 895-0848
Redmond Town Center
Cash, Checks, Visa, MC, AmEx
Two new locations! Whether it's clothing, accessories, bedding, or toys you're looking for, you're guaranteed to find

some of the most dazzling choices here. Items range from affordable and casual, such as the always-popular Cotton Caboodle line which runs from $5 and up, to dressy designer styles. Sizes range from preemie to 14 and there's a good representation of local designers' works, such as the Juliani Children's Wear line. One of the most colorful and intriguing lines I noticed was Buddha Baby's ethnically-inspired clothes costing $25 and up. Besides clothes, Boston Street also carries strollers (Perego and Emmaljunga), baby slings, lots of hats and other accessories, and locally-made (gift quality) baby quilts. The Northgate location sells last season's clothes starting at $3.

■ BRAT PACK
(425) 883-1006
Redmond Town Center
Cash, Checks, Visa, MC, AmEx
The Brat Pack store has an excellent selection of baby products and children's clothes. A wide variety of apparel includes styles by Esprit, Le Top, Sweet Potatoes, Just Kidd'n, and Heartstrings. With so many different brands, there's plenty of play clothes and dressy clothes to choose from. Sizes go from preemie to 10, and prices are moderate to upscale, with a typical baby outfit starting at about $20. Additional items include hats, backpacks, slippers, stuffed animals, toys, cups, frames, lamps, baby supplies and gifts. The staff is very helpful.

■ COTTON CABOODLE
(206) 282-2701
203 W. Thomas
Seattle, WA 98119
Hours: T-Sat.   10:00 a.m.-4:00 p.m.
Cash, Checks, Visa, MC

This is the place to shop if you're a Cotton Caboodle fan looking for a bargain. Located on lower Queen Anne next to the Cotton Caboodle factory, the outlet store sells overstocks far below retail price. On one visit, there was a full rack of half-off items, as well as a container of dresses marked down to $3 and $5, and shorts for $2.50. A cute collar dress was $17 and jumpers were marked down to $8.50. Although merchandise changes seasonally, you'll always find plenty of the basics—knit shirts, pants, tops, bloomers, and jumpers.

■ THE DISNEY STORE

(206) 622-3323
Westlake Center
400 Pine St. #238

(206) 241-8922
Southcenter Shopping Center

(425) 744-9855
Alderwood Mall

(425) 451-0540
Bellevue Square

(206) 368-2656
Northgate Mall

The Disney Store is a fun place to shop, like a little taste of Disneyland right in your own backyard. The window displays are fun and attractive and movie screens show favorite Disney shows while you shop. Children love to go here, which is both good and bad! The store sells clothing items, all depicting some Disney character or scene, and a large selection of gift items and Disney memorabilia. Everything from Dalmatian pencils to Mickey Mouse ties can be found. T-shirts start at $12 and pajamas at around $20. All major credit cards, cash and checks are accepted.

■ FLEECE FARM

(425) 392-5369
(800) 776-5319 phone orders only
3020 Issaquah Pine Lake Rd. #91
Issaquah, WA 98029
Hours: Daily   9:00 a.m.-5:00 p.m.
Cash, Checks, Visa, MC

Good news for all: Fleece Farm has made history by reducing prices! The owners are committed to high quality at the lowest possible prices and they really mean it. Fleece Farm is a local mail order company that sells a full line of colorful and comfortable 100% cotton clothing for kids and moms in 12 colors. Besides mail order, they also do home parties. Their clothing has different screen print designs which can be placed on T-shirts, sweat shirts, dresses and more. The designs are high quality, with such names as Cats 'n' Hats, Horse Haven, Ballet Class, and Polar Bear Nites—29 designs total in the spring/summer catalog. Especially for newborn babies are the "baby sac" style, with hood, long sleeves, and drawstrings at the bottom; it costs $21.95, and a bubble style jersey playsuit for $23.95. Fleece Farm's designs are available in infant sizes all the way up through adults' extra-large, making these great for matching family outfits. If you are looking for high quality leggings this is your final destination. Twelve colors of leggings all are 100% cotton, from infant sizes at $10.50 through size 14/16 for $12.95.

The catalog is interspersed with advice and information on cotton care, and explains that the reason many of the items are on white cotton is so they can be bleached. Especially helpful is the fact that bleaching won't damage the colorful screen-printed designs.

CHILDREN'S STORES

■ FORGET-ME-NOT

(425) 774-0889
514 5th Ave.
Edmonds, WA 98020
Hours: Tu-Sat. 10:00 a.m.-6:00 p.m.
      Sun.   Noon-5:00 p.m.
Cash, Checks, Visa, MC, AmEx
Forget-Me-Not is a delightful store that carries a bright and lively selection of clothing. Play clothes, dresses and accessories are attractively displayed. What makes this store unique is their assortment of collectibles—antique toys, prams, sleds, and children's furniture are attractively displayed throughout the store. Forget Me Not now only sells retail, and is the largest volume retailer of Cow and Lizard. An assortment of handmade and hand painted baby and children's furniture is available that is really quite lovely. Changing tables, chairs and picture frames are among the items that are made by the store's owners. You can choose the theme and colors, and soon have an heirloom quality piece of furniture to begin handing down!

■ GAP KIDS

While most Seattle area malls have a Gap store, Gap Kids are not at all locations. All major credit cards, cash and checks are accepted.

(425) 776-8214
Alderwood Mall

(206) 246-9934
Southcenter Shopping Center

(206) 365-7445
Northgate Mall

(206) 625-1470
Westlake Center

(206) 624-8554
Downtown Westlake Center

(206) 525-2146
University Village Mall

(425) 454-1539
Bellevue Square
The Gap means clean and streamlined clothing for all ages. It is hard to pick the best thing about Gap clothes: styles, price, durability? Gap Kids carries infant and toddler clothing that matches or at least is similar to the stylish adult looks in the regular Gap including jeans, jean jackets, button-down shirts, and t-shirts. The style is comfortable and looks great on kids. Belts, socks, shoes and hair accessories are available to finish off the outfit. Gap sale racks are addictive as prices start at ninety-nine cents!

■ GYMBOREE

(425) 450-9460
Bellevue Square

(425) 771-4558
Alderwood Mall

(206) 366-0133
Northgate Mall

(425) 558-7832
Redmond Town Center

(206) 246-8997
Southcenter Shopping Center
Cash, Checks, Visa, MC, AmEx
Gymboree is a franchise that carries its own label. The styles are simple and comfortable. Most of the clothing is 100% cotton. Gymboree has its own style of mix-and-match clothing utilizing both primary colors and pastels. Sale items are in the back of the store and you'll find bargains here: 25% to 50% percent off, this area is well worth keeping an eye on as you can often buy new Gymboree cheaper than in many of the

resale shops! This is a very well made brand and every kid looks cute in the wild patterns. Some toy items and Gymboree videotapes are also sold here. The sales staff is friendly and helpful, often willing to blow bubbles to amuse your child while you are shopping. You can expect to spend about $14 for leggings and $20 for a sweatshirt.

■ INFANT OUTFITTERS

(206) 283-8042 or (800) OUTFITS
535 W. McGraw
Seattle, WA 98119
Hours: M-Sat.   10:00 a.m.-6:00 p.m.
Cash, Checks, Visa, MC

Gwen Evans started her Infant Outfitters line of baby and toddler clothes in 1984 when her first child was born, and her business has continued to grow since then. Now with a nationwide following, the line is also sold locally at several children's boutiques. The popular playclothes, newborn to size 4, are available in 20-plus different designs and lots of stunning and playful fabrics. Prices for the reversible and nonreversible items start at around $6.95 for a hat and $14.95 for a shirt.

At the retail design studio on Queen Anne, you can come in and personally select fabrics and styles to have custom made, or you can choose from the many one-of-a-kind items available on the racks. There's plenty to choose from, not only in the infant/toddler line, but for older children too. Gwen for Kids features girls sizes 4-10 and unisex clothing to age 10 as well. The girls line features dramatic, yet practical dresses, skirts, vests, jumpers, leggings, and hats for girls ages 2-10. Unusual fabrics, top-quality materials (cotton and washable silk) and fun dress-up styles make this a popular line. Prices range from $20-$80 for most items.

The unisex clothing line offers casual, loose-fitting playclothes to mix and match. Fabrics include chambray and plaids, denims, and plaid flannels. Prices in this line range from $15-$40. Considering that everything is hand-sewn, these are extremely affordable prices. If you can't visit the studio or want to share these great designs with friends and families out of town, call to request a catalog and/or the Infant Outfitters newsletter to keep up with the latest happenings. Gwen will even send you drawings and fabric swatches and work with you to create a special outfit for your child.

■ THE JOY OF CHILDREN

(206) 933-1506
7011 California Ave. S.W.
Seattle, WA 98126
Hours: M-Sat.   9:00 a.m.-6:00 p.m.
Cash, Checks, Visa, MC, Disc, AmEx

This West Seattle store carries new clothing in popular lines, including Le Top, Wee Clancy, Poco Poco, Maddie Jane, Allison Ann, JoLene, After the Stork, Samara, Curious George by Loo Na, Golden Rainbow, and New Potatoes. The styles are great—classic with wonderful matching accessories. The store has two walls of clean and stylish consignment clothes and other consigned items. We found an $18 Gap Kids hat for just $4. Merchandise ranges from casual to very fancy, and includes quilts, swings, rocking horses, videos and tapes, and Boppy nursing pillows. Several hand painted, wooden rocking horse zebras were being sold here for $200 and up, and were pronounced "very cool" by one of our researchers!

■ **JULIANI CHILDREN'S WEAR**
(206) 783-8972
Hours: Call for a studio appointment.
This is one of the most popular Northwestern children's clothing designers. Grasa Adler sells her handcrafted children's clothing at several local and national clothing stores, and at arts and crafts fairs. She uses incredibly colorful fabrics with wonderful patterns for kids, including beach scenes, fish, dolphins, jungle animals, cowboys, farm scenes, celestial designs, and a darling kitten pattern. My personal favorite is a striking sunflower fabric. Her designs are unique and reflect her Brazilian heritage. A swingy collar dress with a scalloped hem is a good example of that influence. Other items include reversible rompers, jumpers, hats, pants, shirts, dresses, and T-shirts with fabric insets that match other separates. Prices are moderate, considering the amount of labor and care that go into handcrafted work like this. Grasa has a high level of creativity and skill; one boutique store manager noted that for sewing quality, her garments are some of the best handcrafted ones available. Because this is basically a one-woman operation, Grasa schedules personal appointments in advance. There's usually lots of merchandise to select from in sizes newborn to 6 and of course she'll take custom orders as well.

■ **KIDGEAR**
(206) 624-0756
1420 5th Ave., Ste. 219
Seattle, WA 98101
Hours: M-Sat.   10:00 a.m.-6:00 p.m.
        Sun.   Noon-5:00 p.m.
Cash, Checks, Visa, MC
Although you'll see some recognizable brands like Flapdoodles and Baby Guess, KidGear's emphasis is on original clothes by individual designers. KidGear's focus is to provide customers with clothing and accessories that are high quality and stylish, very unique, yet functional and lasting. The clothing is attractively displayed with coordinating accessories, so you can easily put together a complete outfit for your little one. Sizes range from newborn to 14. Prices are mid-priced to upscale, although it's usually easy to find an outfit on sale for less than $25. Besides offering many choices in both play and dress-up clothes, the infants and toddlers department has a good selection of baby toys, accessories, parenting and baby books. They carry furniture too—the line of custom made wood items includes a children's table and chair set, rocking horse, toy trunk, and doll beds and chairs. You can also find the Emmaljunga stroller line at KidGear and as a major dealer for the line, they have items in-stock and available for purchase (some stores require special orders). One of the most unique and practical items at KidGear is the Sit 'n' Stroll, a combination car seat and stroller for children newborn to 3 years old. Priced at $149, it's FAA approved for use on airplanes, and is very easy to change from seat to stroller and back again. KidGear also operates a factory outlet, with most items sold below or at

wholesale price. They carry sizes newborn-7. KidGear is located on the second floor of the City Centre Building (across from the Sheraton downtown). Unique is the best word to describe this store; you'll find things here that you won't find in any other children's store in the Seattle area. The outlet center (Mimi Rose) is located in a residential neighborhood in Seattle's northend. Call (206) 361-4675 for directions.

■ KID'S COTTAGE
(425) 481-2106
13300 N.E. 175th St., Ste. 1
Woodinville, WA 98072
Hours: M-Sat.   10:00 a.m.-5:00 p.m.
Cash, Checks, Visa, MC, AmEx
As you first enter the store, you'll see clothes and quite a few accessories for babies, including lots of rattles, toys, stuffed animals, dolls, and bibs. There's a nice selection of new clothes, with brands like Sweet Potatoes and Little Me. Pajamas by Skivvy Doodle that are 100% cotton are the current fastest moving item. Prices are moderate for these lines—infant sleepers and play outfits start in the $20 range. The size range is considerable too—newborn to 14 (girls) and to 16 (boys). The store offers complimentary gift wrap and the staff is friendly and helpful.

■ KINDER BRITCHES
(425) 778-7600
422 Main St.
Edmonds, WA 98020
Hours: M-F   10:00 a.m.-6:00 p.m.
       Sat.   10:00 a.m.-5:30 p.m.
       Sun.   Noon-4:00 p.m.
Cash, Checks, Visa, MC, AmEx
Located downtown at the fountain, Kinder Britches offers a full range of children's wear and accessories. Sizes range from preemie to 8 (boys) and 14 (girls). They have a good mix of both casual and dressy clothes. Unique and fun specialty lines mingle with quality basics such as Esprit and Guess, and some of the dressier lines include Biscotti, Allison Rose, and Tailfeathers for girls and Kitestrings and Golden Rainbow for boys. They offer a full line of specialty preemie clothes by Preemie Yums, in all natural cotton, with tops starting at $6 and sets for $20. Preemie items can be ordered for next day delivery if what you need is not in stock. All-cotton layettes, hand-smocked booties and bonnets, and a fine selection of christening outfits priced from $45 to $85 are also stocked. Kinder Britches is a registered dealer of the Baby Jogger stroller and has them priced competitively. Toys, fanny packs and backpack diaper bags, Lamby Nursery lambskins, fun hats, a great play area for kids, customer service, and free gift wrap are also offered. Baby gifts, crib blankets, comforters, and other gift items and accessories are also available.

■ LIL' PEOPLE
(425) 455-4967
Bellevue Square

(206) 623-4463
Westlake Center
Cash, Checks, Visa, MC
"Cozy cotton artwear" is what Lil' People's business card says, and that's certainly reflected in the fun variety of colorful clothes offered here. The store carries its own line of prewashed, garment-dyed knits in a wide selection of colors. They also feature original prints and designs by their own artists. Besides their own line, Lil' People carries com-

CHILDREN'S STORES

fortable cotton knits by Flaphappy and dresses by Mousefeathers. Other choices include jumpers, pants, vests and stylish tops by Echo Field, Rumbletumble, Warm Heart, Infant Outfitters, and Just Kidd'n. The accessories selection is astounding, with a great assortment of socks, hats, jewelry, suspenders, ties, hairbows, wrist rattles, and more. The "artwear" influence is definitely reflected in these accessories, as well as in special items like the corduroy TV booties with kitty faces (just $7 a pair). Dinosaur water bottles are sure to be a hit with the toddler/preschool set, as will the many stuffed animals and other toys.

■ OILILY
(425) 688-0663
Bellevue Square Mall
Cash, Checks, Visa, MC, Disc, AmEx
The coolest of the cool kids wear Oilily clothes. Of course coolness comes with a price tag. This is a brand that advertises in *Vogue* magazine, so keep in mind "this ain't grunge"! Sales can bring pieces to a reasonable level. This is my favorite "if I win the lottery" store.

■ THE ORIGINAL CHILDREN'S SHOP
(206) 328-7121
4114 E. Madison
Seattle, WA 98112
Hours: M-F   10:00 a.m.-5:30 p.m.
         Sat.   10:00 a.m.-5:00 p.m.
Cash, Checks, Visa, MC
Located in the Madison Park area, Original Children's Shop is a well-stocked children's boutique. They carry lots of cute styles from popular brands like LeTop, Echo Fields, Bambine Penguini, Little Me, Just Ducky, Patsy Aiken, and

Julian's. There's a big selection of Flaphappy hats for $10, and affordable knit tops by Zutano Baby. The store carries preemie sizes and christening gowns too. Most lines are priced at 10% less than retail. Besides clothing, the shop has a full assortment of baby accessories, including infant headrests by Nojo, cute and comfy Padders baby shoes, toys, diaper bags, soft books, and soft sculpture toys that we haven't seen in other stores.

■ OSH KOSH OUTLET
Factory Stores of America
Outlet Center
(425) 831-5688
North Bend, WA
Osh Kosh is one of the brands favored by parents across the country for it's attractive styles and pass me down durability. At the North Bend outlet there is a huge, I repeat—huge, selection of boys and girls Osh Kosh and Baby B'gosh in sizes newborn through 14. You can find both first run and irregulars at 1/3 or more off of retail prices. The sale racks are filled with even bigger bargains if you like to stock up. The selections run about a season behind, which means that since department stores get shipments just prior to a season (ex: fall clothes in August) you can always get season appropriate clothing.

■ REMOND
(360) 384-0446 or 800-426-9244
6105 Portal Way (at Newkirk)
Ferndale, WA 98248
Web site: www.r4babies.com
Hours: M-Sat.   9:00 a.m.-5:00 p.m.
Cash, Checks, Visa, MC
Remond is made in France and apparently the French have a passion for high

quality, gorgeous children's products! You can find everything from silver sets to pacifiers, diapers, natural brushes, bibs and preemie clothes here! Call for the free catalog/new parent book. Remond is located off I-5 (take exit 263).

■ **RISING STARS** [Baby Pages]
(206) 781-0138
7404 Greenwood Ave. N.
Seattle, WA 98103
Hours: M-Sat. 9:30 a.m.-9:00 p.m.
        Sun. 11:00 a.m.-6:00 p.m.
Cash, Checks, Visa, MC, Discover
I love this store! If there is one place that you check out based on this book's advice, let this be it. Rising Stars features

local and Northwest artists/designers and the prices cannot be beat. When I went here with my mother, we went nuts. We saw a two-piece brand-new fall outfit by a local designer for $20. This outfit was comparable to a $40 outfit at an upscale department store. We saw at least 100 hats in the store—all sizes, all styles, all cute. We got my husband a copy of his childhood-favorite Mike Mulligan book. There were chunks of tree that were carved so you could pop them open into mini castles! Magical make believe lives here, not only in the toy selection but in the playroom, which is an indoor tree house! In fact the whole store is "tree lined." There is a section of balms, candles

PREEMIE CLOTHING

One of the most difficult tasks for a parent is coping with the aftereffects of having a premature baby. The hospital, doctors and medications all take their toll. Just as you want to hold and comfort your baby the most, you are told he needs his rest and you can look but not touch. Newborn-sized clothing that seemed so small and tiny before your baby was born now seems like it will never fit. The following stores carry a dedicated selection of preemie clothing or goods. You may wish to call ahead to ask about items currently in stock.

- Baby Depot in the Burlington Coat Factory
- Baby Gap
- Boston Street
- Carter's Outlet Stores
- JC Penney
- Kids Club
- Kinder Britches
- Lamonts
- Merry Go Round Baby News
- Nordstrom
- The Original Children's Shop
- The Tree House

Other ideas:

- **Mothers of Multiples chapters in Eastside, Northend.** Each chapter has twice yearly rummage sales that are advertised in the local parenting newspapers. You can pick up not only preemie clothes but clothes of all sizes, as well as toys and other baby equipment at very reasonable prices!
- **Parents of Prematures Clothing Committee.** Preemie sized clothing is available on a loan basis. This support group also has many other services. Call for information: (206) 363-5934.

and aromatherapy-type stuff for weary parents, as well as an artisan jewelry display. Be sure to look at the book that has bios of all of the Northwesterners whose wares are for sale here. Also, this is the spot to order ceramics by Kim. Her plates and bowls are individually painted with your child's name and other info. Handprints are made at various times during the year as well.

■ THE SHOE ZOO
(206) 525-2770
University Village Mall

(425) 558-4743
Redmond Town Center

(425) 392-8211
240 N.W. Gilman Blvd.
Issaquah, WA 98027
Hours: M-Sat.   10:00 a.m.-6:00 p.m.
　　　　Sun.   Noon-5:00 p.m.
Cash, Checks, Visa, MC, AmEx
If Mommy wears Doc Martens, now baby can too! The Zoo carries three or four styles of kid-sized Docs starting at about $41. The Shoe Zoo is conveniently located across from Kids Club in University Village Mall for Seattle shop-

pers and at Gilman Station (under the clock tower) in Issaquah for Eastsiders. They carry a large selection of shoes for infants to pre-teens, with brands such as Stride Rite, Toddler University, Keds, and Nike. They offer a great selection for any occasion. Regularly priced shoes will cost about $35 to $45. And, if you buy at least one pair of regularly priced shoes a year, you will receive a 15% discount on your child's birthday. The Shoe Zoo is well equipped with accessory items such as socks, backpacks, slippers and hats. You'll find great service at this store which makes it a fun shopping experience for kids and parents.

■ SMALL FRY
(206) 283-4556
3209 W. McGraw
Seattle, WA 98199
Hours: M　　　10:00 a.m.-5:00 p.m.
　　　　T-F　　10:00 a.m.-6:00 p.m.
　　　　Sat.　　10:00 a.m.-5:00 p.m.
　　　　Most Sun. Noon-4:00 p.m.
Cash, Checks, Visa, MC, AmEx
This Magnolia children's shop has a distinctly neighborhood feel, offering personalized service and an excellent se-

---

SPECIAL GIFTS FOR LITTLE ANGELS

If you love angels, you'll love The Angel Store. This store sells "everything angel" and what better way to welcome a new little one into the world than giving him or her their own little angel? What I found of particular interest here were the heart-shaped handpainted porcelain boxes with gold angels on top for the tooth fairy at $12.50, the fairy godmother tie tack/pins for $4.95 and little angel necklaces for $7.95. There is a supply of cards at the cash register that you can slip on to any angel gift that says "a Guardian Angel for your new baby boy/girl." Nice! The Angel Store is located at Old Milltown Mall, 201 5th S., Edmonds, WA 98020, phone (425) 778-5600. Hours are Monday-Saturday 10:00 a.m.-6:00 p.m., and Sundays until 5:00.

lection of apparel, accessories, and gift items. They carry popular children's lines, including Flaphappy, Cotton Caboodle, Zutano. There's always a full selection of darling dresses by Wee Clancy and 100% cotton apparel by Sara's Prints from the layette to size 16. Clothing sizes run from infant to 14. Shoes in infant sizes are available, and larger sizes are often offered in seasonal items like sandals and boots. Small Fry has a good selection of picture frames and dresser decorations, and also carries a line of Beatrix Potter items. There's lots of toys, accessories (plenty of hats!), and unique gift possibilities. Some cute and comfy leather baby booties, lined with flannel, were just $17.95 and would certainly be a treasured baby gift. The store also carries some local baby products, including Teddy Toes blankets.

■ STARS CHILDREN'S WEAR
(425) 392-2900
55 N.E. Gilman Blvd.
Issaquah, WA 98027

Hours:	M-F	9:30 a.m.-9:00 p.m.
	Sat.	10:00 a.m.-7:00 p.m.
	Sun.	11:00 a.m.-6:00 p.m.

Baby Pages

Cash, Checks, Visa, MC, AmEx
Stars is our own local children's superstore, featuring a huge selection of high quality brand-name clothing, accessories, layette, toys and books for children of all ages. Clothing styles are up-to-date and quality is excellent. Sizes run from preemies up to 14 in girls and 20 in boys. A full selection of christening apparel is available, as well as practically anything else you might want for your baby. There are baby toys, furniture and baby equipment, stuffed animals, cards, gifts, books, music, and accessories. Their Great Wall

of Socks features more than 16,000 pairs.

You can find all your favorite brand names at Stars at 20% to 40% below retail every day. There are also periodic sales which bring the bargains to an even greater level. Stars also makes shopping fun with weekend entertainment like clowns and magic acts. It's a day trip!

■ STRIDE RITE
(425) 453-0101
Bellevue Square Mall
Cash, Checks, Visa, MC, Disc, AmEx
Stride Rite carries their own brand of really cute and durable shoes, with an average price of around $38. You probably can remember wearing a pair when you were a kid, but the styles have changed; they are often hip and very cool, but the quality remains! Bellevue Square is the only remaining branch in Washington.

■ TALBOTS KIDS
(425) 450-3375
Bellevue Square
Cash, Check, Visa, MC, AmEx
Talbots Kids has the ubiquitous preppie department, but the store is really much more than that. There are anoraks with thinsulate for $84 and unisex jeans for $38. Really cool primary colored zip necked fleece tops, in sizes 2-16, are $38. On classic items like polos, turtlenecks and sweaters there are "two for" specials. This extends into the baby and toddler lines, which in pastel, are really cute! The cords are two for $40 or $24 each. Talbots are famous for clothes that can be passed down again and again, not only because of their long wearing construction but for their classic stylings.

✍ *Call ahead to confirm hours and locations.*

■ WARNER BROTHERS STUDIO STORE

(425) 646-8738

Bellevue Square

(206) 467-1810

1512 5th Ave.

Seattle, WA 98101

Cash, Checks, Visa, MC, AmEx

The Warner Brothers Studio Store is filled with—you guessed it—Warner Brothers' character clothing and items. Tweety Bird, Batman and Robin, Bugs Bunny and more await you at this lively store! Prices are what you would expect from a specialty store with clothing around $16 on up. There is also unique memorabilia and items that you could not buy elsewhere. Like the other character stores, Warner Brothers is a fun place to shop!

■ WEDNESDAY'S CHILD

(253) 848-2013

9920 152nd St. East

Puyallup, WA 98373

Hours: T-Sat. 10:00 a.m.-6:00 p.m.

Cash, Checks, Visa, MC

If you have a special occasion for your newborn to size 6x youngster, this store will have a special outfit worth the trip. The store features fine children's clothing from the U.S. and Europe like Catimini, miniman, Plum!, Donna Capozzi and other hard-to-find quality clothes lines. There is also a baby registry, free gift wrapping and a children's play area. The seasonal clearance sales are amazing. This is a good place to stock up on holiday clothes for the year.

❧

❧ Call ahead to confirm hours and locations.

RESALE/CONSIGNMENT STORES

■ ABIGAIL'S

Abigail's in the Courtyard:

(206) 325-9903

2812 E. Madison #3

Seattle, WA 98112

Hours: T-Sat. 10:00 a.m.-5:00 p.m.
       Sun.   Noon-4:00 p.m.

Abigail's in View Ridge:

(206) 729-3849

7509 35th Ave. N.E.

Seattle, WA 98115

Hours: T-Sat. 10:00 a.m.-6:00 p.m.
       Sun.   Noon-5:00 p.m.

Cash, Checks, Visa, MC

Abigail's View Ridge is mostly women's clothing, with a nice selection of kid's clothing in the back room. The Madison store is located in a lovely courtyard set back from the north side of Madison Street—look for the old-fashioned baby buggy filled with plants outside. There's an excellent selection of both children's and maternity consignment wear, as well as some new merchandise. The consignment clothes are in great condition and children's outfits average in the $5-$10 range. The maternity section offers many choices too, with barely-used dresses in both casual and career styles ranging in price from $8-$60, most between $20-$40. Besides consignment clothes, the store carries new maternity clothes, including Maternity Blues denim nursing tops ($39.95) and knit maternity shorts ($14.75). There's a large section of Discreet Wear solid-color leggings and stretch pants in ribbed and textured knits for $12.95. Abigail's has a well-stocked center display of nursing supplies, including videos, books, nursing pillows, breast pumps, and more. (The owner noted that they strongly support breastfeeding.) Other new merchandise includes lots of cute kids' hats by Laarni starting at $9.95, a double sling Baby Bundler baby carrier, books, and accessories. More consignment merchandise is upstairs—clothes in children's sizes 4-12, toys, and books. You may also find some equipment such as strollers and swings, and a small supply of bedding.

■ BOOTYLAND
(206) 328-0636
1321 East Pine
Seattle, WA 98122
Hours: M-Sat.   10:00 a.m.-6:00 p.m.
Cash, Checks
Bootyland is for the fun, funky and fashionable baby. It is owned and operated by two mothers in the Capitol Hill area. The store carries both new and used items for infants through size 7. Bootyland is very clean and organized, and offers a wide supply of merchandise from books to clothing to products. We also found several unusual local products at Bootyland; among them, hand-knit fruit and vegetable hats for $12, and a great selection of tie-dye clothing and used baby carriers. I was astounded to see a new-looking pram for $50! Prices begin at about $2 for infant clothing. Bootyland has a great area for your children to play while you shop.

■ FINER CONSIGNER
(206) 522-7441
6407 Roosevelt Way N.E.
Seattle, WA 98115
Hours: T-Sat.   10:00 a.m.-6:00 p.m.
Cash, Checks
Located across the street from Roosevelt Square, Finer Consigner isn't too big, but they carry an assortment of both children's and maternity wear. Prices are good, with maternity jumpers and dresses in the $10-$20 range and some Discreet Wear tops (in great condition!) for just $11 when we visited. Children's clothes offer the greatest choices in newborn-24 months, although the selection in larger sizes is sure to grow as the children of regular customers do too. Prices were inexpensive, about $1-$5 for play clothes. A new, handmade white crocheted sweater with matching cap was just $8. If you're in the neighborhood, this store is worth a stop!

■ FUNKY JANE'S
(206) 937-2637
4738 42nd Ave. S.W.
Seattle, WA 98116
Hours: M-F   10:00 a.m.-8:00 p.m.
       Sat.   10:00 a.m.-6:00 p.m.
       Sun.   Noon-5:00 p.m.
Funky Jane's is located in West Seattle at Jefferson Square (look for the adjacent Safeway store). The emphasis in this large store is on women's wear and you'll find a striking display of stylish clothes and accessories as you enter. Head toward the back right and there's a good-sized section of consigned children's wear in sizes newborn-6x. The condition of clothes is good, and prices are in the $2-$10 range. On the maternity racks, you'll find jeans for around $10 and dresses and jumpers from $20-$30.

■ **GRANDMOTHER'S HOUSE**
(425) 771-4640   *Baby Pages*
7331 196th S.W.
Lynnwood, WA 98036
Hours: M-Sat. 9:30 a.m.-5:30 p.m.
        Sun.   Noon-5:00 p.m.
Located west of Hwy. 99 on 196th S.W.,
the store occupies both the upstairs and
downstairs of a house-turned-store.
Outdoor items (trikes, bikes, strollers,
play equipment) fill the front yard, and
it seems that every available space inside
the cottage is used as well, making for a
fabulous selection. This store has been
in business since 1975, making it the
oldest resale store I know of in the area.
The store buys items outright (no consignment), and merchandise is always
abundant and changing.

There's definitely lots to choose from
here, with rooms full of baby swings,
cribs, car seats and play pens; plenty of
toys, books, bedding, and clothes (in-

cluding a whole rack of OshKosh) too.
The owner puts time and care into
refurbishing used merchandise to make
the clothing and furnishings just like
new. This is a great place to purchase
the original Baby Jogger line, with low
prices and factory-direct delivery via
UPS.

■ **HEAVEN SENT**
(253) 946-2229
1200 S. 324th, Ste. 5
Federal Way, WA 98003
Hours: M-F   10:00 a.m.-6:00 p.m.
        Sat.   10:00 a.m.-5:00 p.m.
Cash, Checks, Visa, MC
Heaven Sent has a great selection of
resale items. Clothes are on racks along
the walls and on circle racks in the
middle of the store, and the store makes
good use of their space with a very well-
organized layout. Besides clothes, they
carry practically everything you might

GIFTS TO CONSIDER GIVING AND RECEIVING

- Front baby carrier
- Baby sling
- Backpack
- Diaper bag/backpack with fold up changing pad and compartments
- Polar fleece bunting, hat and mittens and booties
- Customized playsuits and onesies with handpainting or stitching
- Velour baby union suits
- Child's play tent (to shade an infant in the sun or chill, and give a toddler her own space)
- Kid's music tapes (for those long car rides to the mountains, beach, or sitting in city traffic jams)
- Nursery cassette tape player that attaches to crib
- Membership to the one of Seattle's museums geared to kids.
- Three months of a diaper service.

need for baby: car seats, swings, front and back carriers, jump-ups, bottles, bibs, strollers, bassinets, cribs, mobiles, and wall decorations. They also have a good selection of toys, games, dolls, and play furniture. Prices are very affordable; cribs range from $60-$200, pairs of socks start at 40 cents, and some nice, good quality boys' suits (complete with cummerbunds or vests) cost less than $11.

■ **JUST BEARLY**
(206) 546-8581
17818 Aurora Ave. N (near Fred Meyer)
Shoreline, WA 98133
Hours: M-Sat.　10:00 a.m.-5:00 p.m.
Cash, Checks, Visa, MC
This store packs a punch. It's small but the inventory is great. Maternity clothes are a bargain here: a Japanese Weekend two-piece outfit for $20! A brand new Medela double breast pump for $100! Gymboree infant girl's dress $5, bags of really cool assorted rattles for $6. Prices are more reasonable here than in other consignment stores and the selection is a notch or two higher in quality. This store is definitely worth checking out. It's south of the QFC, on the red brick road, parallel to Aurora Avenue behind the new Kym's Kiddie Corner on Highway 99.

■ **JUST FOR YOU**
(206) 542-3993
19918 Aurora Ave. N.
Seattle, WA 98133
Hours: M,W, F 9:30 a.m.-6:00 p.m.
　　　　T, Th　9:30 a.m.-7:00 p.m.
　　　　Sat.　10:00 a.m.-5:00 p.m.
　　　　Sun.　11:00 a.m.-5:00 p.m.
Cash/Checks/V/MC/AmEx
In business since 1981, Just for You moved and is now located just south of

Costco on Highway 99. Consigned clothes are reasonably priced, with a very large variety of all items from sleepwear to dress clothes in sizes newborn to 14 (girls) and 16 (boys). We also found a selection of swings, strollers, carriers, and high chairs. If you're looking for maternity clothing, Just for You carries a large section with mostly casual clothes and some career dresses.

■ **KIDS BY GOSH**
(425) 432-9336
22035 S.E. Wax Rd.
Maple Valley, WA 98038
Hours: M-F　10:00 a.m.-6:00 p.m.
　　　　Sat.　10:00 a.m.-5:00 p.m.
　　　　Sun.　Noon-5:00 p.m.
Cash, Checks, Visa, MC
Kids By Gosh offers everything under the sun for kids! They carry hard-to-find christening gowns and premature baby clothing, and sell both new and used clothes. Brands include OshKosh b'Gosh, JoLene, Peaches & Cream, Plum Pudding, B.U.M., Esprit, Healthtex, Disney, Weather Tamer, and Beatrix Potter. The store is very well-organized, with walls filled with shelves and hangers of new baby clothes, hats, shoes, socks, and other accessories. Besides things to wear, they have baby furniture, toys, games, puzzles, lullaby tapes, and much more. Prices range from $2.98 and up, and in the consignment area for 98 cents and up. The staff here is friendly and there's a play area for kids, so you can take your time shopping.

ᚬ *Call ahead to confirm hours and locations.*

RESALE STORES

■ **KIDS ON 45TH**
(206) 633-5437
1720 N. 45th St.
Seattle, WA 98103
Hours: M-Sat.   10:00 a.m.-6:00 p.m.
          Sun.   11:00 a.m.-5:00 p.m.
Cash, Checks, Visa, MC, AmEx
Kids on 45th carries a wide variety of
products for babies and children. The
front part of the store offers new clothes,
with an extra large selection of their own
line of cotton basics, affordably priced
from $7-$20. This line is very popular,
as is the consignment section which
offers clothing and other products. On
one visit there were several gently used
swings, strollers, and car seats for sale.
The consignment clothing is well-organized and displayed, with separate racks
for dresses, pants, tops, shirts, overalls,
coats, and shorts. There's also a big
selection of velcro-fastening diaper covers selling for about $2 each. A dollar
rack offers even more children's clothing
bargains. The store sells new baby accessories too. One that looked quite practical was a plastic bib by Roo! that's dishwasher safe and just $4.95.

■ **KYM'S KIDDY CORNER**
(206) 361-5974
11721 15th Ave. N.E.
Seattle, WA 98125
Hours: M-Sat. 10:00 a.m.-5:30 p.m.
          Sun.   Noon-5:00 p.m.

(206) 546-9230
17516 Aurora Ave. N. (near Fred Meyer)
Hours: M-Sat.   10:00 a.m.-5:30 p.m.
With two locations, Kym's Kiddie Corner dominates the north Seattle resale
market. To find either location, just
point your car in the general vicinity and
look for the massive piles of baby equip-

ment that line the streets near the stores
as well as the handmade neon signs
denoting the "huge selection of baby
and kids' toys, clothing and furniture."
When you are within earshot you are
sure to hear Barney or Disney videos
playing in the kids' play area, where
employees' children are often found.

The highlight of Kym's is the equipment—they sell used strollers, high
chairs, trikes, bikes and various play
equipment. Prices are usually 30% to
40% off the new price. Both stores will
put you on a calling list if you are looking
for something in particular.

Each location features new Safety 1st
items (a wall full) and the Black and
White child development toys for the
full retail price. Baby Bjorn carriers at
$69 and Tough Traveler back packs for
$79 are real bargains here.

Kym's carries resale clothing at each
location in sizes newborn to 14. Prices
are reasonable for most items and all are
in good condition. New items like swim
diapers are available seasonally.

■ **LABELS**
(206) 781-1194
7212 Greenwood Ave. N.
Seattle, WA 98103
Hours: T-Sat.   10:00 a.m.-6:00 p.m.
          Th   10:00 a.m.-8:00 p.m.
          Sun.   Noon-5:00 p.m.
Cash, Checks, Visa, MC
Labels is located in the Greenwood area
in a hip little shopping stretch. It offers
some of the most stylish choices in regular women's wear, including some European and better labels. The emphasis on
fashionable clothing can be found in the
maternity section too, where choices in
dresses included several in the Mother-

hood line and in Japanese Weekend for $14-$28. Sun dresses were being offered for under $20 and all clothes were in excellent condition. The children's section includes a nice assortment of outfits, including Gymboree and similar brands, most in the $4-$5 range! (That is not a typo!) This store has the most reasonable prices that I have found. As far as I can figure, the philosophy at this store is price it to sell, and they do. If something catches your eye, buy it because it will be gone later if you plan to think about it. There are also plenty of socks (50 cents), bibs, hats (with original price tags still on them) for $2.50, and other accessories. Kids will stay occupied in the store's play kitchen area while you shop. This is a must-go to shop!

■ LITTLE MUNCHKINS
(206) 244-0616
13635 1st Ave. S.
Burien, WA 98166
Hours: M-Sat.   10:00 a.m.-6:00 p.m.
Cash, Checks, Visa, MC
Little Munchkins is in Burien, where Suzi Q's Consignment Store used to be. The new owners buy used baby clothes and products as well as trade for store credit. The store is nicely organized, with separate racks for dresses, pants, shirts, rompers, overalls, jumpers, etc. This makes shopping much easier and less time-consuming. Sizes range from preemie to 6x. Clothing quality is very good and prices are affordable—Osh Kosh b'Gosh overalls go for about $7, almost-new dresses for $6 and up. A bargain rack offers items for 50 cents.

There's a good selection of rattles, baby and children's toys (Cabbage Patch dolls for $7!), and lots of shoes. Baby equipment includes strollers, cribs, car seats, bassinets, and playpens. We also saw Snugli baby carriers ($15.95) and a nice assortment of bedding. Little Munchkins also offers their own line of handmade dresses, pants, and diaper wraps in cottons and knits. The staff is quite friendly and helpful, and there's a play area for children.

■ LITTLE TROOPERS
(206) 486-2081
6522 N.E. Bothell Way
Seattle, WA 98155
Hours: M-F   10:00 a.m.-6:00 p.m.
       Sat.   10:00 a.m.-4:00 p.m.
Cash, Checks, Visa, MC
Little Troopers is in the Kenmore area in a strip mall off Bothell Way. This is a great place if you're a bargain hunter, as you will find plenty to choose from here. We were impressed with the large selection of toys and stuffed animals at amazingly low prices. The consignment clothes are generally in very good condition and there's a nice variety of items in sizes up to 12. The baby and toddler section has a lot of clothes, bedding, and accessories like diaper bags. The store also sells used shoes, videos and books. Equipment like strollers, cribs, high chairs, and car seats are available from time to time, but usually go fast since the prices are so good. New items for sale include socks, hats, headbands, and other clothing accessories. Little Troopers has a small play area for kids.

⚓ *Call ahead to confirm hours and locations.*

RESALE STORES

■ **LOLLIPOPS**
(206) 243-1795
2038 S.W. 152nd
Burien, WA 98148
Hours: M-Sat.   10:00 a.m.-5:30 p.m.
Cash, Checks, Visa, MC

Lollipops is the only consignment shop we visited that carried clothes for the entire family. The selection of children's clothes is quite good, and condition of clothing ranges from fair to excellent. The merchandise is very well organized by item. When we visited, there was a large selection of baby dresses in practically brand-new condition, most for $5 or less. The maternity section wasn't too big, but prices again were quite good with dresses, denim jumpers, and pants for $10 or less. The store carries baby equipment including toddler beds, swings, strollers, and car seats. There's some baby bedding too, and a wall of plastic stacking baskets—each clearly labeled and filled with toys, books, dolls, doll clothes, diaper wraps, and more.

■ **ME 'N' MOMS /**
   CLASSIC CONSIGNMENT
(206) 781-4827
5514 24th Ave. N.W.
Seattle, WA 98
Hours: M-F   10:00 a.m.-6:00 p.m.
     Sat.-Sun. Noon-5:00 p.m.
Cash, Checks, Visa, MC

You may have noticed that three of the areas' consignment shops are missing! Well, they have merged into one heck of a resale megamall! Located in an ex-furniture store, there are acres of merchandise to look through! Me 'n' Moms still features some of the finest new clothing around, some of which they discount—Flapdoodles is generally 20%

off. The season's end sales are a great place to find bargain prices on clothes for next year. I got a hand-knit hooded cotton sweater for the baby that was $45 new for just $5! There is something for everyone at this store. I had a requested birthday present of a "little bunny that I can sleep with" and there were five styles of the little cuties near the register. The one that won our hearts was wearing a little sweater and had movable jointed arms and legs for $7. If you get weary of shopping, there is a coffee cart just outside the front door!

■ **MOM'S N TOT'S**
(425) 451-4439
137 106th Ave. N.E.
Bellevue, WA 98006
Hours: M-F   10:00 a.m.-5:00 p.m.
     Sat.   10:30 a.m.-5:30 p.m.
Cash, Checks, Visa, MC

Mom's n Tot's, located in Bellevue on 106th Ave. N.E. and Main Street, has been in business on the eastside for more than 12 years. They carry a wide selection of business and casual maternity wear for moms and a first-class clothing selection for tots in sizes from birth to 12 years. The store is clean and well-organized with a variety of toys, books, shoes, bedding and furniture, as well as consignment clothing. Ample parking in the mall setting makes it a very convenient place to shop. Each month, Mom's n Tot's features 20% off on selected items with a color ticket for easy bargain hunting. It's a great store to find super buys.

■ **RE-DRESS**
(425) 746-7984
513 156th S.E.
Bellevue, WA 98007
Hours: M-F   10:30 a.m.-6:00 p.m.
       Th   until 8:00 p.m.
       Sat.   10:30 a.m.-5:00 p.m.
       Sun.   Noon-5:00 p.m.
Cash, Checks, Visa, MC, Disc, Debit
Re-Dress is located in the Lake Hills
Shopping Center, near QFC. The main
focus for Re-Dress has been women's
clothing but it has recently expanded to
include maternity and children's clothes.
Kids' sizes range from newborn to size
14. The management strives to keep
prices low for excellent quality, name-
brand clothing such as Motherhood
Maternity, Carter's, Guess for Kids, Baby
Guess, Baby Gap, OshKosh, and more.
The store is very clean and well-organized, and stroller accessible. The sales
staff is very friendly and helpful in choosing maternity wear for business, casual,
and evening attire.

■ **SATURDAY'S CHILD**
   CONSIGNMENTS
(425) 486-6716
18012 Bothell-Everett Hwy.
Bothell, WA 98012
Hours: M-F   10:30 a.m.-5:30 p.m.
       Sat.   10:00 a.m.-5:00 p.m.
       Sun.   Noon-4:00 p.m.
Cash, Checks, Visa, MC
Saturday's Child is located near Mill
Creek, just east of the 164th S.W. exit
from I-5, on the Bothell-Everett Highway. It's a large store with lots of clothes—
both new and handcrafted as well as
consigned—for boys and girls up to size
14. The prices and quality of the used
clothing are quite good. Many clothing

items for babies and toddlers are in the
$3-$5 range. The store also carries a full
assortment of baby furniture and equipment, including swings, strollers, and
playpens, as well as some bedding, accessories, and toys. You will find many one-
of-a-kind items as the owners continually buy trade show samples. There's
also a nice selection of handcrafted clothing—we noticed a delightful reversible
jumper by Garments of Praise for just
$14.50.

■ **SMALL FRY'S WORLD**
(206) 938-9190
7354-35th Ave. S.W.
Seattle, WA 98126
Hours: T-Sun.   10:00 a.m.-6:00 p.m.
As a mom who had to outfit newborn
twins as well as a preschooler, Kristen
Dobson thought it wise to open a consignment shop. Small Fry's World carries clean, quality clothing, toys, books,
furniture and equipment, all at reasonable prices. Clothing sizes range from
newborn to 14, and name brands include Baby Gap, Osh Kosh b'Gosh,
Cotton Caboodle, Gymboree and Levi's.
A sale rack features clothing marked
down 25%-75% every day. Kids love
visiting this store for its great children's
play room.

■ **THE TREE HOUSE
CHILDREN'S SHOP**
(425) 885-1145
Redmond Center
15742 Redmond Way
Redmond, WA 98052
Hours: M-F 9:00 a.m.-6:00 p.m.
    Th. 10:00 a.m.-8:00 p.m.
    Sat. 10:00 a.m.-5:00 p.m.
    Sun. 1:00 p.m.-5:00 p.m.
Cash, Checks, Visa, MC, Discover
The Tree House is a very unique shop because it offers an especially large selection of both new (about one-third of the inventory) and used/consignment (about two-thirds the inventory) clothing. They've been in business for more than 15 years and have a loyal following. With 3,000 square feet, there's lots of room for merchandise, and it's very nicely organized and displayed. You'll find an extensive section of new baby clothes and accessories to your right as you enter the door. Prices are very moderate. Even preemie clothes, which sometimes carry a premium price at other stores, are available starting at $10 for a Carter's outfit with hat. Other clothing lines include Spumoni, Le Top, OshKosh b'Gosh and Baby b'Gosh, Little Me, Marimekko, and French Toast. Sizes go up to 14. Plenty of baby accessories and supplies are available, including diaper covers, TV booties, hats, and a big selection of rain boots ($6.99). The consignment section is large, with rows and rows of infant and toddler wear, most in good to almost-new condition. Expect to pay about $5 and up for a play outfit. There's also a round rack of consigned maternity clothes, mostly casual wear with pants and jeans for $4-$10 and a few nice dresses in the $8-$20 range. Kids will love the play area at The Tree House, since it features a Little Tikes Gym to climb and play on. The Tree House carries a full supply of Brownie and Girl Scout uniforms here too.

■ **THE UNICORN BOUTIQUE**
(425) 823-4868
12537 116th Ave. N.E.
Kirkland, WA 98034
Hours: T-Sat. 10:30 a.m.-5:00 p.m.
The Unicorn Boutique is across from Drug Emporium in the Totem Lake West shopping area. The store offers consignment clothing in women's, children's, and maternity sizes. The maternity rack has some nice jumpers and dresses for $10-$15, mostly in casual looks. There's a large selection of children's wear and prices are very good, averaging $3-$5. The store also carries some new children's wear by Peekaboo in colorful cotton and knits. Shirts start at $6, pants at $9, and rompers at $16. Besides clothing, you'll find a wide assortment of toys, accessories, socks, hats, baby shoes, stuffed animals, mobiles, books, videos, and small furniture items.

᷄᷄

TOY STORES

Most department stores have toy sections that carry the usual run-of-the-mill Saturday morning advertised toys. The toy stores that are listed here carry the unusual, imagination-capturing, unique toys that we remember into adulthood.

■ **FAO SCHWARZ**
(425) 646-9500
Bellevue Square Mall

(206) 442-9500
1420 5th Ave.
Seattle, WA 98101

■ **THE GREAT TRAIN STORE**
(425) 452-9244
Bellevue Square Mall

■ **IMAGINARIUM**
(425) 453-5288
Bellevue Square Mall

(206) 439-8980
Southcenter Mall

(425) 771-7220
Alderwood Mall
Cash, Checks, Visa, MC

■ **IMAGINATION EXPRESS**
(425) 392-3847
1175 N.W. Gilman Blvd.
Issaquah, WA 98027
Hours: M-Fri.   10:00 a.m.-7:00 p.m.
       Sat.   10:00 am.-6:00 p.m.
       Sun.   11:00 a.m.-5:00 p.m.
Cash, Checks, Visa, MC, Discover

■ **PINOCCHIO'S TOYS**
(206) 528-1100
4540 Union Bay Place N.E.
Just east of University Village
Seattle, WA 98105
Hours: M-Sat.   10:00 a.m.-6:00 p.m.
       Sun.   Noon-5:00 p.m.
Cash, Checks, Visa, MC

■ **TERI'S TOYBOX**
(206) 526-7147
University Village Mall
Cash, Checks, Visa, MC, Discover

■ **TOP TEN TOYS**
(206) 782-0098
104 N. 85th
Seattle, WA 98103
Hours: M-Sun.   9:00 a.m.-6:00 p.m.
       W-F   Open until 9:00 p.m.
Cash, Checks, Visa, MC

■ **TREE TOP TOYS**
(206) 363-5460
17171 Bothell Way N.E.
Bothell, WA 98155
Hours: M-Fri.   10:00 a.m.-9:00 p.m.
       Sat.   10:00 a.m.-6:00 p.m.
       Sun.   11:00 a.m.-5:00 p.m.
Cash, Checks, Visa, MC, Discover

❧

RESALE TOYS

■ TOYS GO ROUND
(425) 778-5600
201 5th Ave. S., Old Milltown Mall
Edmonds, WA 98020
Hours: M-Sat. 10:00 a.m.-6:00 p.m.
   Sun. Open until 5:00 p.m.
Cash, Checks, Visa, MC

Shopping at the Old Milltown Mall in Edmonds is a day of fun. The mall is filled with antique and unique stores. Toys Go Round carries both used toys and clothes. I thought there were two different stores until I realized there were two entrances. The toys are the highlight. I found super deals on a Little Tikes castle, a kitchen, a workbench and more, all for around $40 each. There were also lots and lots of books, dolls and videos as well as a motorized car.

■ TWICE LOVED TOYS
(425) 542-1761
9659 Firdale Ave.
Edmonds, WA 98020
Hours: T-F 10:00 a.m.-6:00 p.m.
   Sat. 10:00 a.m.-5:00 p.m.
   Sun., M 12:30 p.m.-5:00 p.m.
Cash, Checks, Visa, MC, Discover

Twice Loved Toys is in the Firdale Shopping Center, a mile west of 205th/Hwy. 99. This is a shop full of little treasures. Toys are bought outright, then cleaned and refurbished by the owner and resold at 25% to 75% off retail. The store carries everything from vintage 1960's items to today's hot toys. The store maintains a very popular customer request file for any toy-related item ever made. If the toy comes in and you are on

the request list, you will get a call. There are two yearly events that are a must— the annual holiday open house which features a "spin the Barbie" for a discount on any purchase, and the Brio/Playmobil Bash. For the latter, the owner hoards Brio and Playmobil all year and then has a blowout sale day for these super hot items. If you are on the mailing list you will have advance notice of these and any other events or sales. Hands down, this is a great store.

❧

CHILDREN'S BOOK STORES

Books are the key to a child's imagination. A book can keep you company, soothe you when you don't feel good and take you to places all around the world without ever leaving your comfy chair. When you give a child a book, you give him more than paper; you give him dreams.

■ ALL FOR KIDS BOOKS AND MUSIC
(206) 526-2768
2900 N.E. Blakeley
Seattle, WA 98105
Hours: M-Sat. 10:00 a.m.- 6:00 p.m.
   Sun. Noon - 5:00 p.m.
Cash, Checks, Visa, MC

■ **CHILDREN'S BOOKSHOP**
(253) 852-0383
225 W. Meeker
Kent, WA 98032

(253) 445-4790
707 River
Puyallup, WA 98371
Hours: M-Fri.   10:00 a.m.-6:00 p.m.
  Sat.   10:00 a.m.-5:00 p.m.
  Sun.   Noon-4:00 p.m.
Cash, Checks, Visa, MC

■ **PUSS 'N BOOKS**
(425) 885-6828
8086 160th Ave. N.E.
Redmond, WA 98052
Hours: M-T   10:00 a.m.-6:00 p.m.
  W-F   10:00 a.m.-8:00 p.m.
  Sat.   10:00 a.m.-5:00 p.m.
  Sun.   11:00 a.m.-5:00 p.m.
Cash, Checks, Visa, MC, Discover

■ **SECRET GARDEN**
 CHILDREN'S BOOK SHOP
(206) 789-5006
6115 15th Ave. N.W.
Seattle, WA 98107
Hours: M-Sat.   10:00 a.m.-6:00 p.m.
  Th   10:00 a.m.-8:00 p.m.
  Sun.   1:00 p.m.-5:00 p.m.
Cash, Checks, Visa, MC, Disc, AmEx

🕭

LOCAL PRODUCTS/ ARTISTS

■ **AWESOME ANIMALS**
(425) 451-9692
Botanicals Northwest makes natural fruit sugar, chewable animal-shaped vitamins. These contain concentrates of 33 whole fruits and vegetables, ester C (the most easily soluble C), no aspartame, no artificial flavors, dyes or lactose.

■ **BABY ON THE TOWN**
 SHOPPING CART AND
 STROLLER COVER
(253) 813-0110
Zachary's mom started this company after other moms wanted a stroller/shopping cart cover like the one she had made for Zachary. The cover fits into any shopping cart and keeps your baby warm, cozy and clean. Complete with places for toys and snacks, this cover is a lifesaver after your tot begins to feel the need to "help" you shop!

■ **BABY TEE'S**
(206) 542-0100
This company makes iron-ons for T-shirts with your baby's photo on it with messages like "I love my Mommy." I had to get one myself!

■ **BABY'S OWN WEB PAGE**
(360) 876-2280
Web site: www.netcom.com/ ~shawnie1/newbaby.html.
Place your baby's color photograph and custom birth announcement on the Internet for all the world to see.

■ **BIRTH AND BEYOND**
(206) 324-4831
2610 E. Madison St.
Seattle, WA 98112

(425) 402-9366
14450 Woodinville-Redmond Rd.
Woodinville, WA 98072
Birth and Beyond is owned by mother
Lyndsey Starkey. These two unique stores
carry many local products, as well as just
about anything else you would need
during pregnancy. Birth and Beyond
must be a definite stop for you to find
local items or just about anything else
you would want for pregnancy and baby.

■ **BOB'S TOYS**
Bob Langhorne
(253) 862-9391
2006 Tacoma Point Dr. E.
Sumner, WA 98390
The craze has begun. It's hip, it's retro—
it's wood. Wood toys are the rage and
the best of the best are made by Bob
Langhorne, proprietor of Bob's Toys.
He sets up at Pikes Place, and has practically since time began. He makes his
glorious wood pieces by hand with dowel
pins, not nails or screws, which are rubbed
to a glowing finish. These movable toys
all come in a set of about six parts. For
example, the ferry boat set comes with a
ferry, car, loading dock and a truck with
barrels that can be loaded via a pulley
type mechanism that is in the truck.
This is so cool I wanted it for myself! All
of this for $60! One woman I spoke to
used her child's ferry boat as a nursing
stool until she was old enough to play
with it. P.S. They are all guaranteed for
life!

❧ *Call ahead to confirm hours and locations.*

■ **BODYSENSE SEATTLE**
(206) 329-0424
800 5th Ave. #391
Seattle, WA 98104
This company features pillows, packs
and mitts for ailments like sore necks,
backs, hands and feet. Could that possibly be you? All products contain organic
rice and herbs to soothe and penetrate.
Hot or cold, these can help any child's
boo-boos. They even have a unique
microwaveable "comfort toy" for children.

■ **BY GEORGE BABY WRAPS**
(206) 542-1149
By George Baby Wraps are cotton fleece
wraps, something like an envelope with
a zipper, that fit into a stroller or car seat.
These keep baby warm and out of cum-
bersome winter togs while riding in the
car or on a walk.

■ **EDDIE BAUER HOME
   CATALOG**
800-426-8020
Eddie now has a baby bedding line that
features cotton flannel sheets, chenille
blankets, etc. The prices are affordable
and very Northwest in design. On a
more pricey note, the catalog also sells
Child Craft cribs and Kolcraft mattresses.

■ **MARIE MEARS, MURAL
   PAINTER**
(206) 365-4754
Marie has an impressive background in
scenic art—she's worked at most of the
theaters in the area. After having a baby,
she began sharing her artistic talents in a
new way by painting murals and other
room decor in homes. Her consultation
is free and she'll provide an estimate after

meeting with the client, based on a rate of $20 per hour, which includes materials. You can see an example of her murals at Birth and Beyond.

■ MCKENZIE KIDS

(800) 832-0969
P.O. Box 82095
Portland OR 97282

This business started as a business plan en route to finish the owners' degrees but the prototypes were so good they were scooped up by local moms and demand beget this business! McKenzie sells the "everything diaper," Babygear briefcases, parentpacks, packaroos (belt bags) and "everything but the bag" that allows you to make any bag into a diaper bag.

■ NANNY AND WEBSTER

800-392-4975
10838 Main St.
Bellevue, WA 98004
Hours: M-F   8:00 a.m.-5:00 p.m.

Nanny and Webster features baby blankets with a message: "bringing warmth and comfort to children and the people who care for them." Profits from the sale of the blankets are donated to children's charities. The Nanny and Webster blanket is 100% cotton with a two-piece flannel design. The 36" x 42" blanket comes in five different patterns and retails for $24. A quilted flannel blanket with satin trim sells for $30.

■ THE ORIGINAL HOODED TOWEL

(800) 447-6288

This Everett company started it all by making the first hooded towel ever designed just for kids. Three sizes are available in white, pink and light blue to fit most kids. Call for a store near you.

■ POPPE PRESCHOOL PRODUCTS

(509) 886-0579
152 S. Keller
E. Wenatchee, WA 98802

Marie Poppe designs and sells the delightful educational puppets—"folktails"—and many well-tested and beloved preschool-age craft materials.

■ STARWORKS NURSING MOTHER'S COVER UP

21227 S.E. 29th St.
Issaquah, WA 98029

Now you can nurse privately in public. The Starworks' cover-up is made of soft cotton, with a velcro fastener that opens so you can view baby.

■ STITCHES IN TIME

(206) 768-2658
7749 16th S.W.
Seattle, WA 98106

Stitches in Time manufactures the Rosado Sling, a product that allows more freedom of movement for parents. Owner Julianne believes that babies take to the sling because of the closeness, security and comfort it provides. The sling is available in a variety of fabrics and is machine washable and dryable. It has wide fabric which gives you added support and privacy while nursing. It is easy to use as it has a one hand adjustment. Depending on the fabric, the sling costs around $40 and is available via mail order (checks or cash only) or at local retail locations which can be found by calling the number above. The company's other products include nursing tops, diapers and hats.

■ TEDDY TOES

(206) 284-3404
800-51TEDDY
3213 W. Wheeler St., Ste. 254
Seattle, WA 98199

Teddy Toes is manufactured by Sisters 3 of Seattle. The product is an innovative blanket which your baby can wear. An advantage for Seattle natives is that Teddy Toes is water resistant, and won't absorb more than one percent of its weight in water. It insulates even when it is wet. The material is colorfast, machine washable and dryable. Teddy Toes comes in a variety of wonderful colors. The product costs around $45, and can be worn up to 18 months or 30 pounds, saving you money on a coat purchase.

Sisters 3 also offers the Tiny Toes. It's smaller than the original product and is primarily used as a receiving blanket. It's available in a cotton interlock fabric (pastels, primary prints, pastel prints) for $25. It's also offered in a certified organic, undyed, no-bleach cotton thermal, which comes with a hat and costs $33.95. Teddy and Tiny Toes can be purchased in Seattle at Nordstrom stores, Group Health Take Care Stores, and at baby and children's stores, as well as directly from Sisters 3.

■ THE UNCOMMON WALL

(206) 615-7528

Barbara Rich creates "whimsical and sophisticated" hand painted murals, furniture, and personalized items like keepsake boxes. Call her for a free consultation. She'll bring her portfolio and idea book to help you visualize the possibilities. She charges based on the time spent, not the project size.

🐚

BIRTH ANNOUNCEMENTS

■ DRUG EMPORIUM

Drug Emporium is the place to go if you want pre-packaged announcements at a bargain price. Although the selection varies, there are always at least a few different designs to choose from and all are sold at 40% off the retail price. Brands carried include American Greetings and Marcel Schurman. The 40% off applies to all products in those two lines including wrapping paper, ribbons, bows, greeting cards, invitations, thank you cards, stickers, and package decor. Drug Emporium also has a good selection of baby accessories like packaged toys, rattles, bottles, teethers, and more, all at discounted prices.

■ HALLMARK SHOPS

Hallmark Shops are located in malls and in neighborhood shopping areas and offer a great selection of pre-packaged announcements. They have catalogs if you want to order custom announcements. Most stores also have an in-house service that customizes and prints your announcement on a laser printer.

■ LICENSED TO CRAWL

(425) 524-6352
21729 S.E. May Valley Rd.
Issaquah, WA 98027

Here's a unique idea for a birth announcement—a Washington Crawler's License. Postcard size and in full color, these announcements look a lot like a driver's license except they also include the parents' names. The order form comes with detailed instructions on how to get a good picture of your baby, which you send along with all the vital statistics and your check (starting at $30 for 25 "licenses"). Call and get a free sample and order form.

■ THE PAPER TREE

(425) 451-8035
Bellevue Square
Bellevue, WA 98004
Hours: M-Sat.   9:30 a.m.-9:30 p.m.
         Sun.   10:00 a.m.-6:00 p.m.
The Paper Tree is a popular place to shop for birth announcements. In addition to pre-packaged selections, there are more than 20 books of custom announcements that you can choose from. You'll also find plenty of shower invitations, thank you cards, photo albums and frames, and baby books.

■ YOU NAME IT

(425) 391-5899
This Issaquah-based company specializes in custom order stationery for birth announcements, birthday parties, bar/bat mitzvahs and children's stationery. The owner, Stacey Easton, will help you find the perfect announcement! Call for an appointment. All products are always discounted.

■ PAPYRUS

(425) 771-5830
Alderwood Mall

(206) 464-1505
1210 4th Ave.
Seattle, WA 98101
Hours: M-F   9:00 a.m.-6:00 p.m.
         Sat.   10:00 a.m.-5:00 p.m.

(425) 451-4802
Bellevue Square

(206) 363-8055
Northgate Mall

(206) 523-0055
University Village
Papyrus carries both pre-packaged and custom order birth announcements. They also have a nice selection of scrapbooks, photo albums, brag books, mothers' journals, and grandparents' journals.

■ PHOTO TIDINGS

(503) 484-0896
Design your own birth announcement with a photograph of your new arrival. These unique cards are 5" x 7" and can be ordered with or without customization.

■ REAL CARD COMPANY

(206) 325-1854
2814 E. Madison
Seattle, WA 98112
Hours: M-Sat.   10:00 a.m.-5:00 p.m.
At Real Card Company you can select announcements from a wide variety of catalogs but the real emphasis here is on in-house custom designing. Designers make unique creations using calligraphy, letterpress, and/or engraving, to come up with the final result. You can go in while you're expecting and select what you want, then call in the vital statistics when your baby is born. Call for an appointment to ensure undivided attention, as the store can be busy.

ANNOUNCEMENTS

■ SAB-TEC STATIONERS

(206) 523-2106

University Village Mall

Sab-Tec has an excellent selection of birth announcements. They offer pre-packaged sets and you can also order by catalog. In-house, they have a nice assortment of blank cards with colorful borders and matching envelopes. They'll do pen and ink calligraphy on these and the result is very attractive. You pay by the card for in-house work, so you can get as many as you need.

■ "THE STORK GAZETTE"

(206) 633-3988

"The Stork Gazette" is a personalized newsletter that shares the details of your baby's birth. You provide the information, including photographs, and they'll do the rest. Cost is $50 for the first 50 copies, and $10 per 25 for additional copies. The newsletter is printed on both sides of a sheet of high quality card stock.

■ BABY PICTURES

(425) 462-9116

If you'd like to show your child what she looked like before she was born or find out for certain if your baby will be a boy or girl, Baby Pictures can help. For $50 they'll make a 15-minute prenatal ultrasound video, as well as still pictures from the ultrasound. The videos are done by a licensed (RT, RDMS, RVT) ultrasound technician in her home in Bellevue.

❧

DIAPER SERVICES

■ BABY DIAPER SERVICE `Baby Pages`

(800) 562-2229

(206) 634-BABY, Seattle

Hours: M-F   7:00 a.m. - 5:00 p.m.

   Sat.   9:00 a.m. - 1:00 p.m.

(253) 383-BABY, Tacoma

Hours: M-F   1:00 p.m.-5:00 p.m.

   for pick-up

Baby Diaper Service is the largest and one of the oldest diaper services in Washington. It serves customers throughout King, Pierce, Snohomish, Kitsap and Thurston counties. Baby Diaper Service offers a variety of sizes of diapers from preemie to toddler. Baby Diaper Service recommends 70 newborn diapers for $13.35 a week. There is a four week minimum sign-up with the service and if you're a new customer you receive six weeks for the price of four. Similar promotions are available for longer sign-up periods. One other unique feature Baby Diaper Service provides is a day care diaper credit. If your day care charges you for diapers and you provide Baby Diaper Service with a receipt, they will give you a maximum of $15 per month towards any diaper charges.

Baby Diaper Service will deliver diapers before your baby is born. The first set of newborn diaper covers you purchase are offered at a special price of 3 for $10; these covers have space for the umbilical cord as part of their design. All of its diapers are pH balanced and 100% cotton. There is no setup fee for the service. A monthly newspaper entitled *Northwest Baby and Child*, published by Baby Diaper Service, is distributed at no charge throughout the greater Puget Sound area and is delivered free to customers. Baby Diaper Service is also a member of the National Association of Diaper Services.

■ **PURE AND NATURAL**
(206) 767-1807
Pure and Natural's philosophy is to provide quality diapers and excellent customer service. It is owned and operated by parents whose goal is to give you great worry-free service. Pure and Natural has diapers in sizes from preemie to toddler plus training pants. For $12.95 a week you get 70 diapers. This includes weekly pick-up and delivery, a diaper pail, hamper liners, deodorizers, and a free subscription to *Seattle's Child.* Diaper wraps in sizes preemie to toddler are also available for purchase at a competitive price.

Pure and Natural makes emergency deliveries if necessary. I got one when my son was born early so we had preemie diapers and covers waiting for us when we brought him home. We thought this was especially nice because it was actually an exchange—we had our first diapers ordered and delivered early in anticipation and the thought of seeing the "big" newborn diapers was not something we were looking forward to.

Specials are available for parents who sign up for at least one month. The most common promotion offers two weeks free for the first four weeks committed (with a four-week minimum order). Another money-saving special they offer is a referral credit. Pure and Natural also has a total satisfaction promise which means if anything is not right, they will fix your customer concern. Pure and Natural delivers throughout the greater Seattle and Eastside area.

❧

DIAPER SERVICES

DIAPERS FOR PREEMIES
When baby is born early, here are some special "emergency" numbers for delivery of preemie-size diapers. Both Seattle-area diaper service companies carry diapers and wraps for premature babies. If you buy disposable diapers don't forget to ask the manufacturer for coupons!
- Baby Diaper Service: (206) 634-2229
- Pure and Natural: (206) 767-1807
- Preemie Pampers: 800-543-4932
- Preemie Huggies: 800-447-9423
- NW Hospital Supply stocks Preemie Huggies as well as Medela breast pumps: (206) 368-1196, 1530 N. 115th St., Seattle 98133 (they deliver!)

HAIRCUTS FOR KIDS ONLY!

A child's first haircut should be an enjoyable experience for both the parent and child. These salons cater to children with bright decor and toys to play with during the haircut. Many offer special "first haircut" packages.

■ BRAT PACK
(425) 883-1006
Redmond Town Center
Hours: M-F   10:00 a.m.-8:00 p.m.
       Sat.   10:00 a.m.-7:00 p.m.
       Sun.   11:00 a.m.-6:00 p.m.
Cash, Checks, Visa, MC, AmEx

■ HC FOR KIDS
(206) 522-4906
6014 Roosevelt Way N.E.
Seattle, WA 98115
Hours: T-F   10:00 a.m.-7:00 p.m.
       Sat.   10:00 a.m.-4:00 p.m.
Cash, Checks, Visa, MC

■ MC GREGOR'S   *Baby Pages*
GARDEN
(206) 634-2969
2108 N. 55th (Greenlake area)
Seattle, WA 98105
Hours: M-F   10:00 a.m.-7:00 p.m.
       Sat.   9:30 a.m.-5:00 p.m.
Cash, Checks, Visa, MC

■ LIL' HAIR EXPRESS
(253) 839-9412
2014 S. 314th St.
(across from Toys R Us/Hillside Plaza)
Federal Way, WA 98003
Hours: T-F   10:00 a.m.-8:00 p.m.
       Sat.   9:30 a.m.-6:00 p.m.
       Sun.   11:00 a.m.-6:00 p.m.
Cash, Checks, Visa, MC

■ FUN KUTS
(425) 776-7777
3333 184th St. S.W.
(Mervyn's Plaza, across from Alderwood Mall)
Lynnwood, WA 98037
Hours; T-F   10:00 a.m.-7:00 p.m.
       Sat.   10:00 a.m.-6:00 p.m.
       Sun.   10:00 a.m.-5:00 p.m.
Cash, Checks, Visa, MC

■ LI'L KLIPPERS
(206) 633-2158
1418 N. 45th St.
Seattle, WA 98115
Hours: M-F   9:00 a.m.-8:00 p.m.
       Sat.   9:00 a.m.-5:00 p.m.
       Sun.   9:00 a.m.-5:00 p.m.
Cash, Checks, Visa, MC

■ THE EDGE
(206) 633-2158
1418 N. 45th St.
Seattle, WA 98115
Hours: M-F   9:00 a.m.-8:00 p.m.
       Sat.   9:00 a.m.-5:00 p.m.
       Sun.   9:00 a.m.-5:00 p.m.
Cash, Checks, Visa, MC
Both The Edge and Li'l Klippers are at the same location on North 45th; Li'l Klippers is for children under 10 and The Edge caters to older children and teenagers.

CARING FOR YOUR BABY

Seattle is a resource-rich and safe place to be caring for a baby. Years ago, new parents relied on immediate family to give them the support and education they needed to care for a baby. Novice parents in today's fast-paced world often times have long distances between themselves and those wise immediate family members as we become so easily transplanted due to jobs, interests, and adventures. Parents in Seattle can find help, information, health care and resources without too much effort as the resources are well organized and networked and advertised clearly in various places.

Simply picking up the phone and calling one of the many vast resources can connect you with choices of pediatricians, immunization clinics, and child health resources.

Breastfeeding is highly recommended as the ideal way to feed your baby. To help make breastfeeding a positive experience for you and your baby, we've included four pages of resources for lactation consultants and breast pump sales and rentals. For parents interested in feeding their baby organic food, check this chapter for a listing of Seattle's organic food stores.

In addition to the wealth of resources available to babies and parents, Seattle also guarantees that we provide a safe environment for our children. The city of Seattle has the highest national percentage of citizens who know cardiopulmonary resuscitation (CPR) techniques, and has a 25%-30% survival rate for patients suffering cardiac arrest—one of the world's highest survival rates. This is six times the national average! Medic One is an emergency response program that was developed in Seattle and has become a model for other such programs worldwide. This not only helps save our children but helps guarantee that parents and grandparents are going to continue to be a part of their little lives for as long as possible.

ᘓ

Years ago, new parents relied on immediate family to give them the support and education they needed to care for a baby.

ᘓ

CARING FOR BABY

CIRCUMCISION

By Carl Warsowe, M.D., F.A.A.P.

It is a common misbelief that circumcision was a purely religious rite of the ancient Hebrews. In reality, long before its adoption by the Hebrews, circumcision was a widespread practice throughout the ancient Near East. Evidence gathered from historical art and writings date the practice as far back as the Sixth Dynasty in Egypt (2350-2000 B.C.E.) and 2800 B.C.E. in North Syria.[1]

The advent of circumcision as a religious rite is documented in Genesis 17:9-14 where Abraham is commanded: "You shall be circumcised in the flesh of your foreskins, and it shall be a sign of the Covenant between you and me. He that is eight days old among you shall be circumcised; every male throughout your generations..." With the rise of Christianity, the concept of circumcision as a covenant with God was not adopted, and so as Christianity grew and spread, the practice became limited to Jews, Muslims and Coptic Christians, and with some sub-Sahara African tribes, as a rite of passage.

MEDICAL ISSUES AND CONTROVERSIES

Throughout the course of modern medicine, there has been a debate over the pros and cons of circumcision. At times, one philosophy will seem to dominate over the other. For much of the mid-1900s in America, circumcision was considered a medical benefit and was performed with such great regularity in most hospitals that some parents to this day believe that circumcision is required by some state or federal law.

The debate centers on three areas: problems with the foreskin, hygiene, and susceptibility to infectious disease.[2] Removal of the foreskin greatly reduces the risk of penile cancer, but so does adequate hygiene. The chance of infection of the foreskin (posthitis) is eliminated and the likelihood of infection of the glans (head of the penis) is greatly reduced. With removal, however, the glans is constantly exposed to possible irritation which may result in meatal stenosis, where the opening at the tip of the penis becomes constricted and the urine flow is greatly reduced, causing discomfort and rarely, kidney and ureter complications. However, meatal stenosis is not very common.

Phimosis is the most significant problem of being uncircumcised. It occurs when infection, poor hygiene or other causes

≈

After carefully reviewing all the information presented to them, for many the choice is ultimately a personal/ cultural one.

≈

result in a tightening of the foreskin so it is no longer retractable. At times, especially in older men, the stricture can be so severe that it obstructs urine flow and is a surgical emergency. Phimosis is the primary reason why older children and adults undergo circumcision.

With few exceptions, the foreskin of a newborn is not retractable without causing pain, traumatic tears or bleeding. In many children, the foreskin is not fully retractable until the third to fourth year of life. This presents a hygiene problem for the parent. Urine, secretions (smegma), and even stool may accumulate under the foreskin resulting in inflammation and infection. Interestingly, however, this is not a common occurrence. The most that can be done while cleaning the penis is to gently retract the foreskin as far as it can go without discomfort.

As the child grows, a parent needs to show him how to retract the foreskin and clean himself. This becomes a problem as some children develop increasing modesty in the mid childhood years and refuse either parents' attempts to help with or demonstrate proper hygiene. Obviously, with circumcision, hygiene is much easier for the parent and child. However, the first two to three weeks immediately after the circumcision require extra attention to caring for the incision area.

Infections such as gonorrhea, herpes, candidiasis and syphilis are more frequent in uncircumcised males. Most likely, this is because the inner lining of the foreskin is a moist mucosal surface and is not as good a barrier to infection as skin is. Medical studies also give evidence to increased urinary tract infections in uncircumcised males.

CIRCUMCISION PROCEDURE

There are several ways a circumcision can be performed, each determined by the type of surgical tool used. The infant is placed on a form-fitting board with his arms and legs restrained by velcro bands. Most infants are upset by being restrained. Some physicians will not use the arm restraints for this reason. Prior to the 1980s, circumcisions were performed without any anesthesia. However, since a regional anesthesia procedure called dorsal penile nerve block was developed, more doctors are using anesthesia. The doctor injects a small amount of novocaine on either side of the penis where it meets the abdominal wall to block the nerves. Some doctors also give a small superficial injection on the front of the penis where it meets the scrotum to block the few pain fibers that run up the front of the penis. With a good block, there is a very substantial decrease in the discomfort; however, this will not block the pressure or stretching sensations that occur during the procedure.

Many doctors require that an infant not be fed for up to three hours prior to the circumcision for fear of vomiting and aspiration. This is an illogical extension of the rule that patients undergoing general anesthesia must have an empty stomach. In reality, the infant will do much better and be much calmer if he is fed shortly before the circumcision. If the infant were to vomit, there is no more risk of aspiration than if he was in his mother's arms or on his back in bed. With these three changes in the circumcision routine (arms free, dorsal penile nerve block and feeding before the procedure), the procedure of circumcision is much less traumatic for the infant.

Three types of surgical devices are used. The Plastibell is a plastic ring that is placed over the head of the penis and under the foreskin. It has a groove around its perimeter to hold a piece of string that is placed over the foreskin and Plastibell and tied tightly to constrict the blood supply to the foreskin. The remainder of the foreskin is removed, and the Plastibell stays on for several days to a week. When it falls off, there may be a small amount of bleeding.

The Gompco clamp is a bell-shaped device that fits over the head of the penis and under the foreskin. A special ring is then placed over the foreskin and bell and tightened. The entire foreskin is then cut off and the clamp and bell removed.

The last device, the Mogan clamp, is a flat hinged device similar to a scissors, except that the edges are not sharp. The foreskin is pulled up between the blades which are then clamped together. The foreskin is above the blade and the head of the penis is protected below the blade. The foreskin is then removed.

All three devices give the same cosmetic result and have similar complications, the most common being bleeding. It is important to inform the physician if there is a family history of bleeding disorders. Minor bleeding is controlled easily with simple pressure and various foam and gauze wraps impregnated with clotting substances.

Another risk of circumcision is infection at the surgical site. This is rare as the penis has a good blood flow, reducing the risk. For several days to a week after the circumcision, there may be creamy yellow-gray film over the head of the penis. This is not a sign of infection. It may be left or gently washed off.

Accidental surgical trauma to the penis is another risk, though also very uncommon. Parents should inquire as to the experience level of the physician performing the circumcision.

THE DECISION

In most parts of the world, circumcision is not as routinely practiced as it is in this country. Many cultures around the world and some in the United States never circumcise their children. Circumcision rates vary by region within the United States but, in general, about half the boys born in this country will be circumcised. There is an increasing movement by a few to ban it as they see it as a mutilating, barbaric custom. Though these people are vocal, they have had very little success in legally banning the procedure.

When I meet with expectant parents at a prenatal pediatric visit, many of them are still undecided as to whether or not to circumcise their child. For many, after carefully reviewing all the information presented to them, the choice is ultimately a personal/cultural one. Is the father circumcised or not? Do the parents care if the father and the male child have different appearing genitalia? Do they think the circumcised/uncircumcised penis has a more pleasing appearance? Whatever decision the parents make, I stress to them that I feel there is no wrong or right decision.

[1]This and all historical references are taken from Berit Mila in the Reform Context edited by Lewis M. Barth

[2] This data has been taken from Thompson HC et al: Report of the Ad Hoc Task Force on Circumcision, as well as from 25 years of experience, journal reading and discussion with colleagues.

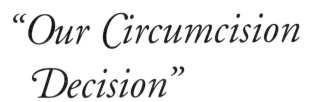

"Our Circumcision Decision"

A Life Experience by Allison Aley

When we first confirmed that I was pregnant, for some reason we both assumed it would be a girl. But as my husband and I adjusted to the idea of having a baby, we started to realize that, while we had always envisioned having a girl first, there was just as much chance that we'd have a boy. We both agreed that we wanted to find out, if that was possible.

We went in for an ultrasound on the day after Christmas and told the technician that we'd like to know the sex if she thought she could tell. Because it was a slow day at the hospital and the images of the baby were particularly clear, she took quite a long time showing us every wonderful detail—fingers, toes, feet, eyes, beating heart, bladder, umbilical cord. We were overwhelmed with the miracle of it all and blissfully happy as we heard words like "normal," "perfect," and "beautiful." We had completely forgotten about the gender question. We were being told that I was carrying what looked like a perfectly healthy baby and that was all that mattered.

As we continued to watch images float across the screen, she said, "So you want to know the sex?" We looked at each other, smiled and then nodded. "Well...it's a boy." "Are you sure?" "Yes, that's his penis." Wow, just like that? No hedging at all when all of my friends had heard things like "It's most likely a girl" or "I can't really tell, the baby is not cooperating." I was still high from the news that he looked normal and this new piece of information was interesting and exciting, but then the thought crossed my mind: "Now we have to address the circumcision issue."

I didn't bring it up right away and when I did I got the reaction that I fully expected. Tom hadn't even considered

that there was a decision to be made. He was circumcised, all of his friends were circumcised, so of course our son would be circumcised. Wasn't it a routine procedure anyway? So began the process of making our first difficult decision as parents. It was such a different experience for us both. We were overwhelmed with the responsibility for the new little life that was growing inside me. And, while we both ended up on the same side of the issue and felt very comfortable and pleased with our decision, we started on opposite sides.

I had done a lot of reading about natural childbirth, breastfeeding and care of the newborn. I knew that circumcision was no longer routine and that the American Academy of Pediatricians no longer recommended that it be done. I was putting so much energy into preparing for a peaceful, natural, welcoming birth, that the idea of cutting off my baby's foreskin seemed contradictory, especially since we had no religious reason to do it. Tom looked at it completely differently. He was less concerned about the pain of the procedure (after all, he didn't remember it), than he was about our son looking different from him and possibly different from his friends as he was growing up.

We discussed it for hours and at times we both got very emotional. We read articles and learned that there is support for every argument on both sides. We quickly realized that it was a decision that had to be made from the heart and gut. We managed to be respectful of each other's feelings, knowing that we each wanted only to do the right thing. I finally said that, although I would choose not to have him circumcised, I thought it should be Tom's decision because he would most likely be the one to explain that decision to our son down the road. I asked only that he really think about it.

After that I didn't bring it up and tried to remain objective when Tom wanted to talk about it. He took the decision very seriously and talked about it with everyone—friends, family, co-workers, and our midwives. We were continually amazed at how misinformed some people were about the procedure and the reasons for having it done. Others were thoughtful and tried to be helpful. My mother assured us that whatever we decided to do would be fine. My

stepmother said he'd look just like all of the Greek statues if he wasn't circumcised. Tom's little brother had a friend who had chosen to be circumcised at 15 because he was the only one of his friends who was not. A lawyer friend had worked on an insurance defense case involving a botched circumcision where the little boy had to undergo reconstructive surgery. All of this was food for thought.

During this time I had the opportunity to watch two circumcisions being performed side by side as part of a clinical rotation. It was hard to watch and I found myself putting my hands protectively over my pregnant belly. The babies were strapped on special boards so that they could not move, and they screamed in what must have been fear and frustration. The obstetricians came in and performed the procedure, each using a different method. Both babies were obviously in pain. The doctors left them strapped to the boards and then the nurses came and swaddled them back up. The parents were not there to comfort them. I felt sick.

When we discussed it at one of our prenatal visits, we learned that, if we chose to have it done (which the midwives did not recommend), the birth center's policy was to have us bring him back to the center when he was eight days old because a baby's blood clots more effectively at that time. We would be there to comfort and nurse the baby immediately. I felt better when I learned this.

Interestingly, my Jewish friends tell me that a ritual bris is done at day eight when the baby is surrounded by family and friends and often given a cloth dipped in wine to suck on to ease the pain. This seems so much more humane. Indeed, many people recommended that we have a mohel perform the circumcision.

One day Tom came home and out of the blue said, "I've decided that we won't have our son circumcised." I was relieved and happy that he had come to the decision that I had hoped for. Looking back now, I am amazed at how much energy and emotion went into that decision, but the process was good for us and helped us to begin to be a cohesive parenting team. And, we both still feel that we made the right decision for us, and for our son, Ben. ❧

IMMUNIZATIONS

■ **KID CARE HOTLINE**
(206) 284-0331
800-756-KIDS (5437)
Call this toll-free line for information and referrals for pediatrician, dental, and immunization services. The goal of this community access program is to help families of low income obtain services. They give referrals to anyone who calls and can help with establishing DSHS eligibility as well as assisting with the application process. Kid Care is also the place to call if you have any concerns about your child's development up to 6 years of age since they can refer you for screening. They are also the contact people for family resource coordination to help families access early intervention programs.

■ **SEATTLE-KING COUNTY DEPARTMENT OF PUBLIC HEALTH**
(206) 296-4949
Call the department's hotline for re-corded health-related information and for the hours and locations of public health centers. The health centers listed below have walk-in clinics and well-child appointments that include immunizations during the hours noted, al-though it's best to call first to confirm those hours and find out about lunch-hour closures. The charge is usually $10 per immunization but no one is turned away if unable to pay. DSHS medical coupons are also accepted. Don't forget to bring your baby's shot record with you each time you go to a clinic.

■ **COLUMBIA CITY PUBLIC HEALTH CENTER**
(206) 296-4650
4400 37th S.
Seattle, WA 98118
Hours: M,T,W,F 8:00 a.m.-6:00 p.m.
        Th   8:00 a.m.-8:00 p.m.

■ **DOWNTOWN PUBLIC HEALTH CENTER**
(206) 296-4755
2124 4th Ave.
Seattle, WA 98121
Hours: M-Th   7:30 a.m.-noon,
                1:00 p.m.-4:30 p.m.
        F   8:00 a.m.-noon,
                1:00 p.m.-4:00 p.m.

■ **NORTH SEATTLE DISTRICT PUBLIC HEALTH CENTER**
(206) 296-4990
10501 Meridian Ave. N.
Seattle, WA 98133
Hours: M,W-F 8:00 a.m.-4:00 p.m.
        T   8:00 a.m.-7:00 p.m.

■ **AUBURN PUBLIC HEALTH CENTER**
(253) 833-8567
(206) 296-8414 from Seattle
20 Auburn Ave.
Auburn, WA 98002
Hours: M,W-F 8:00 a.m.-11:30 a.m.
                1:00 p.m.-4:30 p.m.
        T   8:00 a.m.-11:30 p.m.
                4:30 p.m.-5:30 p.m.

■ EASTGATE PUBLIC HEALTH CENTER
(206) 296-9722
14350 S.E. Eastgate Way
Bellevue, WA 98007
Hours: M-F 8:00 a.m.-12:00 p.m.
              1:00 p.m.-4:00 p.m.

■ FEDERAL WAY PUBLIC HEALTH CENTER
(206) 296-8410 or (253) 874-7639
33431 13th Pl. S.
Federal Way, WA 98003
Hours: M-F 8:00 a.m.-11:00 a.m.,
              1:00 p.m.-4:00 p.m.

■ KENT-SPRINGWOOD PUBLIC HEALTH CENTER
(253) 631-3925
27360 129th Place S.E.
Kent, WA 98031
Hours: M-F 8:00 a.m.-noon
              1:00 p.m.-4:30 p.m.

■ MAPLE VALLEY PUBLIC HEALTH CENTER
(425) 432-1272
22010 S.E. 248th St.
Maple Valley, WA 98038
Hours: Th 8:00 a.m.-6:00 p.m.
(Call to schedule appointment through the Renton Public Health Center)

■ NORTHSHORE PUBLIC HEALTH, FAMILY PLANNING AND TEEN CLINIC
(206) 296-9814
10808 N.E. 145th St.
Bothell, WA 98011
Hours: M-F 10:00 a.m.-11:30 a.m.
              (by appointment) &
              1:00 p.m.-4:00 p.m.
              (walk-in)

■ RENTON PUBLIC HEALTH CENTER
(206) 296-4700
3001 N.E. 4th
Renton, WA 98056
Hours M-F 8:00 a.m.-1:00 p.m.
              2:00 p.m.-5:00 p.m.

■ WHITE CENTER PUBLIC HEALTH CENTER
(206) 296-4620
10821 8th Ave. S.W.
Seattle, WA 98146
Hours: M   9:30 a.m.-5:00 p.m.
        T,Th 1:00 p.m.-4:00 p.m.
        W, F 8:30 a.m.-4:00 p.m.

■ SNOHOMISH COUNTY PUBLIC HEALTH DISTRICT
(425) 339-5220
3020 Rucker Ave., Ste. 108
Everett, WA 98201
Hours: M-F 8:00 a.m.-4:30 p.m.
              (by appointment)
        W   1:00 p.m.-6:15 p.m.
              (walk-in)

(425) 775-3522
6101 200th St. S.W.
Lynnwood, WA 98036
Hours: M-F 8:00 a.m.-5:00 p.m.
              (by appointment)
        W   1:00 p.m.-4:00 p.m.
              (walk-in)

Low fees are charged for immunizations, and DSHS medical coupons are also accepted for payment. Both sites offer walk-in services on Wednesdays and schedule well-child appointments and immunizations during their open hours.

■ **COMMUNITY HEALTH CENTERS OF KING COUNTY**

Auburn Community Health Center
(253) 735-0166
105 A St. S.W.
Auburn, WA 98001
Hours: M,T,Th,F 9:00 a.m.-5:00 p.m.
      W   Noon-8:00 p.m.

Bothell Community Health Center
(425) 486-0658
10414 Beardslee Blvd.
Bothell, WA 98011
Hours: M,T,Th,F 9:00 a.m.-5:00 p.m.
      W   Noon-8:00 p.m.

Eastside Community Health Center
(425) 882-1697
16315 N.E. 87th, Ste. B6
Redmond, WA 98052
Hours: M,T,W,F 9:00 a.m.-5:00 p.m.
      Th   Noon-8:00 p.m.

Federal Way Community Health Center
(253) 874-7634
33431 13th Pl. S.
Federal Way, WA 98003
Hours: M,T,W,F 9:00 a.m.-5:30 p.m.
      Th   12:00 p.m.-8:00 p.m.

Kent Community Health Center
(253) 852-2866
403 E. Meeker, Ste. 200
Kent, WA 98031
Hours: M,W,F   8:30 a.m.-5:30 p.m.
      T,Th   8:30 a.m.-8:00 p.m.

Renton Community Health Center
(425) 226-5536
138 S. 3rd Place
Renton, WA 98055
Hours: M,T,Th,F 9:00 a.m.-5:00 p.m.
      W   Noon-8:00 p.m.

■ **COMMUNITY HEALTH CENTERS OF SNOHOMISH COUNTY**

(425) 775-2589
4111 194th St. S.W., Ste. 101
Lynnwood, WA 98038
Hours: M-Th   8:00 a.m.-11:00 a.m.
                 2:00 p.m.-4:00 p.m.
                 (walk-in for established patients)
         M-F   9:00 a.m.-11:00 a.m.
                 2:00 p.m.-4:00 p.m.
                 (well-child and immunizations for new patients)

(425) 258-1830
1410 Broadway
Everett, WA 98201
Hours: M-F   8:30 a.m.-5:00 p.m.
The Community Health Centers accept DSHS medical coupons and charge low fees on a sliding scale for office visits and immunizations. A well-child visit will be scheduled to coincide with immunizations for new patients and for established patients when appropriate. Call to make an appointment.

🐾

CHILD HEALTH RESOURCES

■ CHILDREN'S HOSPITAL AND MEDICAL CENTER RESOURCE CENTER

(206) 526-2201 (center/education info)
(206) 526-2500 (resource line)
4800 Sand Point Way N.E.
Seattle, WA 98105
Web site: www.chmc.org
Hours: Resource center hours:
       M-F   8:00 a.m.-4:00 p.m.
       Resource line:
       Daily   7:00 a.m.-midnight

Children's Hospital offers the most comprehensive child health, safety, and parenting resource service in Washington State. On the fifth floor of the hospital (5A) you'll find the Parent Resource Center. It's filled with racks and filing cabinets of free brochures, articles, and booklets related to parenting; including information on feeding, immunizations, community resources, and special needs programs, as well as safety and health issues. There is also a lending library of books and videos for viewing in the Center on parenting issues.

Children's also operates a resource line, staffed by pediatric registered nurses. You may call for free, confidential information on child health and parenting, as well as referrals to physicians and community resources. They will even send out written materials upon request.

A leader in community education, Children's offers classes for parents: Babysafe, Toddlersafe, Child and Infant CPR. They offer preadolescent classes including Better Babysitters; For Girls Only: A Heart-to-Heart Talk on Growing Up; and For Boys Only: The Challenges of Growing Up. Classes are offered at various times and are affordable. For more information on classes, visit the resource center or the Children's web site. Class information and events are also published in a quarterly newsletter, "Good Growing," along with a great deal of other useful parenting and children's health information.

■ COMMUNITY INFORMATION LINE

(206) 461-3200

Operated by the Crisis Clinic's Resource Center, this phone line provides information and referrals to over 2,000 social service agencies in King County. The center maintains a current data base of agencies and also publishes an annual directory called "Where to Turn" which lists agency addresses and phone numbers. A larger "Where to Turn PLUS" directory includes more detailed information on agencies, including a service description, eligibility requirements, fees, and branch locations.

■ MED-INFO AT NORTHWEST HOSPITAL

(206) 633-4636

Northwest Hospital provides their 24-hour MED-INFO line as a free community service. When you call, you'll talk to a registered nurse who can answer medical questions and refer you to additional resources as necessary.

■ PARENT PROVIDER RESOURCE LINE

(425) 259-2973

This phone line is operated by the Child Care Resource and Referral of Volunteers of America in Snohomish County. Besides providing phone referrals to agencies, parent support groups, and classes, a Parent Resource Guide is published quarterly which lists information on programs for parents. This publication is published by Lifenet in conjunction with the Volunteers of America.

■ PARENTS ANONYMOUS

(206) 233-0139 (Family Help Line)
800-932-HOPE (outside Seattle)

Parents may call the help line 24 hours a day to get assistance in dealing with crisis situations and to locate local resources. They'll also send written material on positive parenting. Parents Anonymous offers free self-help support groups throughout the community, including free child care.

■ SEATTLE TIMES/CHILDREN'S HOSPITAL INFOLINE

(206) 464-2000

Call this number to hear recorded messages on various child/teen health topics.

ᴁ&

BREASTFEEDING RESOURCES

■ BABY'S FIRST CHOICE

(206) 789-0959
7033 7th Ave. N.W.
Seattle, WA 98117

Beverly Fissel, RN, IBCLC, has been a certified lactation consultant for about three years in addition to being a nurse practicing in the maternity and pediatric setting for 20-plus years. She offers both office visits and personal home visits for $38 and $50 respectively. She also has an assortment of breast pumps for rental and purchase as well as many breastfeeding aids and supplies. If you are looking for a friendly, supportive lactation consultant with a wealth of experience to draw on, this is the person to call.

■ BESTFEEDING

(425) 672-6825
19823 Damson Rd.
Lynnwood, WA 98036

Bestfeeding is dedicated to promoting and supporting breastfeeding through consultations, rentals and sales of a wide selection of breast pumps and other useful equipment, instruction in pump use and expert help in choosing the right pump, and information and support so that breastfeeding can be an enjoyable experience for mother and baby. Judy Hulse, RN, MS, IBCLC, is a mother of four breastfed children. She is a nurse/ lactation consultant at a local hospital, teaches breastfeeding classes for a local childbirth education group, speaks at regional breastfeeding conferences, and has been an International Board Certified Lactation Consultant since 1987. She is available evenings and weekends, has reasonable rates, and even does home visits in the local area.

■ **BIRTH AND BEYOND**   *Baby Pages*
(206) 324-4831 or 800-348-4831
2610 E. Madison St.
Seattle, WA 98112

(425) 402-9366
14450 Woodinville-Redmond Rd.
Woodinville, WA 98072
Birth and Beyond offers breastfeeding accessories such as nursing bras, shirts, and other attire. They have a large selection of breast pumps for rental and for purchase. Also available are books, Boppy nursing pillows, Avent bottles, and a supportive environment for the nursing mother staffed by experienced salespeople with breastfeeding expertise. The stores feature weekly product demonstrations and informational workshops that are free and include topics and products of interest for breastfeeding mothers.

■ **CEAS BREASTFEEDING SERVICES**
(206) 789-0883
10021 Holman Rd. N.W.
Seattle, WA 98177
The breastfeeding counselors at the Childbirth Education Association of Seattle are registered nurses and childbirth educators who have had special training as lactation specialists. They offer help for nursing mothers and their babies in the early days after birth and during the following months of breastfeeding. CEAS offers free telephone counseling on weekdays 9:00 a.m. to 3:00 p.m. and on weekends, generally from 9:00 a.m. to noon. To reach a counselor on the weekends, after hours, or on holidays you can

use a telepager at (206) 615-8078. If you need more than telephone counseling, a specialist can provide you an individual consultation for about $65. CEAS also offers two classes on breastfeeding. One class is the breastfeeding class included in the eight-week childbirth classes but can be taken anytime as a separate class. The other class is "The Breastfeeding Expectant Father"—a two-hour class that is offered every other month. The cost for classes is $20 per couple.

■ **DECENT EXPOSURES**
(206) 364-4540 or 800-524-4949
(206) 364-5160 brochure request line
P.O. Box 27206
Seattle, WA 98125
Web site: www.decentexposures.com
Decent Exposures offers a bra that is designed by two sisters who were unable to find comfortable fitting bras during their pregnancies. They offer an "Un-bra" which can fit women in every size from 28AAA to 58K. The bra that they offer can be lifted up or down for nursing. This Seattle company also offers nursing pads, underpants and other clothing items for nursing mothers. The Un-bra costs between $25 and $50 depending on the size and material you choose. You will need to call for an appointment to be fitted. Shipping is included. They also have expanded into the baby clothing line with their 100% cotton and organic cotton hats, washcloths, blankets, bibs, and other baby accessories.

■ **EVERGREEN PROFESSIONAL CENTER**
(425) 899-2790
12304 N.E. 130th Lane
Kirkland, WA 98034
Hours: M-F   9:00 a.m.-7:00 p.m.
        Sat.   9:00 a.m.-2:00 p.m.
All of Medela breast pumps and the Nurture III pumps and accessories are available at this pharmacy for rental or for sale. They also carry many nursing accessories such as nursing pillows. The Evergreen Hospital Postpartum Center is across the street with lactation consultants who are available if needed.

■ **FAMILY RESOURCES**
(425) 485-3295 (call for appointment)
21029 W. Richmond Rd.
Bothell, WA 98021
Family Resources offers a complete line of breastfeeding supplies, including Medela pumps to rent and pumps to own (even a rent-to-own plan). Accessories include pillows, pads, baby slings, and more. There's a large assortment of nursing bras (32A-48J), gowns, and other clothing. Owner P.J. Jacobsen (former owner of two highly popular local children's stores in the '80s—Babakies and Kinderkies) is a board certified lactation consultant and offers her services at a very economical rate.

■ **HEALTHTEAM NORTHWEST**
(425) 482-4000 or 800-888-4429
2525 220th S.E.
Bothell, WA 98021
An affiliate of Children's Hospital & Medical Center, this agency provides in-home breastfeeding support by registered nurses with lactation expertise as well as temporary child care and newborn care.

■ **HEARTFELT CENTER**
(425) 670-2481
Marcia David, LMP, CD is a licensed massage therapist, certified doula, and lactation consultant. She carries all Medela breast pumps for rental or for purchase as well as many supplies, including nursing bras. She provides 24-hour phone consulting to clients and in-home lactation visits.

LA LECHE LEAGUE OF GREATER SEATTLE

La Leche League is the world's largest resource for breastfeeding and related information. League members give support, education, information, and encouragement to women who want to breastfeed. Call (206) 522-1336 or 800-525-3234 to hear a recording which will supply you with a list of leaders in your area whom you may call with your nursing questions. The League strongly believes in nursing and they will do all they can to support you towards this goal. Your local leader will provide you with information about monthly meetings. She will also mail you a free catalog featuring books and products related to breastfeeding.

■ MILK DIAPERS
800-929-0218
P.O. Box 961
Camas, WA 98607
Milk Diapers is a locally owned company that offers washable nursing pads. The nursing pads are available at local retail outlets or by mail order. The company also sells nursing sleep wear and bedjackets.

■ NORTHWEST MEDICAL SUPPLY
(206) 368-1196
1530 N. 115th St. #108
Seattle, WA 98133
Hours: M-F   9:00 a.m.-6:30 p.m.
        Sat.   9:00 a.m.-1:00 p.m.
Northwest Medical Supply, located on the Northwest Hospital campus, is a Medela breast pump rental station. Lactation consultants provide support for breastfeeding mothers as well as Home-to-Work Transition support and training. Northwest Medical Supply has satellite stations in both King and Snohomish counties which offer a full line of breastfeeding supplies. They offer on-call pump delivery and a 24-hour breastfeeding answer line.

■ PACIFIC MOTHERS SUPPORT, INC. (P.M.S.I)
(425) 462-0577 or 800-578-2260
1407 132nd N.E., Ste. 10
Bellevue, WA 98005
Hours: M-F   9:00 a.m.-5:00 p.m.
        Sat.   11:00 a.m.-3:00 p.m.
P.M.S.I. has only hospital-approved breast pumps for rental or purchase. One pump they sell is the highly recommended Nurture III breast pump for

about $100. This double pump has a five-year warranty. There is a certified lactation consultant on staff. All breastfeeding supplies and accessories are available at the office during normal business hours and any other time by appointment. They will bill insurance companies for you if you have prior authorization for equipment and will accept DSHS medical coupons.

■ SPECIAL BOND
(253) 839-6401
30819 14th Ave. S., Ste. D
Federal Way, WA 98003
Diane Herforth and Pamela Golliet, both certified doulas with more than 40 years experience between the two of them, are committed to helping families achieve their goals in childbirth and breastfeeding. Diane is a certified lactation consultant and offers breastfeeding consultations by appointment. They also offer childbirth classes and labor support and offer home visits. They have breast pumps and equipment to both rent and sell.

■ THE TAKE CARE STORE
Central:
(206) 326-3496
306 15th Ave. E.
Seattle, WA 98112
Hours: M-F   9:30 a.m.-5:30 p.m.
        Sat.   10:00 a.m.-3:00 p.m.

Northgate:
(206) 527-7878
9800 4th Ave. N.E.
Seattle, WA 98115
Hours: M-F   9:00 a.m.-1:00 p.m.,
               1:30 p.m.-5:00 p.m.
        Sat.   9:00 a.m.-1:00 p.m.

BREASTFEEDING

■ THE TAKE CARE STORE

Redmond:

(425) 883-5052

2700 152nd Ave. N.E.

Redmond, WA 98052

Hours: M-Th   9:30 a.m.-6:00 p.m.

           F   9:30 a.m.-5:30 p.m.

           Sat.   10:00 a.m.-3:00 p.m.

Medela portable breast pumps are available for purchase. There is also a hospital style breast pump that may be rented by the day or month. Both pumps have the single or double pumping option, depending on the parts that you purchase or receive from your hospital. The stores offer a full supply of accessories like pads and pillows, and are well-known for their excellent selection of educational books on a wide variety of health topics. Although located at Group Health, you don't have to be a co-op member to shop at the stores, and all three are open on Saturdays to make shopping even more convenient.

■ WOMEN, INFANTS, AND CHILDREN (WIC)

800-841-1410

Serving Seattle-King County

This 800 number will give you (in English or Spanish) the nearest WIC office in your area. WIC is for pregnant or lactating women and their children under 5 years of age who are assessed to be at nutritional risk. The group offers prenatal nutrition counseling and vouchers for specific nutritious foods.

                 ❧

FEEDING BABY: ORGANIC BABY FOOD

All of the following grocers carry various organic produce and baby foods, and a large variety of other organic foods. If you are just looking for Earth's Best baby food and organic produce it can most often be found at the larger grocer chains such as Albertsons, Larry's Markets, Safeway, and QFC's.

■ CENTRAL CO-OP GROCERY

(206) 329-1545

1835 12th Ave.

Seattle, WA 98122

Hours: M-Sun.   9:00 a.m.-10:00 p.m.

Central Co-op carries Earth's Best baby food, Healthy Times teething biscuits and cookies, grains, organic juices, and lots of organic produce. Also available are organic dairy products, soy alternative products such as nondairy cheeses and milk, as well as a large selection of bulk foods such as cereals and grains. They accept membership from any co-op; if you're not a member you pay a 15% surcharge for purchases over $5. To become a member you pay an initial fee of $5, and then $2 each month you shop until you've paid $60. Look for their new store to open soon at 16th and Madison.

■ MANNA MILLS

(425) 775-3479

21705 66th Ave. W.

Mountlake Terrace, WA 98043

Hours: M-F   9:30 a.m.-8:00 p.m.

         Sat.   10:00 a.m.-6:00 p.m.

This store is a little hard to find. Take the 220th St. S.W. exit from I-5 and proceed west. Turn right at 66th W. and you'll see the store on your right a few blocks down. Inside you'll find organic juices, cookies, crackers, and a big selection of whole grains in bulk containers. Prices are very good on bulk items and, since they are a mill, flours are fresh as they are ground right on the premises. You will also find good, affordable organic produce here and even natural blend cotton disposable diapers.

■ **PUGET CONSUMERS CO-OP (PCC)**
(425) 828-4621
10718 N.E. 68th
Kirkland, WA 98034
Hours: Daily   8:00 a.m.-10:00 p.m.

(206) 525-1450
6504 20th Ave. N.E.
Seattle, WA 98115
Hours: Daily   9:00 a.m.-9:00 p.m.

(206) 525-3586
7504 Aurora Ave. N.
Seattle, WA 98103
Hours: Daily   8:00 a.m.-11:00 p.m.

(206) 723-2720
5041 Wilson Ave. S.
Seattle, WA 98118
Hours: Daily   7:00 a.m.-10:00 p.m.

(206) 526-7661
6514 40th Ave. N.E.
Seattle, WA 98115
Hours: Daily   8:00 a.m.-10:00 p.m.

(206) 937-8481
2749 California Ave. S.W.
Seattle, WA 98116
Hours: Daily   8:00 a.m.-10:00 p.m.

(206) 632-6811
716 N. 34th
Seattle, WA 98103
Hours: Daily   8:00 a.m.-11:00 p.m.
PCC is the largest natural foods co-op in the country, owned by over 40,000 active members. All of their full-service grocery stores have an in-store deli and they feature baked goods from a number of different suppliers throughout the community. They have a large organic produce section, bulk grains and spices, organic juices, organic milk, butter and cheeses, goat's milk, and also carry Earth's Best baby food. The co-op has a large selection of free literature, and sells popular books on healthy eating and living. They also offer a variety of cooking and nutrition classes that address parents' and children's eating needs. To join you'll pay $8, then make regular payments towards a $60 lifetime membership that is fully refundable if you resign your membership.

■ **RAINBOW GROCERY**
(206) 329-8440
417 15th Ave. E.
Seattle, WA 98112
Hours: Daily   9:00 a.m.-9:00 p.m.
At Rainbow Grocery you'll find Earth's Best baby food, organic juice and produce, goat's milk, crackers and rice cakes.

艹

CHILD SAFETY AND FIRSTAID/CPR

■ AMERICAN HEALTH AND SAFETY TRAINING

(425) 485-2529

This company provides a six-hour CPR/ first aid course for $30 per person and a group CPR class for $125 (up to 20 people per group). They also offer private classes for $75/class. Sessions are held at sites in Kirkland, Bothell, and other locations.

■ AMERICAN RED CROSS

King County Chapter:
(206) 323-2345
1900 25th Ave. S.
Seattle, WA 98144
Hours: M-F   9:00 a.m.-4:30 p.m.

Snohomish County Chapter:
(425) 252-4103
2530 Lombard Ave.
Everett, WA 98201
Hours: M-F   9:00 a.m.-4:30 p.m.
The American Red Cross has been teaching courses for more than 80 years. Their courses are standardized nationwide and are kept up-to-date with the latest information available. They offer a nine-hour class on Community First Aid and Safety, which teaches first aid and adult and infant/child CPR. The class costs $55. They also teach a five-hour infant/child CPR class which covers CPR for infants and children and care for breathing emergencies. This class costs $30. Classes are held days, evenings, and Saturdays at many sites throughout the community.

■ BABY BLOCKERS, LLC

(425) 837-8660
P.O. Box 1658
Issaquah, WA 98027
Baby Blockers specializes in child home safety for Eastside families. They stock more than 100 different safety products, including locks and guards for banisters, cabinets, toilets, appliances and windows. In addition to sales, Baby Blockers will provide product installation and home safety consultations.

■ BABY SAFE BUDGET CHILD PROOFERS

(425) 397-8468 or 888-586-9966
P.O. Box 758
Lake Stevens, WA 98258
E-mail: bbsafe@aol.com
Hours: M-F   8:00 a.m.-8:00 p.m.
        Sat.   9:00 a.m.-3:00 p.m.
This national mail order company offers child safety products for do-it-yourself childproofing: brand-name gates, latches, outlet covers, hearth and furniture padding, kitchen and bathroom safety products, window and door safety products, stair and deck protection and much more. All products come with simple installation instructions; most install without tools. If tools are required, they are pictured next to the product description in the catalog. Prices are always discounted, and usually much lower than in other catalogs. And BabySafe Budget Child Proofers is a local company.

■ **CHILDBIRTH EDUCATION ASSOCIATION OF SEATTLE (CEAS) AND CHILDREN'S HOSPITAL & MEDICAL CENTER (CHMC)**

(206) 789-0883 registration info

The following classes, co-sponsored by CHMC and CEAS, are offered at various times and dates at Children's Hospital:

Infant and Child CPR: This American Heart Association Pediatric Basic Life Support class is taught by pediatric registered nurses. Topics include pediatric risk factors, healthy heart living, infant/child CPR, choking and safety. Review classes are also available. Cost is $25 per person.

Babysafe and Toddlersafe: A safety class for expectant parents and others who care for children. Topics include developmental stages, risk factors, home/personal safety, injury prevention, and CPR/choking rescue demonstration and practice. Babysafe addresses infants; Toddlersafe focuses on children 1-5 years of age. Cost is $20 per family for each class

■. **EVERGREEN HOSPITAL MEDICAL CENTER**

(425) 899-3000 registration/information

Evergreen Family Maternity Center offers an Infant and Child CPR course. Learn the special CPR skills needed to aid an infant or child. The fee is $20 per person or $35 per couple.

■ **FIRST STEP FIRST AID/CPR**

(206) 328-1377

P.O. Box 22997

Seattle, WA 98122

Taught by a professional fire fighter, the First Step program is certified by the Department of Labor and Industries and provides a full eight-hour infant/child/adult CPR and first aid course for $35. A three-hour CPR class is offered for $15. Recertification classes are also available. Slides and videos are used to supplement the basic curriculum and the focus is on providing a flexible and low-stress environment for learning. Classes are held on a regular basis throughout the community and groups can also arrange to have a First Step course provided at their site. Discount rates are available for groups.

■ **HEART START**

(888) 235-7106

Heart Start offers first aid and CPR classes scheduled regularly at a location in Bellevue. Groups may also request a course at their own site. The cost for individuals is $39 for a full eight-hour infant/child/adult First Aid and CPR session or $15 for CPR only. Group rates are slightly less, averaging $25 (full course) and $11 (CPR only) per person. Discounts are available for new clients.

CHILD SAFETY

■ HOLISTIC CHILDBIRTH EDUCATION AND YOGA CENTER

(206) 547-9882
4649 Sunnyside Ave. N., Rm. 300
Seattle, WA 98103
E-mail: yogaaiki@ix.netcom.com
The center offers separate infant CPR (for ages birth to 1 year) and child CPR (ages 1 to 8) workshops. You may bring your infant to the infant CPR class but pre-crawling infants only, please. The cost is $25 per person or $35 per couple for a 2-1/2 hour session.

■ MEDIC FIRST AID

(425) 747-5252
A national program, Medic First Aid is taught by EMTs both on-site and at group locations. The rate for a group of ten to twelve is $350, and includes a full eight-hour first aid and CPR session.

■ MEDIC II

Seattle Fire Department
(206) 684-7274
Free CPR classes are offered to Seattle/ King County residents at community locations, including fire stations. The classes are free but donations are appreciated. They offer a three-hour adult class, a four-hour pediatric/infant class and a 1-1/2 hour adult refresher course.

■ NORTHWEST HOSPITAL

(206) 368-1784, Childbirth Education Northwest's three-hour infant CPR and Safety class teaches infant CPR, accident prevention and product safety to parents, grandparents and babysitters (over age 14) who care for infants, newborn to 12 months. The cost is $15 per person. First aid classes are also available.

■ OVERLAKE HOSPITAL MEDICAL CENTER

(425) 688-5259 education office
Overlake Hospital offers the following safety classes:

Car Safe Kids: A class that will help you learn how to select an appropriate seat for your child and use it properly. Participants will receive a coupon for $5 off a Toys "R" Us car seat. The cost is $15 per person or $25 for two family members.

Infant CPR and Safety Proofing: A course for parents covering accident prevention, product and equipment safety, infant CPR/choking (birth to 1 year) with mannequins.

Kid Safety + Workshop: A two-part course covering safety and accident prevention, basic first aid and CPR. For parents, foster parents and child care providers. DSHS certified. Ages 11 to adult.

■ PROVIDENCE GENERAL MEDICAL CENTER

(425) 261-4565
Birth and Family Education at Providence General Medical Center in Everett offers the following classes:

Car Safe Kids Class: This class will teach you how to keep your babies and older children safe while in a car. Come learn from the experts of the Washington State Safety Restraint coalition. Offered monthly.

Infant Safety and CPR: This 2-1/2 hour class for expectant and new parents covers information on keeping your child safe at home, in the car and when at play. Infant CPR instruction and airway management is also covered. The class is taught by an American Heart Association Certified CPR instructor.

■ ST. FRANCIS HOSPITAL
(253) 952-7957 or 888-825-3227
CPR/Infant Safety: The Franciscan Health System Family Education offers this one-time class for parents, parents to be, grandparents, and baby-sitters. Learn resuscitation techniques and practical tips for making your home safe for children. Certification for the course is available. The cost is $20 per person or $30 per couple.

■ SAFETY FOR TODDLERS *Baby Pages* OF KIRKLAND
(425) 487-3460 or 800-775-3460
Safety for Toddlers offers top of the line, quality, not easily found safety products for your home to create a safer environment. Well known in the Seattle area, they offer home installation of products or you can purchase direct from them and install them yourself. They also give community service safety presentations to any parent support groups and offer in-home consultations.

■ SAFETY RESTRAINT COALITION
(425) 828-8975 or 800-BUCK-L-UP
If you have questions about choosing a car seat or using it correctly, this is the place to call. They can provide car seat recall information, or tell you where to find car seat distribution programs. Kids can join the Buckle Up Helper Club. It's free and teaches good seat belt habits. Buckle Up Helpers get free stickers and club mailings. If a seat belt, child car seat or air bag saved you from injury or death in a car crash, you can join Washington's Saved by the Belt Club. You just need to call to join and get a free license plate frame.

■ SWEDISH MEDICAL CENTER
(206) 386-3606
An Infant Safety and CPR class is offered that teaches infant CPR, safety tips for accident prevention and basic first aid for burns, poisonings, head injuries and other emergencies. It is an excellent choice for anyone who will be responsible for infant care. This one-session course is offered the second (and periodically the fourth) Wednesday of each month from 7:00-9:00 p.m. at Swedish Medical Center/Ballard. There is also a class offered at Swedish Medical Center in Seattle at various times during each month.

■ WASHINGTON POISON CENTER
(206) 526-2121 or 800-732-6985
TDD: (206) 517-2394 or 800-572-0638
The Washington Poison Center, affiliated with Children's Hospital and Medical Center, managed approximately 135,000 patient concerns in 1995-96. The center, located in Seattle, handles calls regarding poisonous and hazardous substances from individuals and organizations from throughout Washington state.

■ WASHINGTON TRAFFIC SAFETY COMMISSION
(360) 753-6197
1000 S. Cherry St.
P.O. Box 40944
Olympia, WA 98504
The Commission provides information on child car seats, child passenger safety, and state seat belt laws. They also have information on impaired driving, bicycle and pedestrian safety and other traffic safety issues.

CHILD SAFETY

WATER SAFETY RECOMMENDATIONS

Experts agree that there is no single measure to prevent childhood drownings. The key appears to be a combination of efforts including constant supervision, multiple barriers, and CPR training. In order to be effective, it is extremely important that parents and caregivers are knowledgeable of these measures not only for our own personal safety, but for helping to educate the community as a whole.

The following measures can be taken to help prevent drownings.

MAINTAIN CONSTANT ADULT SUPERVISION

Constant visual supervision should be practiced near all bodies of water. Most children who drown are seen five minutes or less before being missed. Drownings occur suddenly and without warning. There is usually no splash and no cry.

- Do not allow children to play in water unsupervised.
- Keep toys out of the pool area.
- Have a phone near the pool or water and post 9-1-1 on the phone.
- Do not let children play roughly in water.
- Have a designated "child watcher" when there are several children in the water.

INSTALL PROPER POOL BARRIERS

If you own a pool, proper pool barriers such as fences, motorized pool covers or self-closing, self-latching doors are a necessity.

- Know the current building ordinance for pool barriers in your community.
- Keep items which can be used for climbing away from pool fences.
- Inspect and maintain barriers on a regular basis.

KNOW CPR AND PRACTICE WATER SAFETY

Once an incident occurs, survival depends on rescuing the child quickly, and initiating proper CPR. Seconds count.

- Learn CPR and recertify every two years.
- Enroll your child in swimming classes.
- Do not consider children to be "drown proof" just because they have been enrolled in swimming classes.

This information was reprinted with permission from a brochure produced by the Drowning Prevention Coalition of Central Arizona.

SPECIAL CONCERNS

If you are considering becoming a parent, are pregnant, or have a child with special health care needs, Seattle is the place to be if you would like some help. Seattle is a family-friendly city with a wealth of resources available to meet the array of needs a family may present. It is not uncommon for a pregnant woman to, at some point, have concerns for the welfare of that small wonder that is maturing within her womb. The Greater Seattle region has more than a half dozen major hospitals and medical centers that provide cutting edge maternity and newborn services and are staffed by highly-skilled medical professionals.

Upon the delivery of an infant requiring special medical care and treatment, Airlift Northwest will transport that infant to the best facility to care for it until it is stable enough to return to the birth hospital closer to home or to home for good. If that infant continues to require care or has any disabilities that require care and services, there is no need to worry about availability of resources. There are multiple resources to be tapped for support for medical as well as psychosocial needs.

The University of Washington School of Medicine's nationally recognized Department of Pediatrics is based at Children's Hospital & Regional Medical Center in Seattle.

Being a parent in the Seattle area is just a little more comfortable knowing that the resources are here just in case you might need them.

ও

Being a parent in the Seattle area is just a little more comfortable knowing that the resources are here just in case you might need them.

ও

SPECIAL CONCERNS

"The Perfect Baby"

By Sheryl Rosner

As most people expect, I truly felt that my pregnancy and the birth of my first child would be marked by joy and emotional bliss. I had a very uneventful pregnancy; in fact, I hardly ever felt sick. I went through all of the usual pregnancy screening tests without a hitch. I had three ultrasounds, all of which showed a perfectly healthy developing fetus. All signs showed that I would have an unremarkable birth of an undoubtedly remarkable baby.

My labor began when my water broke as I sat watching "Get Shorty" at the movie theater, just two days before my expected due date. My husband and friends whisked me off and the doctor on call instructed me to come in to the hospital since I would need to deliver the baby within 24 hours. My doctor was not on call that night so I was introduced to a doctor who I had never met before. My labor progressed rapidly and the baby was born after just a few hours of pushing.

As the baby emerged I could see my husband David's face, as the head was flipped around. I said, "Is it a girl or a boy?" and I heard David ask the doctor, "Is that a cleft lip?" The doctor looked quickly at the baby and stated matter of factly, "Yes, I believe it is." At that moment, everything had changed. The blissful birth that was expected turned into one of the most stressful and traumatic moments of my life. I screamed, "Is the baby okay? Can I see it?" and David said, "It's a girl and she has a cleft lip." All I wanted to do was hold the baby and make sure I would be able to feed her.

Samantha was born with a bilateral, incomplete cleft lip. Her palate was intact, which allowed her to nurse right away. I had already been slightly familiar with clefts since a friend of mine from work had a baby with a cleft just six months prior to Samantha's birth. When her baby was born, I did some rough research since I was curious about the condition. I was relieved to learn that it is predominately a cosmetic condition that can be fixed through plastic surgery.

The next few days in the hospital involved frustration, fear, confusion and sadness. I felt very uninformed about Samantha's condition, although I did receive some assurance from Samantha's pediatrician that things were going to be all right. I tapped into every resource in the medical community that I knew to help us locate the best plastic surgeon to conduct Samantha's surgery. All avenues pointed us to one local hospital's team of highly skilled plastic surgeons and craniofacial experts. I was unable to get an appointment for Samantha until one week after she was born, but in the meantime, she was turning out to be the most delightful, adorable child I had ever seen. She nursed easily and we bonded instantaneously.

Our doctor helped reassure us that everything was, in fact, going to be fine. We scheduled Samantha's surgery for 12 weeks after she was born. I was told that she would not be able to nurse for two weeks after the surgery, so I would need to get her used to a special bottle. She would also need to wear cuffs around her elbows so that she would be unable to touch her lip after the surgery.

The surgery was long and heart-wrenching, but thanks to the plastic surgeon's genius, Samantha looks gorgeous. People often stop me and tell me how beautiful she is. She will probably need a few more small procedures before she is 12 and she will ultimately need a lot of dental work—but all in all, we feel extremely lucky and thankful to have such a wonderful, perfect child. ❧

CHILDREN WITH SPECIAL NEEDS

■ ADVOCATES FOR RETARDED CITIZENS

(206) 364-4645, ext. 21
10550 Lake City Way N.E., Ste. A
Seattle, WA 98125
ARC has been serving people with developmental disabilities and their families since 1936. A Parent-to-Parent Program that offers emotional support and information by connecting parents with other parents is a free and confidential program that ARC offers. They also publish a monthly newsletter, provide printed resource materials, and have a lending library. Family social events and educational workshops are offered by facilitators who are parents who have "been there," and offer understanding, resources, knowledge and group support. ARC has information about community resources to help your child learn and develop to his/her fullest potential and can also direct you to resources for your entire family.

■ AMERICAN DIABETES ASSOCIATION

(206) 282-4616
557 Roy St., Lower Level
Seattle, WA 98109
Wondering what to do with your child with diabetes for Halloween? Call the ADA youth program and get information on the Halloween party they are having for children with diabetes. They plan various other children's events throughout the year as well as a summer camp for children affected by diabetes. Also offered are educational meetings and support groups throughout King County. The association also makes referrals to medical specialists and offers free diabetes screening through the University of Washington Medical Center. They have a complete library stocked with educational videos for loan and numerous books for loan and for purchase. They can also provide you with informational pamphlets on diabetes and specific care issues. Many of the library resources are geared towards various developmental levels and are printed in a variety of different languages.

■ AMERICAN HEART ASSOCIATION

(206) 632-6881
4414 Woodland Park Ave. N.
Seattle, WA 98103
The Association promotes education about heart defects and conditions and provides educational materials for the general public and people diagnosed with cardiac conditions. It raises funds for research through various activities and fund-raising programs it sponsors in Seattle neighborhoods. Another service provided is training CPR instructors who provide CPR classes to interested people in the Seattle area.

■ AMERICAN LUNG ASSOCIATION

(206) 441-5100
2625 3rd Ave.
Seattle, WA 98121
Children with respiratory conditions will appreciate the support of the local American Lung Association, which includes education and support, and a camp for 6- to 12-year-olds with asthma. They also can refer you to various support groups, including parent and peer groups, that meet throughout the Seattle area.

■ **ASHLEY HOUSE**
(360) 825-6525
40903 236th Ave. S.E.
Enumclaw, WA 98022
Ashley House was established in 1989 in response to a statewide task force which determined that medically fragile children were staying in hospitals longer than necessary, were going to adult nursing homes, or were being referred out of state. It is housed in three homes built as private residences which are located in Enumclaw, Tacoma, and Olympia. Ashley House was developed as a transition between the hospital and home for children who are technology dependent. Children will receive very skilled nursing care while the family can adjust and prepare for their child's homecoming at a much lower cost than if the child stayed in the hospital. The program offers transitional care for medically fragile or medically intensive children—24-hour skilled nursing care, weekly physical, occupational and education services, and comprehensive counseling support in a homelike setting. Ashley House developed from the belief that no child should have to live permanently in an institutional environment. Several beds are available for children whose families need some brief "time out." Respite care enables parents or guardians of medically fragile or medically intensive children to spend time with other family members, as well as the opportunity to manage important family business or crises which may arise, or simply to go on vacation. The overall goal of the program is to help families cope with crisis, by providing a warm, caring environment in which they may learn how to deal with their child's disabilities.

■ **AUTISM SOCIETY**
(360) 943-2205
203 East 4th Ave.
Olympia, WA 98501
The Society provides information, referral, and advocacy for children and adults with autism, and their families. They also offer information on support groups in the Seattle area.

■ **BIRTH TO THREE DEVELOPMENTAL CENTER**
(253) 874-5445
35535 6th Pl. S.W.
Federal Way, WA 98023
A United Way agency, Birth to Three is "a special place for special children." Classroom and private sessions provide special needs children with physical, occupational and speech and language therapy in a play group setting. Feeding and dressing skills are taught along with cognitive skills, sign language, and songs. Both developmentally delayed and typically developing children participate in the program. Parent participation is encouraged.

■ **BOYER CHILDREN'S CLINIC**
(206) 325-8477
1850 Boyer Ave. E.
Seattle, WA 98112
The clinic provides diagnostic evaluation and treatment for children with developmental delays, cerebral palsy, neurological impairments, or other disabilities. Special evaluation and treatment for children birth to 3 years old are offered.

SPECIAL NEEDS

■ **CENTER ON HUMAN DEVELOPMENT AND DISABILITY (CHDD)**
(206) 685-1253
University of Washington
P.O. Box 357920
Seattle, WA 98195
The CHDD provides assessment and diagnosis for developmental delays and retardation including fetal alcohol syndrome and autism. They also offer high-risk infant follow-up and a PKU clinic.

■ **CHILDREN WITH SPECIAL HEALTH CARE NEEDS (CSHCN)**
(206) 296-4610
Seattle-King Co. Health Dept.
First Interstate Center
999 3rd Ave., Ste. 900
Seattle, WA 98104
This federally and state funded program assists children up to age 18 who are disabled or have a physical condition that places him or her at risk of becoming disabled. Eligibility for the program will depend on the nature of your child's condition and your family's financial resources. Eligibility is determined by the CSHCN program of your local health department. CSHCN's focus on case management/family resource coordination helps you, regardless of financial resources, to assess your child's needs, plan for his/her medical care, and work with other people and agencies to help provide treatment for your child. Other support includes assistance with the cost of medical care such as evaluation, surgery, and medical equipment; and helps you find resources and obtain the services your child needs.

■ **CHILDREN'S CYSTIC FIBROSIS CENTER**
(206) 526-2024
Children's Hospital & Medical Center, CH-18
4800 Sand Point Way N.E.
Seattle, WA 98105
Upon referral from a primary physician, your child may be seen at this specialty clinic that sees patients with cystic fibrosis. The clinic is staffed by physicians, pediatric nurse practitioners, respiratory therapists, social workers, and dieticians who all have expertise with the cystic fibrosis population. Also offered is a parent support group for families coping with cystic fibrosis.

■ **CHILDREN'S HOSPITAL & REGIONAL MEDICAL CENTER**
(206) 526-2000 (526-2223 TTY)
4800 Sand Point Way N.E.
Seattle, WA 98105
Web site: www.chmc.org

Children's Bellevue
(425) 454-4644
400-112th N.E. #110
Bellevue, WA 98004
Children's Hospital provides general and acute in- and outpatient medical and surgical services for sick and disabled children. They offer special services for premature and critically ill infants, and for children with cystic fibrosis, cardiac defects, neuromuscular disease, and many other illnesses. Testing is available for specific health problems, including speech and language difficulties, developmental delays, learning disabilities, and other conditions. Branch locations offer more limited services.

■ CHILDREN'S RESOURCE CENTER

(206) 526-2500

Located at Children's Hospital, the Resource Center provides information and education on children's health issues including development, parenting, specific diseases and illnesses, grief and loss, nutrition and safety through books for loan, free pamphlets, and videos.

■ CHILDREN'S SERVICES OF SNO-VALLEY

(425) 888-2777

1407 Boalch Ave. N.W.

N. Bend, WA 98045

Developmentally delayed and disabled children up to age 3 and their families can benefit from this individualized education and therapy program serving the Snoqualamie Valley. Specific services include occupational/physical therapy, special education, family resource coordination, home visits, and parent support groups.

■ CHILDREN'S THERAPY CENTER OF KENT

(253) 854-5660

10811 Kent-Kangley Rd.

Kent, WA 98031

The Center provides physical, occupational, and speech therapy for children from birth to 10 years (preference to children under 3) who have developmental or other disabilities. Most of the children attend the center upon referral from a physician or a public health nurse. Insurance may cover the cost of therapy or it may be covered by funding received from the state if the child qualifies for Division of Developmental Disabilities (DDD) funding. They also provide an early childhood education program for children with disabilities, ages birth to 3, that works with the children on socialization to help get them ready for beginning school at age 5. The groups usually range from two to eight children and have a physical, occupational, or speech therapist involved.

■ COMMUNITY INFORMATION LINE

(206) 461-3200

Operated by the Crisis Clinic's Resource Center, this phone line provides information and referrals to over 2,000 social services agencies in King County. The center maintains a current data base of agencies and also publishes an annual directory called "Where to Turn" which lists agency addresses and phone numbers. A larger "Where to Turn PLUS" directory includes more detailed information on agencies, including a service description, eligibility requirements, fees, and branch locations.

■ COMMUNITY SERVICE CENTER FOR THE DEAF AND HARD OF HEARING

(206) 322-4996 V/TTY

1609 19th Ave.

Seattle, WA 98122

E-mail: cscdhh@juno.com

Services are available in American Sign Language and include information and referral to community resources and to interpreters. The center also has a resource library, bookstore, and a community advocate on staff.

SPECIAL NEEDS

■ COMMUNITY SERVICES FOR THE BLIND AND PARTIALLY SIGHTED

(206) 525-5556
9709 3rd Ave. N.E. #100
Seattle, WA 98115
This organization provides information and referral to community resources, as well as counseling and support groups. Also on-site is a retail store open M-F from 9:00 a.m. to 5:00 p.m.

■ CRISIS NURSERY—CHILD CARE SITE CHILDHAVEN

(206) 328-KIDS
The Crisis Nursery is a free, self-help program designed to keep families together while also preventing child abuse and neglect. When families are facing crises and have few or no other resources, parents voluntarily place their children into licensed respite provider homes for up to 72 hours.

■ CYSTIC FIBROSIS FOUNDATION

(206) 282-4770 or 800-647-7774
100 W. Harrison N. Tower #510
Seattle, WA 98119
Learn from peers how to be an advocate for your child with cystic fibrosis. The parents involved have experienced first hand some of the many feelings and struggles you are facing as a parent learning about your child's lifetime disease. They can help you find information, refer you to many community resources, as well as lend a listening ear and help problem solve, based on their own experience and expertise.

■ DEAF-BLIND SERVICE CENTER

(206) 323-9178
2366 Eastlake Ave. E. #206
Seattle, WA 98102
The center offers information and referral to community resources, as well as other services to assist deaf-blind persons. They also provide public education about deaf-blind people and issues.

■ DEVELOPMENTAL DISABILITIES, DIVISION OF DSHS

(206) 720-3300 (720-3325 TTY)
1700 E. Cherry St.
Seattle, WA 98122

(253) 872-6490
1313 W. Meeker, Ste. 102
Kent, WA 98032
These offices coordinate state services for the developmentally disabled, including clients with mental retardation, cerebral palsy, autism, epilepsy, and Down syndrome.

■ EASTER SEAL SOCIETY

(206) 281-5700 or 800-678-5708
521 2nd Ave. W.
Seattle, WA 98119
The Easter Seal Society provides information and referral services for disabled children and adults. They also operate camps for children with disabilities.

■ EPILEPSY ASSOCIATION OF WASHINGTON

(206) 547-4551
800-752-3509
3800 Aurora Ave. W. #370
Seattle, WA 98103
This organization provides support and information for persons with epilepsy

and for their families. They have a peer support group and support groups for parents of children with epilepsy.

■ EXPERIMENTAL EDUCATION UNIT
(206) 543-4011
University of Washington
P.O. Box 357925
Seattle, WA 98195
The Experimental Education Unit offers an Infant-Toddler Program (ITP). Any child from birth to age 3 with an identified developmental delay is eligible for this free program, which provides center- and home-based small group sessions, home visits, baby and toddler groups, and parent groups. The ITP is a training facility for UW graduate students in disciplines which emphasize working with special needs children, from special education to audiology and social work. All services are at no cost to parents.

■ HEALTHTEAM NORTHWEST
(425) 482-4000 or 800-888-4429
2525 220th S.E.
Bothell, WA 98021
A subsidiary of Children's Health Care System, HealthTeam Northwest offers a variety of pediatric services to patients including intermittent nursing visits, therapy, social work services, home phototherapy, mother/baby visits, as well as hourly care from private duty nursing personnel. Also offered are IV infusion and respiratory therapies to patients of all ages and supply and delivery of ancillary supplies and equipment if needed.

■ HEARING, SPEECH AND DEAFNESS CENTER
(206) 323-5770
1620 18th Ave.
Seattle, WA 98122
The Center has been offering evaluation and treatment for speech, hearing, and other communicative disorders over the past four decades. They provide therapy, information and referral, and parent emotional support with the goal of assisting parents, family members and caregivers to create an environment which promotes the development of the whole child. A Parent-Infant Program (PIP) for families with hearing impaired children ages birth to 3 is offered. This program's services may include home visits for speech/language therapy, infant/toddler play groups, parent support groups, individual or family counseling, sign language classes, and family resource coordination. Also available are audiological services, including a trial hearing aid program and a lending library of books and video tapes. A satellite clinic in Renton also offers speech services.

■ HEART TO HEART SUPPORT GROUP
(206) 526-2015
Children's Heart Center
Children's Hospital & Medical Center
4800 Sand Point Way N.E.
Seattle, WA 98105
Being a parent of a child with a heart defect can be isolating and challenging. Heart to Heart offers parents an opportunity to talk with other parents of children with heart disease. The support group meets regularly to learn from and discuss with other parents and professionals (physicians, psychologists, teach-

ers, social workers) about such topics as the "normal heart," family stresses, the history of pediatric cardiology and surgery, siblings, as well as taking operating room tours.

■ JUVENILE DIABETES FOUNDATION

(206) 545-1510
1333 N. Northlake Way
Seattle, WA 98103

Volunteers provide support to parents whose children have been diagnosed with diabetes. The foundation also provides informational literature and referrals for medical care and supplies.

■ KID CARE, COMMUNITY HEALTH ACCESS PROGRAM

(206) 284-0331 or 800-756-5437

Telephone referral, information and a resource guide is available for families of developmentally disabled children. They can refer you to the Child Find office of your local school district so that you can get free screening and evaluation for your child, and find out about special educational programs for preschoolers. This is the place to call if concerned about your child's development.

■ KINDERING CENTER

(425) 747-4004
16120 N.E. 8th
Bellevue, WA 98008

The school provides an educational preschool and home training for developmentally disabled or abused children. They also offer a support group for fathers, parent training, respite care, and foster home licensing.

■ LEARNING DISABILITIES ASSOCIATION

(425) 882-0792 or 800-536-2343
7819 159th Pl. N.E.
Redmond, WA 98052

The association offers information on learning disabilities and attention deficit disorder. They provide parents with professional referrals for speech and language services, occupational therapy, testing, counseling, and tutoring. Parent support is offered by telephone to assist with school related issues, to give feedback and support to parents as they work through school systems and any difficulties encountered in management of a learning disabled child. They assist parents to advocate for their child and can give suggestions and ideas on educational issues. The association also maintains a list of resources of schools that have programs specifically designed to meet the needs of children with learning disabilities.

■ LEARNING DISABILITIES HOTLINE

(206) 621-9768
P.O. Box 46188
Seattle, WA 98146

This phone referral and information line is run by volunteers. They can provide literature on learning disabilities, as well as someone to talk to who's learning disabled herself and can help address concerns.

■ **LEUKEMIA SOCIETY OF AMERICA**
(206) 628-0777
2030 Westlake Ave.
Seattle, WA 98121
The Society provides information and referrals for persons with leukemia. They offer financial help for medication, blood transfusions, lab tests, and transportation.

■ **MARCH OF DIMES BIRTH DEFECTS FOUNDATION**
(206) 624-1373 or 800-291-DIME
1904 3rd Ave., Ste. 230
Seattle, WA 98101
Web site: www.modimes.org
The goal of the March of Dimes is to promote awareness about birth defects and reduce infant mortality. They accomplish this by community service programs, research, and legislative advocacy.

■ **MUSCULAR DYSTROPHY ASSOCIATION**
(206) 283-2106; will accept collect calls
701 Dexter Ave. N., Ste. 106
Seattle, WA 98109
MDA provides diagnosis and ongoing medical care in their clinic at Children's Hospital as well as support for those with neuromuscular diseases. They also offer social activities, and a summer camp; no fees are charged and there is a $1700 allowance towards purchase of a wheelchair or braces.

■ **NATIONAL FATHERS NETWORK—WASHINGTON STATE FATHERS' NETWORK**
Kindering Center
(425) 747-4004
16120 N.E. 8th St.
Bellevue, WA 98008
Web site: www.fathersnetwork.org
A national organization that refers fathers of children with special needs to support groups throughout the country. The Washington State Fathers' Network advocates for and provides for all men and their families who have children with special needs. The organization is funded by the Office of Children with Special Health Care Needs, Washington State Department of Health. The mission of the Network is to promote fathers as crucially important people in their children's and families' lives. This is accomplished through the many activities of the Network such as sponsoring evening or weekend programs specifically designed for fathers of children with special needs, developing father support and mentoring programs, presenting at statewide parent and professional conferences, assisting organizations in reviewing their current services and making their offerings increasingly "inclusive" of men, and networking through "Connections," a father-driven newsletter.

SPECIAL NEEDS

■ **NORTHWEST AIDS FOUNDATION**
(206) 860-6241
127 Broadway E., Ste. A
Seattle, WA 98122

(425) 867-1551
16315 N.E. 87th St. #B-1
Redmond, WA 98052

(425) 255-7348
305 S. 43rd St.
Renton, WA 98055
This agency provides support services, public information and education programs on HIV and AIDS. Also provided are grants to individuals in crisis and to organizations for education about the disease.

■ **NORTHWEST CENTER CHILD DEVELOPMENT PROGRAM**
(206) 286-2322
2919 1st Ave. W.
Seattle, WA 98119
A child care program that integrates disabled and typically developed children four months through 5 years old is what you will find when you visit this center. Also included are parent education and support and there is a registered nurse on-site. Other staff include therapists and early childhood teachers. A variety of funding sources are available, depending on your specific financial needs.

PUBLIC SCHOOL PROGRAMS

To find out if your baby qualifies for assistance from a school program, call the school district serving your area and ask about its infant and toddler program. Free assessment is available. Services may include individual early intervention, weekly home visits, mother/child support groups, and speech and physical therapy. The services are free. Check with your school district's office for details of its program since they vary from one school district to another. The programs are designed for all developmentally delayed infants from birth to age 5.

Auburn	(253) 931-4927	Lake Washington	(425) 828-3201
Bellevue	(425) 455-6077	Mercer Island	(206) 236-3330
Edmonds	(425) 670-7176	Northshore	(425) 489-6000
Federal Way	(253) 941-0100	Renton	(425) 204-2200
Highline	(206) 433-2125	Seattle	(206) 298-7805
Issaquah	(425) 557-7000	Shoreline	(206) 367-6111
Kent	(253) 859-7513	South Central	(206) 901-8000

■ NORTHWEST HOSPITAL SPEECH AND LANGUAGE SERVICES

(206) 368-1848
1550 N. 115th St.
Seattle, WA 98133

This division of Northwest Hospital provides services, evaluation, individualized treatment, parent training, free screenings and community presentations for children with speech, language and hearing special needs. They offer a comprehensive program that can assist you and your child in areas such as stuttering, vocal cord problems, orofacial myofunctional disorders, delayed language, language learning disabilities and more. Parents who suspect their child has a speech, language or hearing problem may schedule a free screening at the above number.

■ PARENT PROVIDER RESOURCE LINE

(425) 259-2973

This phone line is operated by the Child Care Resource and Referral of Volunteers of America in Snohomish County. Besides providing phone referrals to agencies, parent support groups, and classes, a Parent Resource Guide is published quarterly which lists information on programs for parents. This publication is published by Lifenet in conjunction with the Volunteers of America.

■ PARENTS OF BLIND CHILDREN (NATIONAL FEDERATION OF THE BLIND-WASHINGTON)

(425) 823-6380

Volunteer groups of parents that have sight-impaired children provide support for families of blind and visually impaired children by working with children and parents on the day to day issues. This may be helping them with learning Braille or help with cane walking. They may also assist parents with advocacy for their children when dealing with educational issues in the school systems as well as holding an annual conference that promotes networking among parents of blind or visually impaired children.

■ PARENTS ARE VITAL IN EDUCATION (PAVE), WASHINGTON BRANCH

(253) 565-2266
800-5-PARENT
6316 S. 12th St.
Tacoma, WA 98465

One-on-one peer support for parents of children with disabilities is offered by this parent-to-parent training project. Program participants learn about the rights of children with special learning needs, so they can increase their skills in working with teachers, therapists, etc. to obtain appropriate educational services. Workshops, lending library, and a quarterly newsletter make this a worthwhile program. Another program offered through PAVE is the Toddler-Infant Program at 800-298-3543.

SPECIAL NEEDS

Seattle Baby Resource Guide

■ PEDIATRIC INTERIM CARE CENTER

(253) 852-5253
233 2nd Ave.
Kent, WA 98032

Caring for drug-affected and medically fragile infants is the specialty of this center. They also recruit and train foster families to care for drug-affected infants and provide support services and follow-up for people caring for these babies. A 24-hour hotline is operated to answer questions about care and also tell how to refer a baby that will be born drug-affected.

■ SCOTTISH RITE CENTER FOR CHILDHOOD LANGUAGE DISORDERS

(206) 324-6293
1155 Broadway Ave. E.
Seattle, WA 98102

This center provides free assessments and therapy for children ages 2-8 with communication disorders. Therapy usually consists of one-on-one clinic therapy between the child and a speech pathologist. They also help with obtaining support services within the community, and offer training for parents to help their child articulate better in day to day interactions at home.

■ SEATTLE AIDS SUPPORT GROUP

(206) 322-AIDS
303 17th Ave. E.
Seattle, WA 98112

Free support groups for persons with AIDS or HIV and their families and friends are offered weekly as well as information and referral to resources, and support services. Some of the evening support groups currently meeting are: Gay Couples Group (Mondays), Parents or Caregivers of Children with HIV (Tuesdays), and Mother's Group (Wednesdays).

■ SIBSHOPS (SIBLING SUPPORT PROJECT)

(206) 368-4911
University of Washington,
Experimental Education Unit

Sibshops is for siblings of children with special needs. These sessions give brothers and sisters a chance to meet each other, talk, learn, and have some fun. They are sponsored by the Sibling Support Project at Children's Hospital, ARC of King County, UW's EEU and Seattle Public Schools. Call for schedule of sessions.

■ WASHINGTON STATE SERVICES FOR CHILDREN WITH DEAF-BLINDNESS

(206) 439-6937 or 800-572-7000
Puget Sound Educational Service District
400 S.W. 152nd St.
Seattle, WA 98166
E-mail: fankhaus@psesd.wednet.edu

If your child's behaviors lead you to think he or she might have a visual and a hearing impairment you will want to call the Washington State Services for Children with Deaf-Blindness for assistance with concerns.

❧

INFERTILITY

Seattle residents are touched by infertility as are other city dwellers throughout the country. Among the many causes of female and male infertility are polycystic ovaries, uterine abnormalities, decreased sperm motility, various medications, luteal phase defect, endometriosis, low sperm count, or age, just to name a few; they all can be found in clients seeking infertility services in King and Snohomish counties. There have even been some links to caffeine and fertility.

For men, there is conflicting evidence on whether caffeine is good or bad for sperm counts. For women, recent research has suggested that women who consume more than 500 milligrams of caffeine a day take 11% longer to get pregnant than those who consumed no caffeine. To consume this much caffeine, however, one must drink the equivalent of 13 sodas, 10 cups of tea, or five cups of coffee. Overall, the greatest caffeine-consumers studied had a 45% greater risk of waiting more than nine months before becoming pregnant, according to a report in the *American Journal of Epidemiology*. The jury is still out on this one, so java drinkers who frequent those ever-so-popular latte stands in the Seattle area don't need to cut themselves off completely yet. Everything in moderation is a good suggestion to follow—so watch the consumption of those Starbucks treats while trying to conceive.

❧

The good news for people in the Seattle area is the wide variety of infertility services available.

❧

SERVICES AVAILABLE IN SEATTLE

The good news for people in the Seattle area is the wide variety of infertility services available. The most well known is the University of Washington Medical Center Fertility and Endocrine Center which happens to be the only facility in the Pacific Northwest to have four physicians on staff who, in addition to being board certified in obstetrics and gynecology, also are certified or board-eligible in the subspecialty of reproductive endocrinology. The Fertility and Endocrine Center Assisted Reproductive Technology (ART) Program was initiated in 1984 and has steadily grown to become the largest ART Program in the Northwest United States.

Also in the area is the Virginia Mason Fertility and Reproductive Endocrine Center offering a full range of services, including reproductive technologies and fertility conserving surgeries for the reproductive tract.

INFERTILITY

Research continues to improve options given to clients seeking fertility assistance. Greater Seattle is recognized around the world as a center for medical research. The University of Washington ranked first among all public universities in the receipt of federal research grants which indicates only good news for those waiting for innovative, new technologies in the area of fertility. One area of study gaining attention lately has been the emotional impact of infertility and infertility treatment for couples and other nontraditional dyads or single persons seeking fertility assistance. There are multiple resources available to assist with this difficult and frequently overwhelming time throughout King and Snohomish counties as well as many national organizations.

ዬፉ

FERTILITY RESOURCES

■ **FERTILITY AND ENDOCRINE CENTER**
(206) 548-4225
University of Washington
4225 Roosevelt Way N.E., Ste. 101
Seattle, WA 98105
University of Washington's Fertility and Endocrine Center is the Pacific Northwest's largest fertility clinic, serving the Washington, Alaska, Montana and Idaho region. The two primary areas of practice are reproductive endocrinology and infertility. They also offer programs to help patients cope with the stress of infertility and its treatment.

■ **GYFT CLINIC**
(253) 475-5433
Puget Sound Hospital
3582 Pacific Ave., 3rd Fl.
Tacoma, WA 98408

■ **PACIFIC GYNECOLOGY SPECIALISTS**
Swedish Hospital
(206) 682-2200
Nordstrom's Medical Tower

1229 Madison, Ste. 1050
Seattle, WA 98104
This clinic specializes in infertility and oncology gynecology.

■ **REPRODUCTIVE TECHNOLOGY**
(206) 386-2483
1229 Madison, Ste. 710
Seattle, WA 98104
Reproductive Technology is Seattle's largest sperm bank. You will need to be referred by a physician to utilize their services. Laboratory technicians and embryologists perform sperm testing, IVF, GIFT and ZIFT procedures. They also have a donor egg program.

■ **RESOLVE**
(206) 524-7257
Resolve offers information and support for individuals touched by infertility. It offers a facilitated support group, information on a variety of medical procedures, referrals to fertility specialists and therapists, and to adoption agencies. Resolve serves the greater Seattle area and also offers monthly topic meetings in Seattle and Tacoma.

■ **VIRGINIA MASON MEDICAL CENTER**
(206) 223-6190
1100 Ninth Ave.
Seattle, WA 98111
The Fertility and Reproductive Endocrine Center has experts in both male and female fertility. Patients receive a full range of services, including reproductive technologies. Fertility conserving surgeries for gynecologic problems such as uterine fibroids, endometriosis and congenital abnormalities of the reproductive tract also are offered.

᚛᚛

PREGNANCY AND CHILD LOSS

■ **CHILDREN GRIEVE TOO**
(206) 246-6142
This program of Family Services offers counseling and support for children (and their parents) who have lost a loved one.

■ **COMPASSIONATE FRIENDS**
(206) 241-1139 (Seattle-King County)
(425) 259-1048 (Snohomish County)
P.O. Box 66896
Seattle, WA 98166
Compassionate Friends is a self-help organization offering friendship and understanding to bereaved parents. The purposes are to support and aid parents in the positive resolution of the grief experienced upon the death of their child, and to foster the physical and emotional health of bereaved parents and siblings. Healing is slowly and gently promoted as parents gain insight and understanding, have an opportunity to ventilate their feelings in an accepting atmosphere,

and as they are able to reach out to the newly bereaved.

■ **INFORMATION AND CONSULTATION SERVICES-COMPASSIONATE FRIENDS**
(206) 241-5650
Grief support for children who have lost a parent or sibling.

■ **JOURNEY: A GRIEF SUPPORT PROGRAM**
(206) 526-2062
Children's Hospital & Medical Center
Social Work Department
P.O. Box C-5371
Seattle, WA 98105
Family support services offered are individual family assessment; follow-up telephone contact; support groups for children, adolescents and adults; individual and family counseling; information about and referrals to community resources; and audiovisual and a wide range of printed material about loss and grieving. There is no charge for the initial family meeting. The support groups have a minimal monthly donation, and counseling is available on a sliding fee scale.

■ **PARENTS OF STILLBORNS (P.S.)**
(206) 782-0054
P.O. Box 17451
Seattle, WA 98107
For those experiencing stillbirth, newborn death or miscarriage, P.S. provides telephone contact with a trained volunteer parent and monthly meetings to discuss common concerns and experiences and share information. Regular presentations by experts in various areas and a bimonthly newsletter are available for all in need.

PREGNANCY/LOSS

■ SIDS FOUNDATION OF WASHINGTON

(206) 548-9290 or 800-533-0376
c/o Children's Hospital, CG-07
P.O. Box 5371
Seattle, WA 98105

The SIDS Foundation offers programs of emotional and informational support to those who have experienced a baby's death due to SIDS. Peer contacts are available by telephone 24 hours a day, can assist in funeral planning, and may visit during the pregnancy and infancy of a subsequent child. The SIDS Foundation also has a speakers' bureau available for presentations and sends out a bimonthly newsletter as well as targeted mailings. Crisis situations are handled on a 24-hour on-call basis.

■ SWEDISH MEDICAL CENTER

(206) 386-2712
747 Broadway
Seattle, WA 98114

The Women and Infants Social Work Services at Swedish offer the following support groups:

Difficult Decisions: If fetal testing reveals a genetic or developmental abnormality that results in your choosing pregnancy termination, this support group can offer help and support. Sharing and receiving the support of other couples who have made the same decisions can be helpful and assist in arriving at a comfortable resolution to your grief. The group meets monthly.

Pregnancy After Loss: For expectant parents who have experienced a miscarriage, stillbirth or the death of an infant, contemplating or celebrating a new pregnancy can be difficult. This group meets monthly to share experiences with couples in similar situations.

Support After Miscarriage: If you have had a pregnancy that resulted in miscarriage, you know it is a real and very devastating loss. Sharing personal experiences and identifying methods to cope with loss with other parents can be helpful in working through grief. Swedish's "Following Miscarriage" grief support group is facilitated by a masters-prepared social worker with experience in perinatal grief and loss. Attendees are women and their partners who have experienced spontaneous miscarriage within the last twelve months. The group allows parents to talk about the unique loss of miscarriage in a safe, confidential setting by helping parents process the grief of miscarriage, reducing parents' isolation and normalizing the experience, identifying coping strategies to deal with loss, and focusing on miscarriage as a unique perinatal loss. The group meets the fourth Monday of the month, from 6:30 - 8:00 p.m. and charges a fee of $10 per person, or $15 per couple.

❧

PREMATURE INFANT RESOURCES

■ **PARENTS OF PREMATURES**
(206) 283-7466
P.O. Box 3046
Kirkland, WA 98083
Parents of Prematures is a voluntary organization made up of parents in the Puget Sound area who have experienced a high-risk pregnancy and/or the birth and hospitalization of a premature baby. Helping others since 1973, they offer an outreach program, parent education meetings, a bimonthly newsletter, guidelines for breastfeeding, premature clothing lending, and a lending library. They meet monthly in various Seattle locations for parent support or to hear guest speakers.

FACILITIES SERVING PREMATURE INFANTS

If your baby is born eight to ten weeks prematurely, he/she may be able to remain at the hospital where you delivered, if it has a Level II special care nursery. These hospitals include Evergreen, Group Health Central, Northwest, Overlake, Providence, Stevens, and Valley Medical Center. The hospitals have neonatologists on staff or on call, and most offer surfactant therapy. For births more than ten weeks early, or when other medical conditions require, infants are transferred to the Level III nurseries at Children's Hospital & Regional Medical Center, University of Washington Medical Center, or Swedish Medical Center.

Children's Hospital & Regional Medical Center • (206) 526-2041   19 beds
Children's infant intensive care has an attending staff of 12 neonatologists, six from the community and six from the University of Washington Medical Center (UWMC). They handle the most complex newborn medical and surgical procedures. Children's does the most major infant surgeries in the area, and is the only hospital that offers Extra Corporeal Membrane Oxygenation (ECMO). Children's offers surfactant therapy and high frequency ventilation, as well as newer and experimental treatment. The staff at Children's and UWMC work closely together in determining which of their two hospitals can best treat babies being transferred from other hospitals.

Swedish Medical Center • (206) 386-2430   30 beds
Swedish's special care nursery is a comprehensive facility to care for premature infants born at 24-36 weeks gestation. They have 11 neonatologists on their attending staff (five on-service at any given time). They offer surfactant therapy and neonatal surgery. Infants requiring complex cardiac surgery and certain other treatments are transferred to Children's.

University of Washington Medical Center • (206) 548-4606   32 beds
The UWMC's neonatal intensive care is considered the regional center for high-risk obstetrics and perinatal services. They offer surfactant therapy and high frequency ventilation and other new therapies as they are available. Seven senior neonatologists are on staff. Infants requiring immediate surgery are transferred to Children's.

HELP IS ON THE WAY!

When baby is born early, here are some special "emergency" numbers for delivery of preemie-size diapers. Many services even offer preemie-size diaper wraps for sale and delivery as well. If you buy disposable diapers, don't forget to ask the manufacturer for coupons!

- Baby Diaper Service: (206) 634-2229
- Pure and Natural: (206) 545-1075
- Preemie Pampers: 800-543-4932
- Preemie Huggies: 800-447-9423
- NW Hospital Supply stocks Preemie Huggies as well as Medela breast pumps: (206) 368-1196, 1530 N. 115th St., Seattle 98133 (they deliver!)

MULTIPLE BIRTH RESOURCES

■ MOTHERS OF MULTIPLES

(425) 882-3271
This organization operates branches throughout the area. Groups offer family social events, as well as monthly meetings that feature a guest speaker. They encourage pregnant women to join, so they can have the support of others early on.

■ N.W. ASSOCIATION OF MOTHERS OF TWINS CLUB

For general information:
Sue Thompson, (425) 337-7624
Members of the N.W. Assoc. of Mothers of Twins operate individual clubs. Clubs serve as both a social and support group for families containing multiples. Groups sponsor activities such as clothing and toy sales, and offer resources on parenting.

■ NORTH SEATTLE FAMILIES OF MULTIPLES

(206) 781-1552
Olympic View Elementary School
504 N.E. 95th St.
Seattle, WA 98115
Meetings are the second Tuesday of every month at 7:30 p.m. Activities include children's parties, summer picnics, clothing, toy and equipment exchanges, and a monthly newsletter. If you have questions or just need to talk to someone who's been there, the members of this group can help.

ૐ

SINGLE PARENTING RESOURCES

■ APPLE PARENTING CLASS

Highline-West Seattle Mental Health Center
(206) 248-8226
1010 S. 146th St.
Seattle, WA 98146
On a quarterly basis, Highline-West Seattle Mental Health Center offers a

course which involves an educational presentation on parenting issues to help people cope with the stresses of parenting. This is a nonprofit parenting program for families who are having a challenging time with their children or for those simply wishing to make parenting a more fun and rewarding experience. Children are incorporated into the learning process by means of parent-child lab activities. Usually one class per quarter is in Spanish.

■ CHILDREN'S HOME SOCIETY

(206) 524-6020
3300 N.E. 65th
Seattle, WA 98115

(253) 854-0700
4338 Auburn Way N.
Auburn, WA 98002

(253) 850-2582
213 South 4th Ave.
Kent, WA 98032

This nonprofit organization provides multiple services to children and families. Single parent workshops, support groups, and counseling are offered.

■ DIVORCE LIFELINE CHILDREN'S PROGRAM

(206) 624-2959

This organization offers supportive therapy groups for separating and divorced persons, and for children of divorce. Counseling groups for children (ages 6-17) meet weekly and are offered throughout the school year at sites in Seattle, East King County, South King County, Everett, and Bremerton. Professional group leaders facilitate discussion and activities in these age-appropriate groups in an atmosphere that fosters

acceptance, expression, and problem-solving. One parent also attends three meetings for feedback, education, and support concerning the child. These groups provide a place for children to talk about feelings and to learn healthy ways of expressing anger, hurt, fear, and loneliness. They provide support to parents so that they can help their children cope with changes in the family. Fees for group counseling are based on a sliding scale so that all children may participate. As a program of Lutheran Social Services of Washington and Idaho, Divorce Lifeline is committed to helping all people regardless of ability to pay.

■ PARENTS WITHOUT PARTNERS (PWP)

(425) 776-5811 Lynnwood
(206) 440-7596 Seattle Metro
(206) 517-2700 East King County

PWP is an international nonprofit, nonsectarian education organization, devoted to the interest and welfare of single parents and their children. To be eligible, one need only be the single parent of at least one living child; custody is not a factor. An orientation meeting must be attended before joining PWP. There is a fee of approximately $30 to join. They offer social events for single parents and their children, as well as education and referral services.

■ SOLO PARENTING ALLIANCE
(206) 720-1655
139 23rd Ave. S.
Seattle, WA 98144
E-mail: solo@accessone.com
Solo Parenting Alliance is a grass roots, nonprofit organization created by and for solo parents to strengthen their community by promoting self-sufficiency. This group offers a unique Family Home Share program bringing together single parent families to share expenses and experiences in the same house. A resource center in Seattle's Central District and a quarterly newsletter are two other benefits of membership. The Alliance sponsors support groups and parenting classes at family support centers and other community locations.

❧

TEEN PREGNANCY

■ ARBOR HOUSE
(425) 489-1838
19019 100th N.E.
Bothell, WA 98011
Arbor House is a nine-unit apartment building housing young pregnant and parenting women (18-21) and their babies (under age 3). The units are totally self-contained, and allow resident mothers the opportunity to live independently with their babies, while retaining access to a live-in house parent. Each resident attends weekly parent support groups and monthly resident meetings during her stay of up to 18 months, in addition to working towards educational/vocational and life skills requirements.

■ CAMPFIRE TEEN PARENTS PROGRAM
(206) 461-8550
8511 15th Ave. N.E.
Seattle, WA 98115
Campfire holds three-day retreats twice a year to Vashon Island for teen parents and pregnant teens. Seminars are also offered on leadership, employment, and education opportunities.

■ CATHOLIC COMMUNITY SERVICES-PREGNANCY SUPPORT SERVICES
(206) 323-6336
100 23rd Ave. S.
Seattle, WA 98144
This agency provides housing, health, and referral services for pregnant and parenting teens.

■ CHILDREN'S HOME SOCIETY TEEN PARENT HOME
(206) 322-8918
339 22nd Ave. E.
Seattle, WA 98112
Single moms, ages 14-18, are housed in a foster home setting, work on self-esteem and nutrition, and attend weekly parenting classes to encourage the best possible future for themselves and their children.

■ COLUMBIA HEALTH CENTER
(206) 296-4650
4400 37th Ave. S.
Seattle, WA 98118
Medical exams and tests, counseling, family planning, adoption referrals, and obstetrical services are provided on a sliding scale as part of Columbia Health Center's confidential services.

■ DSHS FIRST STEPS PROGRAM HEALTHY MOTHERS, HEALTHY BABIES
800-322-2588

Call the toll-free number for more information on state medical and support services for teens who are pregnant or new parents. Services include child care, education, financial assistance, case management, transportation, and family planning. A free prenatal packet and baby book are available to any pregnant woman (in seven languages). This is also the WIC referral line.

■ EASTSIDE HEALTHY START
(425) 869-6658

This family support program offers voluntary, home-based support services to young families with a mother 21 years or younger who is pregnant or parenting her first infant. The program serves young parents in Bellevue, Bothell, Issaquah, Kirkland, Mercer Island, Redmond, Skykomish, and Woodinville. Parents are provided support, information, and referrals to help them make healthy choices for themselves and their families. This early intervention program is provided until the child reaches school age. There are no fees charged. Services include social/support groups (including child care and transportation to the group) and linkage to community resources. Eastside Healthy Start is a joint program of Northshore Youth and Family Services, Youth Eastside Services, Friends of Youth, Children's Home Society, and Seattle-King County's Public Health.

■ FRIENDS OF YOUTH
(425) 392-6367
414 Front St. N.
Issaquah, WA 98027

Eight-week long parenting classes are offered quarterly in Systematic Training for Early Childhood Issues, counseling, and teen parent support by this organization. A Teen Shelter Line is also provided for teens who need temporary housing.

■ GROUP HEALTH HOSPITAL-CENTRAL
(206) 326-2656
200 15th Ave. East
Seattle, WA 98112

The teen clinic offers prenatal and postnatal care as well as teen prenatal classes.

■ GROUP HEALTH HOSPITAL-EASTSIDE
(425) 883-5151
2700 152nd N.E.
Redmond, WA 98052

The hospital offers a teen pregnancy program with prenatal and postnatal support groups.

■ KING COUNTY WORK TRAINING PROGRAM
(206) 296-5220
700 5th Ave., Ste. 3700
Seattle, WA 98104

Pregnant teens and teen parents (ages 16-21) who live in King County, outside of Seattle, can participate in an integrated program of employment services, medical care, parenting training, counseling, and case management.

TEEN PREGNANCY

■ MEDINA CHILDREN'S SERVICES

(206) 461-4520
123 16th Ave.
Seattle, WA 98122
School-site classes and GED assistance are offered by this interagency group, as well as counseling and crisis intervention at no charge for parents 14-18 years old. Child care is provided for participants. They offer a program for teen fathers called Project Mister and a program called TAPP (Teenage Pregnancy, Parenting, and Prevention) at two Seattle locations.

■ MY PLACE

(425) 356-1229
This support group focuses on pregnancy and parenting issues and community services geared to teens. Child care is provided on site. The program is sponsored by Deaconess Children's Services, Everett YMCA, Camp Fire, and Family Opportunities Council.

■ PROGRAM FOR EARLY PARENT SUPPORT (PEPS)

(206) 547-8570
4649 Sunnyside Ave. N., Rm. 346
Seattle, WA 98103
PEPS offers support groups for teen parents and their children, ages birth to 3. Groups are held at schools, community centers, and private homes throughout the community.

■ TEEN PARENT CHILDCARE HOTLINE

(206) 329-3481
1265 S. Main St. #210
Seattle, WA 98144
This organization, funded by the city of Seattle, provides free assistance to teen parents in finding child care so they can attend school.

■ TEEN PARENT WIC PROGRAM

(206) 296-4786
Teen parents are considered to be at nutritional risk under the guidelines of the Women, Infants and Children (WIC) program. They can receive vouchers for food, as well as nutrition education and other services. There are centers located throughout King and Snohomish Counties.

■ TRANSITIONAL LIVING CAMPUS

(425) 486-6774
20208 Bothell Way N.E.
Bothell, WA 98011
This Friends of Youth program is geared towards young women (18-21) who require the supportive, structured environment of a family living model. TLC is a spacious home that can accommodate five mothers and babies (under one year of age), each family unit occupying a separate bedroom. Kitchen, living room, recreation room and dining room are shared, and form the focus of family interaction. A house parent lives on-site.

■ **UNIVERSITY OF WASHINGTON-ADOLESCENT CLINIC**
(206) 543-3453
1959 N.E. Pacific
Seattle, WA 98105
The adolescent clinic offers primary and specialty medical care for adolescents including prenatal and postnatal care for pregnant teens. The staff includes two midwives, a maternity nurse, social worker, and nutritionist.

■ **YOUNG PARENTS SUPPORT GROUP**
(206) 364-7930
North Seattle Family Center
13540 Lake City Way N.E. #5
Seattle, WA 98125
Come together to share your stories, ideas and opinions while giving and receiving support from each other. Volunteer facilitators lead the drop-in group which is continuous throughout the year. The program is free, and free child care is available for participants.

■ **YOUTH FAIR CHANCE AMERICORP RESOURCE MOTHER'S PROGRAM**
Southwest Community Career Center
(206) 764-1933
6335 35th Ave. S.W.
Seattle, WA 98126
This program offers support services to promote and protect the health and well-being of teen parents and their infant children. It serves teen parents and young adults, ages 14-29, who live in West Seattle, including High Point, Parklake Homes, Roxbury Village, White Center, and Southpark. Services include referrals, advocacy, outreach, emergency food and clothing assistance. Also available through the Career Center are G.E.D., high school reentry, and ESL classes.

ADOPTION IN SEATTLE

🕭

International

adoptions

seem to be

more

prevalent on

the West

Coast, with

an

abundance of

international

adoption

agencies in

the state of

Washington.

🕭

Adopting infants and older children in the Seattle area is governed by various state statutes and regulations. The area has many licensed placement agencies well-versed in these legal requirements. Adoptive parents may also choose to seek a child through the State of Washington Department of Social and Health Services (DSHS) or a private placement through an attorney. Regardless of what agency they may use, adoptions are finalized only after completing a home study, the birth parents have terminated parental rights, a consent to adoption has been approved by the court, and a post-placement investigation has been conducted.

International adoptions seem to be more prevalent on the West Coast, with an abundance of international adoption agencies in the state of Washington. Seattle is especially unique in its prevalence of international adoptions from Asian countries. This may have something to do with the large Asian population in the Seattle metropolitan area, the strong ties of this particular culture, or simply the social fabric of the Northwest where people seem to be more accepting of cultural differences.

Most international adoptions require a home study to be submitted to the immigration and naturalization services of the particular country. In most countries the adoption is completed in the adoptive child's country and the parents must apply for a visa to return to the United States. If a married couple is adopting a child they should both travel to the country to adopt the child or a full visa is not given and the parent who didn't travel would need to re-adopt the child once he or she arrives in the state.

Once the adoptive parents arrive home to Washington, the state does not require anything else to be done. Most adoption agencies in the area suggest or require that you do re-adopt, however, to get a birth certificate and other legal documents of adoption as well as to keep good relationships with the countries by demonstrating that the child is valued and loved.

Certainly international and in-state adoptions require energy, time, and often financial burdens. The Seattle area has much to offer in resources such as information and assistance to adoptive parents, children, and families before, during, and after the adoptive process.

■ ADOPTION RESOURCE CENTER

(206) 524-6020
Children's Home Society of Wash.
3300 N.E. 65th St.
Seattle, WA 98115

This resource center offers a variety of services to assist those whose lives are touched by adoption. Information, education, support and counseling are available, as well as training and consultation for professionals. They offer a resource line and data bank of services for special needs adoptive families post-placement, as well as a book store stocking hard-to-find adoption titles. The Center does not place children for adoption. It's designed to be an objective source of information and education for people interested in adoption and offers the area's only staff of psychotherapists who specialize in adoption issues.

Many workshops and courses are offered throughout the year. They include Adoption: A Lifelong Process, Intercultural Adoption, Sharing the Birth, Adoption for Gay and Lesbian People, Childbirth Education for Prospective Birth Parents, and more. Fees depend on services provided. Ongoing support groups are also held, including Birth Parent Support Group, Multi-Racial Family Group, Support Group for Gay and Lesbian Parents, Adoptive Parent's Support Group, and The Kid's Group.

■ AMERICANS ADOPTING ORPHANS

(206) 524-5437 or 800-467-7426
12345 Lake City Way N.E., Ste. 2001
Seattle, WA 98125

This agency offers assistance with adopting children from China. After adopting two children from China, the owners began this business as a way to share the knowledge they gained from the experience as well as to help all the children they had to leave behind. The agency is licensed by the State of Washington and accredited by the People's Republic of China. Their program is unique in that they make it a point to have parents really participate in the process so that it becomes "their adoption." They allow parents to do as much or as little of the work as they want to, as they feel it is empowering to conquer the bureaucratic obstacles to reach one's child—not to mention the fact that it saves the prospective parents money when they do the work themselves. As an added bonus, the agency distributes a newsletter to interested parties and holds monthly support group meetings for parents wishing to adopt.

■ BETHANY CHRISTIAN SERVICES

(206) 367-4604
19936 Ballinger Way N.E., Ste. D
Seattle, WA 98155

This agency offers complete pre- and post-placement services to families and individuals interested in adoption and provides orientation and training for people interested in domestic, international, and special needs adoptions. Through their "Partners in Placement" program, Bethany Christian Services is also able to assist in adoptions where a birth mother has already independently chosen an adoptive family for her child and in certain situations, can place a birth mother in a licensed "Shepherding Home" as an added service.

ADOPTION

■ **CATHOLIC COMMUNITY SERVICES**
(206) 323-6336
100 23rd Ave. S.
Seattle, WA 98144
The agency provides complete pre- and post-placement services to families and individuals interested in adoption. They provide orientation and training for people interested in special needs, international, and domestic adoptions. Classes and training are included in the cost of the home study.

■ **JEWISH FAMILY SERVICE**
(206) 461-3240
1601 16th Ave.
Seattle, WA 98122
This agency provides many different services focused on the Jewish community, including licensed adoption services.

■ **LDS BIRTH PARENT PROGRAM**
(206) 624-3393 or (425) 228-0074
220 S. 3rd Pl.
Renton, WA 98055
This program is operated by the Church of Jesus Christ of Latter Day Saints and offers free counseling, information, referral, and other support services for girls and women with unplanned pregnancies. They also offer adoption placement for church members.

■ **LUTHERAN SOCIAL SERVICES**
(425) 672-6009
6920 220th St. S.W., Ste. K
Mountlake Terrace, WA 98043
They provide counseling for women with unplanned pregnancies, and adoption planning and placement for infants and special needs children. Open adoption is available and services are customized to meet individual needs.

■ **MEDINA CHILDREN'S SERVICES**
(206) 461-4520
123 16th Ave.
Seattle, WA 98122
Medina Children's Services provides free counseling to pregnant women and their partners. They also offer special programs for families adopting older children, disabled children, African-American, Native American and biracial children of any age, and Caucasian infants.

■ **NEW HOPE CHILD AND FAMILY AGENCY**
(206) 363-1800
2611 N.E. 125th #146
Seattle, WA 98125
Counseling for birth mothers, birth fathers, and families considering adoption is offered by this agency. They provide a support group and referral to residential facilities for pregnant mothers. Adoption services for prospective adoptive parents are also offered.

■ NORTHWEST ADOPTION EXCHANGE
(206) 292-0082 or 800-927-9411
1809 7th Ave., Ste. 409
Seattle, WA 98101
This information and referral agency specializes in special needs adoptions. They not only facilitate adoptions but also give information on a wide range of adoption issues, and advocate for and develop projects to expand support services for families throughout the adoption process. They also provide consultation, training, and technical assistance to adoption agencies, caseworkers, and adoptive parent groups.

■ ONE CHURCH, ONE CHILD
(425) 235-4772
451 S.W. 10th St., Ste. 120
Renton, WA 98005
This organization recruits prospective African American foster and adoptive parents for children waiting for placement throughout the state. They also provide training and seek to recruit at least one family from every church congregation to adopt or foster parent a child.

■ OPEN ADOPTION AND FAMILY SERVICES
(206) 723-1011 or (206) 440-1605
800-772-1115
P.O. Box 27173
Seattle, WA 98125
Open Adoption and Family Services provides a full range of counseling and adoption services, including home studies, pre-placement adoption reports, seminars on adoption, support groups for birth and adoptive families.

🔊

ADOPTION

CHILD ABUSE RESOURCES

■ CHILD PROTECTIVE SERVICES (CPS)

(206) 721-6500 King County
(425) 339-3900 Snohomish County
You can call the 24-hour CPS line to get information on child care and foster care or to report violations of licensed child-care centers. This is also the number to call if you need information about child abuse or need to report suspected abuse or neglect.

■ CRISIS CLINIC

(206) 461-3222
King County Crisis Line
(425) 258-4357 or 800-584-3578
Snohomish County Crisis Line
These 24-hour phone lines handle calls dealing with mental illness, emotional distress, abuse, violence, and relational distress. They are linked to emergency services and resources. They also serve as referral numbers for support groups and other resources.

(206) 461-4922 Teen Link
This hotline is run by teens, for teens, from 6:00 p.m. until 10:00 p.m. Sunday through Thursday. They handle the same types of calls as the Crisis Clinic Line above, use the same data base, but offer a source to teens who might find it difficult to speak with an adult.

■ FAMILY HELP LINE

(206) 233-0139 or 800-932-HOPE
(206) 233-0446 (TDD)
No parent wants to hurt their child, but everyone has moments when they feel they might lose control. The Family Help Line is available seven days a week so that help is only a phone call away. This service is provided by Parents Anonymous Washington State for all parents in the state to access and is funded through a special contract with DCFS, DSHS State of Washington. Being a parent is a very difficult, often frustrating job with little support or recognition. Sometimes parents feel alone with their problems and need to talk with someone about their kids in an open and honest way. The Family Help Line can assist parents in many ways. They offer supportive listening since sometimes just talking to a caring listener who is not critical can make all the difference. They can assist parents in locating parenting classes, support groups, family counseling, and respite child care. They are also available 24 hours a day for crisis intervention. If you request literature, they will send you handouts on positive parenting subjects including time outs, methods of dealing with an angry child, and alternatives to spanking.

❧

SEATTLE FAMILY LIFE

Clearly, Seattle has become a children's town. Neighborhoods are filled with baby joggers and strollers. Everywhere you look there are children!

Along with this, postpartum care for mothers, babies and families is booming. Doulas will come to your home and nurture the family, helping it adjust to the new little person and to the increased work load. If the adjustment is difficult, then Seattle has many groups and meetings that focus on postpartum depression, a typical aftereffect of pregnancy, which usually lifts after the first year. Many moms find that sharing their anxieties helps speed this process along.

Hand in hand with this new baby boom are new businesses and child-related activities springing up all over town. It is clear that Seattle is both willing and interested in nurturing well-rounded, fun-loving, educated children for our future. As Generation Xers begin to have more babies, our children are all getting the benefit of their inquisitive minds. We found a micro computing class for 3-year-olds! You'll also find hands-on science and nature classes, which are more than a walk in the park—true interactive learning and working models that have "cultural, environmental and global" impact.

Seattle is a great place for parent-child activities. Most museums have parent-child classes, where adults can learn alongside their kids. And if you want to shop but can't find a sitter, the newest trend at several of the Northwest's larger retailers is drop-in child care. These stores offer child care, generally with an 8:1 child/caregiver ratio by a staff person who has at least some formal training in childhood education. Call for specific site details.

&

It is clear that Seattle is both willing and interested in nurturing well-rounded, fun-loving, educated children for our future.

&

- QFC University Village (206) 523-5160
- Fred Meyers
  Auburn (253) 931-5574
  Bellevue (425) 865-8583
  Burien (206) 443-6423
  Federal Way (253) 952-0123
  Lynnwood (425) 670-0223
  Renton (425) 204-5223
  Benson Plaza, Renton (425) 235-5373
- IKEA, Renton (425) 656-2980
- Incredible Universe, Auburn (425) 804-3800

"Stay-at-Home Dad"

A Life Experience by Andrew Brandt

Tell people you are a stay-at-home father, and the one thing you won't be astonished to hear is, "Oh, I think it's wonderful that you're doing that." People blurt this out unrelentingly, and they mean it to be complimentary. Nevertheless, it is one of those conventionalized utterances (such as another thing I often hear, "Your baby has such beautiful blond hair") that evokes an ambiguous response in me. "Wonderful," in the context of their phrase, is probably meant as "admirable," but with undertones of "freakish." Historically, of course, stay-at-home fatherhood is freakish, but today it should not be regarded as particularly admirable or particularly exceptional.

For my wife and me, the choice was easy. We could afford to lose my salary, but not hers. And while my wife may feel ambivalent about continuing to work, I feel unambivalent about staying home. Without talking about practical problems, like diapering and other dirty subjects, the chief problem I confront socially is the idea that there must be something different about the father, as opposed to the mother, watching the kids. But for me there is no difference. Why should there be, after all? The physical acts of "mothering" are easy to learn. As for the other part, what comes under the heading of "nurturing," I don't believe men are as incompetent on that score as they are made out to be.

Of course there are people out there who deplore the notion that the woman should work just because she makes more money. These people are right to the extent that being able to afford a mini van should not be regarded as the highest aspiration of family life; but we should completely reject the prejudice, whatever its source, that says that watching the baby is women's work.

I have noticed, however, that if traditional society regards baby watching as women's work, then taking the kids to the playground seems to be the male contribution. Just the other day at the playground, a guy—there with his three kids—asked me, "Did your wife make you take them out?" Well, that's what I get for going to the playground after five o'clock. If I take the kids in the morning, I look merely unemployed. But that too depends on where I take the kids. In some areas of town, a stay-at-home father can pass. In others, he's a fish out of water. These differences reflect differences in political attitudes, but for economic reasons that seem irresistible in our society, the stay-at-home father is becoming more a fixture, and less a freak.

Politically speaking, couples should feel free to decide, for the reasons that suit them best, who watches the baby—mother, father, granny, sitter, or whoever. The only enemy is the feeling that still on some level pervades society, that men lose status by staying home with the kids. My hope is that by bucking thousands of years of tradition, stay-at-home fathers can raise not just their own status, but the status of parenting in general, for all the wrong reasons, let us admit. But the result would still be one worth hoping for. ❧

SUPPORT GROUPS

■ FATHERS SUPPORT GROUP
(206) 721-5542
Southeast Youth and Family Services
3722 S. Hudson St.
Seattle, WA 98118
Fathers in Action presents this support group for dads on the second and fourth Wednesday of each month, from 6:00-7:30 p.m. Open forum discussions explore the personal experiences of fathers.

■ FATHERS WHO LOVE THEIR KIDS
(206) 781-7045
Call this number and ask for Paul and he can give you information on this informal group of dads who meets in Seattle once a month. They talk about fathering and spend time together creating friendships and community. Meetings are the first Monday of each month and they usually have one other event (for the whole family) each month. The group is looking for new dads (old dads, single dads, stay at home dads, working dads and unemployed dads, even granddads and stepdads) who are willing to join and get connected with other dads.

■ F.E.M.A.L.E.
(425) 462-8890, Bellevue chapter
(425) 774-3666, Mill Creek chapter
(425) 880-4579, Redmond chapter
(253) 471-7985, Tacoma chapter
(425) 844-2641, Woodinville chapter
(206) 248-2333, West Seattle chapter
(206) 367-8821, SnoKing chapter
Formerly Employed Mothers at the Leading Edge (F.E.M.A.L.E.) is a national organization for women who have chosen to take a break from their full-time careers to stay at home with their children. Local chapters meet twice or more a month in the evening, without children. Most chapters also have play groups and family functions. The groups provide a place where moms can find intimacy and support from other moms.

■ KALEIDOSCOPE
(206) 461-4546
Kaleidoscope, a support group for gay, lesbian, and bisexual parents, holds meetings from 6:30 to 8:00 p.m. on Tuesdays at Stonewall Recovery Services, 430 Broadway Ave. E. in Seattle. Another group meets on the Eastside from 6:30 to 8:00 p.m. on Wednesdays at the Eastside Recovery Center in Rockwood Office Park, 1412 140th Pl. N.E., Bellevue. Children are encouraged to be part of Kaleidoscope through the Child Care Program which meets in conjunction with the support groups.

■ LISTENING MOTHERS
(206) 521-8093
Listening Mothers is a community service program sponsored by the Center for Object Relations (COR) that offers support and information, helping mothers explore the concerns, frustrations and joys of the first year of motherhood. Small groups of five mothers, usually with their infants, meet with knowledgeable leaders once a week for six weeks. There is a sliding fee scale. Groups are available in Seattle, Mill Creek, and Bellevue. Call for classes meeting in your area.

■ **LYNNWOOD FAMILY SUPPORT: DADS MAKE A DIFFERENCE NIGHTS**

(425) 670-8984
6309 196th St. S.W.
Lynnwood, WA 98036

Looking for a father-friendly environment? This group is for dads, dads-to-be, and noncustodial dads who value involvement in their child's life. They meet from 6:30-8:30 p.m. the second and fourth Thursdays of the month with a volunteer facilitator, a father himself. Fathers meet to speak about the joys of fathering and provide support, parenting strategies, and ways to strengthen parenting involvement.

■ **MOPS, INTERNATIONAL**

(303) 733-5353

Boulevard Presbyterian Church
(206) 243-2600
1822 S. 128th St.
Seattle, WA 98168
Meets the second and fourth Tuesday of each month from 9:00-11:30 a.m.

Shoreline Community Church
(206) 362-4790
125 N.E. 185th St.
Seattle, WA 98155
Meets first and third Fridays of each month from 9:00 -11:00 a.m.

Southminster Presbyterian Church
(206) 878-8133
19834 8th Ave. S.
Seattle, WA 98148
Meets second and fourth Mondays of each month from 9:00-11:30 a.m.

Westside Presbyterian Church
(206) 935-4477
3601 California Ave. S.W.
Seattle, WA 98116
Meets first and third Fridays of each month from 9:00 -11:30 a.m.

MOPS is a national mother's support and networking organization with about 100 groups in the state of Washington. The purpose of these church-sponsored groups is to nurture all mothers of preschoolers by meeting their distinct needs. Even though the groups are church-sponsored, you do not need to attend the church or any church to join the MOPS group. The meetings generally take place twice a month and include networking time for mothers along with various activities, such as guest speakers on a specific preschool developmental or safety issue or some type of craft activity. The children are on-site in a different room with supervised child care and activities for their age group. There are various groups meeting in the Seattle area. Call the above number for a location near you. Listed above are just a few Seattle MOPS groups and meeting times.

■ **MOMS AND MOPPETS**

Eastside Foursquare Church
(425) 488-2500
N.E. 145th & 100th N.E.
Bothell, WA 98011

Moms and Moppets offers weekly get-togethers each Tuesday from 9:00-11:30 a.m. for mothers and their children from newborn through age 5. These meetings include parenting and health topics, crafts, and decorating. Refreshments and small group discussions are also offered.

SUPPORT

■ MOM'S GROUP
St. John's Episcopal Church
(425) 827-3077
105 State St.
Kirkland, WA 98033
This free group for mothers meets weekly from 9:30-11:30 each Tuesday morning for discussions, parties, special programs, and other activities such as crafts. Child care is available for children through kindergarten age. This is usually a low-key get-together so if you are looking for a non-structured group, this may be the one for you.

■ MOMS AND TOTS GROUP
(425) 487-1479
This mother's group originally started off as a traditional MOPS group, but now offers a slightly different group atmosphere. Members of the group meet the 2nd and 4th Tuesdays of each month. Meetings include parent-child field trips which include trips to the Children's Museum, pumpkin patches at Halloween time, and the Northwest Puppet Center. This group still has the MOPS charter and benefits with the national charter's resources and quarterly newsletter, "Moms Sense." The number listed above offers a quarterly schedule of activities.

■ MOMS CLUB
(425) 481-1607
Cedar Cross United Methodist Church
1210 132nd St. S.E.
Mill Creek, WA 98037
Meets the 1st Tuesday of each month from 10:00-11:30 a.m.

(360) 691-6940
Granite Falls Community Center
Meets the 1st and 3rd Tuesday of each month from 10:00-11:30 a.m.

(425) 836-1944
Redmond United Methodist Church
16540 N.E. 80th St.
Redmond, WA 98033
Meets the 1st Wednesday of each month from 9:30-10:30 a.m.

(425) 392-6446
Faith United Methodist Church
3924 Issaquah/Pine Lake Rd. S. E.
Issaquah, WA 98029
Meets the 1st Friday of each month from 10:00-11:30 a.m. Meets on Wednesdays for activities and local outings.
This national nonprofit organization has many local chapters that meet throughout King and Snohomish counties. The group that meets in the Snohomish/Bothell/Mill Creek area meets monthly as a large group for support and activities while the children are supervised in the nursery or working on crafts. They also have playgroups that usually meet once a week and a monthly children's outing planned. The moms also have various activity groups such as a recipe exchange group, a museum group, and a group that does community service work. Then once a month they plan a mom's night out and leave the kids behind for a night of fun with other moms. Other local groups have similar activities and groups and meet at various times during the month. By contacting the groups listed you can find the one that best fits for you and your children's needs.

■ MOTHERS AND OTHERS

(425) 226-6600
St. Madeleine Sophie Catholic Church
4400 130th Pl. S.E.
Bellevue, WA 98006

This support group, which meets Mondays from 9:30-11:30 a.m., is for mothers, fathers, nannies, grandparents, and anyone else who nurtures children. Child care is available for babies and toddlers, with supervised play activities for preschoolers. The adults meet in one room while the children are entertained in another room, allowing for some break time for the adults. They discuss a variety of topics such as: better love life, parenting, and childhood concerns. There are also times set aside for fun activities such as cooking or crafts. This is a great group to join if you are looking for educational and inspirational support networking with other mothers.

■ NEW MOM SUPPORT GROUP

(206) 386-3606
Swedish Medical Center
747 Broadway
Seattle, WA 98114

The New Mom Support Group meets weekly at Swedish and provides a forum for discussion on a variety of topics. It covers the first three months of motherhood and costs $60 for the three-month session or $20 per month. Topics vary based on class needs but may include topics such as maintaining and nurturing identity as a parent, returning to work or staying at home.

■ NORTHWEST ASSOCIATION FOR POST PARTUM SUPPORT (NAPS)

(206) 955-6155

This is a free referral line for post partum doulas. Just call and a representative will call you back, assess your needs and give you the names and numbers of several registered doulas to call and interview. Referred doulas are trained in pediatric CPR and first aid, have undergone a police background check and received training as a doula. In addition, they participate in ongoing doula education.

■ PROGRAM FOR EARLY PARENT SUPPORT (PEPS)

(206) 547-8570
4649 Sunnyside Ave. N.
Seattle, WA 98103
Hours: M-F   8:00 a.m.-4:30 p.m.

PEPS services include facilitating community-based parent support groups for parents with children ages birth to 3, publishing and distributing a new parent resource list, and staffing a resource and referral line. The Neighborhood PEPS groups meet at members' homes for six months on a weekly basis, and provide education and support for parents whose children are ages birth to four months when the group starts. The Neighborhood Program costs $75. A free Outreach Program provides ongoing weekly groups at community centers for parents with children up to 3 years old. The goal of PEPS is to support all families through mutual support and shared information, building on their strengths as parents. The programs are offered to all families regardless of income (scholarships are available for the Neighborhood Program). PEPS also offers special programs for teen parents.

■ **SEATTLE-KING COUNTY DEPARTMENT OF PUBLIC HEALTH MOTHER-INFANT GROUP**
(206) 296-4765
North Seattle Public Health Center
10501 Meridian Ave. N., Rm. H-200
Seattle, WA 98133
These groups meet once a week for six weeks, and discussion topics include coping with crying, illness care, safety, growth and development, and nutrition and feeding. No preregistration is required and classes are free (donations accepted). Classes are held on Tuesday afternoons from 1:00 p.m. to 2:30 p.m. at the Ballard Community Center. The address is 6020 28th Ave. N.E. You may bring your baby with you to these classes and do some networking with other mothers.

PARENT EDUCATION COOPERATIVES

Community colleges and vocational schools throughout the area offer parent education programs that include a cooperative preschool component. These programs serve several purposes including parent education, opportunities for children to learn and socialize with other young children, and a built-in support group for parents. Programs vary but generally they include some on-campus time with other parents and a preschool/playschool for the children that meets one to three times a week, usually at neighborhood locations. Classes have an assigned teacher and parents rotate as helpers in the classroom. There are some fees for these programs, but usually they cost much less than a regular preschool. Some of the schools offer programs for parents with young babies (prewalkers). Many of the co-ops offer an open house in the spring, in preparation for fall enrollment, and classes do fill up quickly. For more information, call the school nearest you:

Bates Technical	(253) 596-1760
Bellevue Community	(425) 641-2366
Clover Park Vocational	(253) 589-5569
Edmonds Community	(425) 640-1665
Everett Community	(425) 388-9300
Green River Community	(206) 464-6133
Highline Community	(206) 878-3710
Lake Washington Technical	(425) 739-8100
North Seattle Community	(206) 527-3783
Renton Technical	(425) 235-2352
Seattle Central Community	(206) 587-6906
Shoreline Community	(206) 546-4593
South Seattle Community	(206) 764-5321

■ SOUND PARENTING
(425) 775-4059
P.O. Box 1625
Edmonds, WA 98020
Sound Parenting offers weekly parent support and education groups in Snohomish and North King counties to give parents the opportunity to meet others in similar circumstances, share experiences, exchange information, and learn about a wide variety of topics. Six to eight group members and their babies meet for two hours every week for 12 weeks. Quarterly gatherings are also organized and open to all past and present participants. Lasting friendships are made, playgroups are formed, and babysitting is often shared between members. All groups are facilitated by Julie Hanson-Lynn, M.A.

🍂

FAMILY SUPPORT CENTERS

Family Support Centers operate in many communities in the metro Seattle area. These centers provide resources, education, referrals, support groups, and more. Types of programs offered include parent-child activity time, WIC and maternity health support services, new parents support groups, an "evening out" (free drop-off care for your kids), and single parent and teen parent groups. The centers are operated by nonprofit organizations, often with financial support from local counties, cities, and communities. Most are open weekdays and some evenings; call for specific hours and a current list of programs.

SEATTLE

■ NORTH SEATTLE FAMILY CENTER
(206) 364-7930
13540 Lake City Way N.E., Ste. 5
Seattle, WA 98125

■ SOUTHWEST FAMILY CENTER
(206) 937-7680
4555 Delridge Way S.W.
Seattle, WA 98106

■ ATLANTIC STREET CENTER FAMILY CENTER
(206) 723-1301
7301 Beacon Ave. S.
Seattle, WA 98108

■ BALLARD FAMILY CENTER
(206) 706-9645
549 Ballard Ave. N.W.
Seattle, WA 98117

■ BITTERLAKE FAMILY CENTER
(206) 368-0172
13035 Lynden Ave. N.
Seattle, WA 98133

■ GARFIELD FAMILY CENTER
(206) 461-4486
2323 E. Cherry St.
Seattle, WA 98122

■ MEADOWBROOK FAMILY CENTER
(206) 366-9256
10517 35th Ave. N.E.
Seattle, WA 98125

■ **RAINIER FAMILY CENTER**
(206) 723-8590
4600 38th Ave. S
Seattle, WA 98118

METRO AREA

■ **AUBURN FAMILY RESOURCE
CENTER**
(253) 854-0700
4338 Auburn Way N.
Auburn, WA 98002

■ **LYNNWOOD FAMILY
SUPPORT CENTER**
(425) 670-8984
6309 196th St. S.W.
Lynnwood, WA 98036

■ **REDMOND FAMILY
SUPPORT CENTER**
(425) 869-6699
16225 N.E. 87th, Ste. A-5
Redmond, WA 98052

■ **SHORELINE FAMILY
SUPPORT CENTER**
(206) 362-7282
17018 15th Ave. N.E.
Shoreline, WA 98155

❧

GAY AND LESBIAN PARENTING RESOURCES

■ **CHILDREN OF LESBIANS
AND GAYS EVERYWHERE
(COLAGE)**
(206) 325-4449
618 12th Ave. E.
Seattle, WA 98102
Web site: www.colage.org
This international agency run by and for
kids of gay, lesbian, bisexual, and transgendered parents has been around since
1990. The mission of COLAGE is to
foster growth of daughters and sons of
gay, lesbian, and transgendered parents
of all racial and class backgrounds. They
help start peer groups for mostly adolescents of gay parents but also have some
adult groups. They provide education,
peer support, and encourage community awareness as well as advocate for
their rights and those of their families,
promoting acceptance and awareness that
it is love that makes a family. In addition
to support groups, there is an annual
conference offered in different cities
around the country and a quarterly newsletter called "Just For Us."

■ **GAY AND LESBIAN PARENTS
COALITION
INTERNATIONAL**
(202) 583-8029
P.O. Box 50366
Washington, DC 20091
This organization offers annual conferences, information sheets and videos for
educational purposes, and publishes a
quarterly newsletter for members called
"Network," packed with news, inter-
views, resources, cartoons, stories, and
more.

■ **GAY AND LESBIAN AND TRANSGENDERED FAMILY CENTER**
(206) 323-1768
628 12th Ave. E.
Seattle, WA 98102
Seattle Counseling Services For Sexual Minorities facilitates this organization that offers seminars and forums on a bimonthly basis. Topics include legal and parenting issues, adoption, dealing with school systems, and more. They also plan social events to build community for gay and lesbian families.

■ **GAY FATHERS ASSOCIATION OF SEATTLE**
(206) 324-4359
1122 East Pike St., Ste. 1270
Seattle, WA 98122
Gay and bisexual men dealing with such issues as coming out, parenting, separation, and divorce may want to tap into this organization for resources and educational forums. Support groups meet every other Thursday at 7:30 p.m. at Group Health Hospital on Capitol Hill in room D-618.

■ **KALEIDOSCOPE OF FAMILIES**
(206) 517-6252
430 Broadway Ave. E.
Seattle, WA 98102
This is a gay, lesbian, bisexual, transgendered parenting support group. The peer support groups meet weekly in Seattle and Bellevue locations for sharing experiences, educational workshops, and family time. They also publish a newsletter every two months.

■ **LAVENDER FAMILIES**
(206) 325-2643
P.O. Box 21567
Seattle, WA 98111
This resource network provides information, attorney referrals, advice, and emotional support for lesbian, gay, and bisexual parents on issues of custody and visitation, child rearing, donor insemination, and adoption.

■ **SUPPORT GROUP FOR GAY AND LESBIAN PARENTS**
(206) 527-6068
This group is sponsored by the Adoption Resource Center of Children's Home Society and meets monthly to discuss the unique issues faced by adoptive gay and lesbian parents. Prospective adopters are welcome. The group is limited to gays and lesbians.

ᨊ

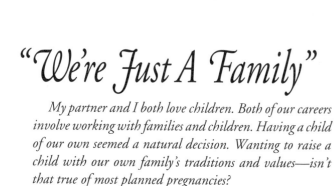

"We're Just A Family"

My partner and I both love children. Both of our careers involve working with families and children. Having a child of our own seemed a natural decision. Wanting to raise a child with our own family's traditions and values—isn't that true of most planned pregnancies?

Being gay has never been the first word I'd use to describe myself, but I did have to ponder the ramifications of having a child. I am not given to being "out" in public, but as the parent of any talkative preschooler knows, home life gets broadcast to anyone and everyone. My partner and I have vowed not to lie about who we are in relationship to our daughter when she tells the checkout person, the swim teacher, the clown at a friend's birthday party, etc., that she has two moms and two dads.

It took several heterosexual friends to finally convince us that we have the same gifts to share with a child as they do: love, emotional and financial stability, a desire to make the world a better place—both for our child and because of our child. After having initial misgivings, all of our families are very supportive and involved. We feel fortunate to have a known donor/father for our child. We both feel that fathers are important, and have a close friendship of many years with this couple. Our daughter sees them on a regular basis.

I feel that in our home we are just a family, not a "lesbian-mom family." We play Candyland, watch "Barney," negotiate desserts and go to church most Sundays. It is outside that is sometimes different—our daughter has already felt twinges of wanting to be like everyone else.

I don't think I am burying my head in the sand, ignoring the potential pain my daughter will face. Neither do I see myself as a rebel. We chose to be a family for traditional reasons. Not being traditional in our composition did not seem enough reason not to go forward. It is our hope that we will raise a daughter who is self-assured, kind and caring, with an open mind and a strong sense of family in all its various forms. ❧

PARENTING CLASSES

The various hospitals throughout the Puget Sound area are a good source of parenting classes. Check with their education departments for information. Listed below are a few of the consistently taught offerings. Watch the newspapers and hospital newsletters for other special classes and events offered throughout the year.

■ BETTER BEGINNINGS
(800) 422-5820
Elizabeth Pantley is nationally known as a parenting expert based right here in Seattle. Author of *Kid Cooperation* and several other publications, she offers a straightforward approach to parenting. Elizabeth is available to speak at schools and support groups.

■ EVERGREEN HOSPITAL MEDICAL CENTER
(425) 899-8000
The following parenting and relationships classes are offered throughout the year:
- The Dynamics of Mothers and Daughters
- Raising Boys to Men
- Parenting With Love and Laughter
- Siblings Without the Rivalry
- Finding and Choosing Quality Childcare
- Surviving Your Terrific Toddler
- Pulling the Plug on Power Struggles
- Parenting With Love and Logic

■ NORTHWEST HOSPITAL
(206) 368-1784
The following parenting classes are offered at different times throughout the year:
- Parenting Your Infant
- Parenting Your Toddler
- Positive Parenting

■ ODESSA BROWN CHILDREN'S CLINIC
(206) 329-7870, ext. 233
2101 E. Yesler Way
Seattle, WA 98122
Odessa Brown, located in Seattle's Central Area, is a Children's Hospital & Regional Medical Center satellite program. They offer the following parenting classes:

First-time Parenting: First-time parents with infants under 1 year of age are encouraged to attend this free nine-session series. Topics include building self-esteem in young children, communication, nurturing and discipline. Babysitting and transportation are available.

STEP: Systemic Training for Effective Parenting: STEP seminars assist parents in developing effective ways to discipline and to teach responsible behaviors to children, and in understanding child growth and development.

■ OVERLAKE HOSPITAL
(425) 688-5259

You and Your New Baby: Overlake Hospital offers this five-week support class for new parents on an ongoing basis. Topics covered include infant feeding, sleep patterns, fussy babies, new parent adjustments, and more. Classes are held once a week at Overlake Hospital in Bellevue and at Issaquah Medical Center in Issaquah, and cost $40 per person.

Positive Parenting: This six-part series emphasizes skill-building in communication, encouragement and logical consequences. Time is given to individual problems. It is designed for parents of infants through teenagers. Karen Joslin, M.A., author of *Positive Parenting from A to Z* teaches the class and the $80/family tuition includes Joslin's book.

Other classes offered throughout the year include:

- Baby Grows Up: Understanding the Transition From Infancy to Toddlerhood
- Planning for Potty Training
- Potty Training Challenges
- Time For Bed: Do You Snooze or Lose?
- Dealing With Your Child's Temper Tantrums
- Raising Your Spirited Toddler and Preschooler
- Talking to Young Children About Sex
- Anger: Yours and Your Child's
- As Girls Grow Up: Pizza Night Out for Parents and Daughters
- As Boys Grow Up: Pizza Night Out for Parents and Sons
- Turf Battles: Understanding and Managing Sibling Rivalry and Fighting

■ PROVIDENCE GENERAL MEDICAL CENTER
(425) 261-4565

Various Parenting classes are offered:

- "Car Safe Kids Class"
- Teens With Kids
- Parenting Young Children—A Systematic Training for Effective Parenting (STEP)
- Diagnosis and Treatment of Attention Deficit Hyperactivity Disorder in Children
- Surviving Your Child's Teenage Years: Parenting During Adolescence
- Parenting Teenager— A Systematic Training for Effective Parenting (STEP)

■ ST. FRANCIS HOSPITAL
(253) 952-7957 or (888) 825-3227

Love and Logic Parenting: This 8-10 week class is a practical guide to teaching children responsibility through love and logic. It provides sound strategies for dealing with almost any problem adults face in communicating with children. Participants will learn specific "how-to's," not theoretical concepts.

❧

PUBLICATIONS OFFERING SUPPORT

■ **A NEW ARRIVAL, SEATTLE'S CHILD, EASTSIDE PARENT, SNOHOMISH COUNTY PARENT**

(206) 441-0191
Seattle's Child, Eastside Parent
Web sites: www.seattleschild.com,
www.eastsideparent.com
(425) 252-1355
Snohomish County Parent
Web site: www.snohomishparent.com
These three publications are published by Northwest Parent Publishing, Inc. Run by two mothers, these news magazines are well known for their editorial content. *A New Arrival* is published twice a year and is geared solely to new and expectant parents. Free copies are available at maternity and baby stores as well as local libraries. The monthly publications—*Seattle's Child, Eastside Parent*, and *Snohomish County Parent*—have a large circulation and are available free of charge at children's stores, child care centers, libraries, and almost any place children visit. You may also subscribe for monthly issues to be delivered to your doorstep for $15 for one year or $25 for two years. Articles are for parents of children of all ages, rather than just infants and toddlers. The paper includes an extensive listing of activities for families, as well as classes and support groups for parents.

■ **NORTHWEST BABY & CHILD**

(206) 232-0301
Web site: www.family.com
Published by Baby Diaper Service, *Northwest Baby & Child* is a free monthly publication that offers wonderful information regarding infancy and the toddler years. A regular monthly column offers advice on breastfeeding; there are also many articles on health, safety and environmental issues. It is available at baby and maternity stores, toy stores, and other children-related spots and delivered to Baby Diaper Service customers in five counties. The paper also includes a monthly calendar of support groups and other happenings for parents and children.

■ **NORTHWEST FAMILY MAGAZINE**

(360) 734-3025 or 800-494-3025
1014 12th St.
Bellingham, WA 98225
Web site: www.nwfamily@family.com
This monthly magazine can be picked up free from many schools and businesses in North King and Snohomish Counties or you can subscribe for $15/year to have it delivered to your home. It features many family subjects such as developmental issues, families' personal experience stories, and reviews of kid-friendly places to visit on family outings. Regular departments include: Bulletin Board with coming events, Northwest Teen Calender, Family Travel, In Review, and a monthly Family Calender, just to name a few.

🐚

POSTPARTUM DEPRESSION

■ DEPRESSION AFTER DELIVERY

(206) 283-9278
P.O. Box 59973
Renton, WA 98058
This nonprofit group provides support to women with postpartum mood/anxiety disorders, and their families. They provide education to the public concerning the nature and management of this disorder, and promote related research. The phone number above connects you to an information line that provides names and phone numbers of women who have experienced postpartum mood/anxiety disorders.

POSTPARTUM DEPRESSION SUPPORT GROUPS

The listing below provides you with support group meetings. Infants, husbands, and other support persons are welcome at the meetings.

■ SOUTH KING COUNTY

Good Neighbor Center
305 S. 43rd
Renton, WA 98056
Meets the first Tuesday of every month at 7:00 p.m. in the small conference room.

■ NORTH END/KING COUNTY PUBLIC HEALTH CENTER

North District Multi Service Center
10501 Meridian Ave. N., Rm.. C-110
Seattle, WA 98133
Meets the second Wednesday of every month at 7:00 p.m.

■ EASTSIDE

Kirkland/Evergreen Hospital
12040 N.E. 128th Street
Bellevue, WA 98034
Meeting dates: first and third Thursday of every month at 7:00 p.m. Check in at main desk for room information.

■ EVERETT

Everett-Providence General Medical Office Building
14th and Colby
Everett, WA 98206
First and third Tuesday of every month at 7:00 p.m. Meets in the Mt. St. Helens Room.

■ TACOMA

Tacoma General Hospital
315 S. K St.
Tacoma, WA
Meetings the fourth Tuesday of every month in conference room three.

POSTPARTUM DEPRESSION THERAPY GROUPS

Both therapists mentioned below will refer you to other local therapists if they are booked or geographically inconvenient.

■ DAWN GRUEN, ACSW

(206) 281-7610
222 Etruria, Ste. 130
Seattle, WA 98109

■ ABBY MYERS, ARNP

(206) 522-3543
4026 N.E.. 55th, Ste. A
Seattle, WA 98105
Postpartum therapy groups meet weekly, focus on adjustment to the new role as parents, relief of symptoms, teaching of

coping and relaxation skills, and medication education if needed. Babies are welcome. Every fourth session your partner is encouraged to attend a multicouples session.

❧

POSTPARTUM DOULAS

Doulas, also called postpartum caregivers, are women who give nonmedical support and hands-on help to the new mother and her family. Doulas are trained in breastfeeding, new baby care, and postpartum depression. They cook, make sure the mother gets to rest, do laundry, and help with older children. A doula's service is especially helpful in today's transient society where relatives are often too far away to help. Most doulas charge an hourly rate and have hourly minimums. Here are several Seattle services:

■ **BEGINNINGS**
(425) 486-5164
Beginnings offers in-home postpartum care for parents. Owned by two registered nurses, Carol Crow and Karen Januto, the service offers well newborn and sibling care, light housekeeping, meal preparation and breastfeeding support, in the North end. The hourly rate is $25 per hour with a two-hour minimum.

■ **MOTHERCARE OF AMERICA DOULA SERVICE, INC.**
(425) 672-8011
MotherCare was Washington State's first doula service, and at 10 years old, is among the nation's oldest. Owner Dorothy Harrison, mother of six children and a grandmother, uses her own practical experience in hiring support care for mothers during the postpartum period. MotherCare provides infant care, new mother support, sibling care, breast-

---

MOVIE THEATERS WITH SOUNDPROOF "CRYROOMS"

- **The Crest**: (206) 363-6338, N.E. 165th & 5th N.E.
- **Guild (45th)**: (206) 633-3353, 2115 N. 45th St.
- **Metro**: (206) 633-0055, 4500 9th Ave. NE
- **Northgate**: (206) 363-5800 10 Northgate Plaza
- **Varsity**: (206) 632-3131, 4329 N.E. University Way

If you're not sure your toddler can make it through a feature without a fuss, these glass booths are a lifesaver. The Northgate's cry room is good-sized; most others are small. You'll need to call to find out if the movie you want to see is being shown in the "cryroom" in multi-screen theaters.

DOULAS

feeding and bottle feeding support, light housekeeping, errands and family meal preparation. You can pick and choose what services you want during a pre-delivery interview with a care provider. The cost for this service is $20 per hour with a 12-hour minimum. MotherCare is now associated with Overlake Hospital. If you give birth at Overlake, they will defray the cost of your MotherCare doula!

■ **NEW FAMILY NURSE**
(425) 867-0678
Barbara LaFayette, R.N., is your "new family nurse." She is available to teach baby care and breastfeeding. She will also do your errands and chores, prepare

gourmet meals and virtually anything you need her to do to make your life easier with baby. The cost for her service is $25 per hour with a four-hour minimum.

■ **THE SECOND NINE MONTHS**
(206) 955-9431
Renee Beebe, M.Ed.
Like most doulas, Renee helps new parents with newborn care, household chores, shopping and meal preparation. In addition, she is a board certified lactation consultant as well as a La Leche League group leader since 1991. Her job, she feels, is to help new parents trust their instincts and develop their parenting style, which she aids them in doing by

FREE CHILDREN'S BIRTHDAY TREATS!

Many local eateries and national chains offer kids a special treat on their birthday of ice cream or a kid's meal. This also indicates that these are kid-friendly restaurants in general. Look in the phone book for one of the many locations near you.

- **Dukes**: free sundae, to all ages
- **Alderwood/Northgate/Tacoma Malls**: free surprise package through age 17. Mail name, address and birthday to KCPQ Kids Club, 4400 Steilacoom Blvd. S.W., Tacoma, WA 98499
- **Red Robin**: Mile High Mud Pie to all ages
- **The Sweet Factory**: a handful of candy, through age 12
- **TGIF Fridays**: free dessert, all ages
- **Taco Time**: kid's meal, through age 12
- **Alfy's Pizza**: mini pizza, to age 12
- **Azteca Mexican Restaurant**: free dessert, all ages
- **Baskin-Robbins Ice Cream**: ice cream cone, through age 12
- **Billy McHales**: ice cream cone, all ages
- **Burger King**: kid's meal, BK kids club members through age 12
- **Chili's Bar & Grill**: sundae, all ages
- **Denny's**: kids meal, through age 10

helping them feel well rested, nourished and nurtured. Most of her clients are over 30 first time parents or C-sections and those whose families are not close geographically. She charges $22 an hour.

■ **SEATTLE MIDWIFERY SCHOOL**
(800) 747-9433
(206) 322-8834 (Seattle area)
The Seattle Midwifery School offers training for both birth and postpartum doulas, and their training meets the requirements for certification through the National Association for Postpartum Care Services. This training provides doulas with the knowledge to provide wisdom and practical information to new parents. Doulas will care for a new baby while mom naps, prepare meals, straighten up a bit, read to an older sibling and teach the family how to bathe and care for a newborn. The Seattle Midwifery School keeps a listing of certified doulas they have trained and can give you names and numbers of doulas in your area.

❧

MASSAGE RESOURCES

■ **BABY MASSAGE VIDEO**
(888) 222-9868 to order
Pacific Communications (PACCOM) introduces the newest video on using the power of touch to soothe, heal and nurture our babies, "Baby Massage: A Video for Loving Parents." Companion piece to the best-selling book by Vimala McClure, *Infant Massage, A Handbook For Loving Parents*, this 70-minute video features certified infant massage instructor Elly Leduc, RN, and music by composer/percussionist Mickey Hart of The Grateful Dead. The video offers a combination of quality videography, a beautiful setting, inspiring information and clear instructions. The public can order this video by calling the toll-free number of by mail for $29.95, plus $4 shipping and handling.

■ **HEARTFELT CENTER**
(425) 670-2481
406 Main St., Ste. 111
Edmonds, WA 98020
Marcia David is the answer when it comes to one-stop birthing. She has been a certified birth doula for six years and offers prebirth and labor services as well as a postpartum follow-up visit. She is also a licensed massage practitioner who does relaxation massage during pregnancy and postpartum in her office or private home sessions. She teaches infant massage locally at Stevens Hospital. The last class offered was a five-session class for parents and infants with each class consisting of 90 minutes of hands-on practice and instruction. Marcia is also a lactation consultant, and carries a full line of Medela breast pumps and accessories, plus nursing bras.

■ **LAURA STUSSER, LMP**
(206) 634-1549
Laura Stusser, LMP, is a Certified Instructor with the International Association of Infant Massage and is a mother of one son. She also specializes in pregnancy and postpartum massage therapy. Laura combines her love for babies and massage with her parenting experience to create playful, hands-on classes and offers support to new parents. Learning

MASSAGE

the ancient art of infant massage is easy and one of the most rewarding and loving activities you can share with your baby. Regular massage can help your child sleep better, improve development, enhance bonding and attachment, and relieve gas and symptoms of colic. Laura teaches private and group infant massage classes.

OTHER MASSAGE RESOURCES

Many Seattle area hospitals offer infant massage classes. Listed are some of the hospitals that currently offer these classes.

■ **EVERGREEN HOSPITAL MEDICAL CENTER**
(425) 899-3000

■ **PROVIDENCE GENERAL MEDICAL CENTER**
(425) 361-3247

■ **STEVENS MEMORIAL HOSPITAL**
(425) 640-4066

ئ◆

FAMILY ACTIVITIES

■ **AQUA BARN RANCH**
(425) 255-4618
15227 S.E. Renton-Maple Valley Hwy.
Renton, WA 98058
Cash/Check/MC/V/Discover
Swimming and camping are the main activities at Aqua Barn. (Aqua Barn no longer offers horseback riding.) It's a good place to take your young child for RV or tent camping, as there is a full service, kid-friendly restaurant right there. The Aqua Barn is open different hours each day for swimming, so it's a good idea to call and check times before you go.

■ **BAY PAVILION**
(206) 624-5673
Pier 57, Alaskan Way
Seattle, WA 98101
Hours: Daily   11:00 a.m.-8:30 p.m.
You'll find the only indoor carousel in Seattle here, along with some fun, touristy shops with souvenirs and great munchies. Stop by Seattle Fudge, where they often have free samples. The Pavilion is just a short stroller ride from the Aquarium, and outside there's a bright observation deck with walkways and benches.

■ **BELLEVUE DOWNTOWN PARK**
(South end of Bellevue Square)
A great place to visit during a shopping trip to Bellevue Square. Fountains, waterfalls and a play area make this a fun place for children.

■ **BELLEVUE SQUARE "PLAY BOAT"**
(425) 454-4340 or (425) 454-8096
Bellevue Square Mall, First Floor
Hours: M-Sat.   9:30 a.m.-9:30 p.m.;
             Sun.   11:00 a.m.-6:00 p.m.
Everyone loves this padded tug. Parents have plenty of sitting room nearby to watch as the kids, 6 and under only, ride the imaginary waves.

■ CARNATION FARM

(425) 788-1511

28901 N.E. Carnation Farm Rd.

Carnation, WA 98014

Carnation Farm offers free tours for the public on Saturdays, 10:00 a.m.-3:00 p.m., May through September. Reservations are required for groups only. Here's your chance to visit a real milking barn, see baby calves, and run wild in the grassy fields. This is a treat for kids to see how things were in the "olden days" and to really see where milk comes from!

■ CHILDREN'S MUSEUM

(206) 441-1768

Seattle Center House, Lower Level

Seattle, WA 98109

Hours: Daily   10:00 a.m.-5:00 p.m.
           Sat.,Sun. 10:00 a.m.-6:00 p.m.
Cost: $5.50 per person; under 1 free.
        First Tues. each month is "pay
        as you can" donations,
        4:00-8:00 p.m.

The Children's Museum more than doubled in size with its 1995 expansion and offers many wonderful hands-on exhibits for children and families. A child-sized neighborhood, toddler play center, mountain forest habitat, Imagination Station art studio, regularly scheduled hands-on workshops, and much more await visitors.

■ CHILDREN'S MUSEUM OF
TACOMA

(253) 627-6031

925 Court C

Tacoma, WA 98402

Hours: T-F   10:00 a.m.-5:00 p.m.
        Sat.   10:00 a.m.-4:00 p.m.
        Sun.   Noon-4:00 p.m.
Cost: $3.75 per person; under 2 free

The museum has hands-on exhibits, creative play areas, and special activities and workshops. The "Nigerian Village" exhibit features replicas of a marketplace, schoolhouse, king's hut and women's quarters where role playing, games and activities encourage fun learning. Fridays are "family night" with free admission from 5:00 to 9:00 p.m.

■ COULON BEACH PARK

(425) 235-2560

1201 Lake Washington Blvd. N.

Renton, WA 98055

Hours: Daily   8:00 a.m.-dusk

At the newest major park on Lake Washington, you'll find a big swimming beach, boat rentals, trails for walking, biking, and jogging, and a large playground with modern equipment. There's also an Ivar's Seafood Bar in the park, open seasonally. Biking is not permitted.

■ DECEPTION PASS STATE
PARK

(360) 675-2417

Whidbey Island, WA 98278

Hours: Daily   6:30 a.m.-dusk

This park has beaches, lakes, camping, fishing, meadows, trails, and beautiful views. Take I-5 north to the Anacortes exit and go west on State Highway 20, following signs to Whidbey Island. The park actually begins on Fidalgo Island and continues on Whidbey Island, which is accessed by crossing Deception Pass (an inlet of water, crossed by a very high bridge). At Rosario Beach (on the Fidalgo side), you'll find tide pools to explore and a 30-foot tall wood carving of Ko-Kwal-Al-Woot ("Maiden of Deception Pass"). Three new restrooms are located at the Cornet Bay Road entrance.

■ **DISCOVERY PARK**
(206) 386-4236
3801 N. Government Way
Seattle, WA 98199
Hours: Daily 6:00 a.m.-11:00 p.m.
          Visitors Center:
          Daily   8:30 a.m.-5:00 p.m.
A great place to introduce your kids to
the outdoors, Discovery Park has acres
and acres of forests and meadows to walk
through. Trails are well-marked, but it
helps to stop by the Visitors Center and
get a map too. Nature walks led by park
rangers are offered frequently on the
weekends. There are beaches and a light-
house, but both are a bit of a hike to get
to. You'll also find some nice playground
equipment near the Daybreak Star Art
Center, which is a great place to see
Native American art. The best part—it's
all free!

■ **EDMONDS PUBLIC FISHING
PIER**
At the foot of Dayton St.
Edmonds, WA 98020
Even if you're not fishing, this is a wonderful place to take kids. Check the tide
tables in the newspaper or Yellow Pages,
and come close to the low tide. Kids will
likely find shells and interesting rocks on
the beach, and during low tide you can
walk from the pier north to (and under!)
the ferry dock. Besides the splashing
waves, you'll hear the sounds of sea gulls,
ferry boat horns, and trains going by.
There's a large grassy area for picnicking
just north of the pier, and you can't beat
the views of the Olympic mountains on
a clear day. On the other side of the ferry
dock is another beach park adjacent to
Edmonds Underwater Park, where you'll
often see divers descending into the deep.
(They even carve pumpkins underwater
at Halloween!)

BEATING SEATTLE'S RAINY DAY BLUES

Rainy days are a fact of life in Seattle, and our kids can easily become stir
crazy on those days. Here are a few hints to beat the boredom blues:

■ Sing and dance to music.

■ Create an obstacle course of pillows, cushions, and blankets for a crawler
to navigate.

■ Play a simple form of hide and seek. Babies shriek with delight when they
are "found."

■ Make special "rainy day" food: tomato soup with animal crackers, grilled
cheese in cut out shapes—your older baby will love to help!

■ Dress up in rain gear and go and jump in the puddles.

■ Look for the rainbow!

■ ENCHANTED VILLAGE AND WILD WAVES WATER PARK

(253) 661-8001
36201 Enchanted Pkwy. S.
Federal Way, WA 98003

Hours: April-Labor Day; call for hours
Cost: Enchanted Village only: $11, $8 for those 48" or taller, $6 if under 48". Both parks: $17.95-$19.95 (again by height)

Cash/Check/MC/V/AmEx

Enchanted Village is a great place to bring a picnic and enjoy amusement rides, bumper boats, wading pools, puppet shows, magic shows, the Antique Doll and Toy Museum and mini-golf, all of which are included in the price of admission. Wild Waves is geared for older children but there are some small slides and water rides for younger kids.

■ FARMER DAN'S

(425) 432-1705
26634 S.E. 196th
Hobart, WA 98025

Farmer Dan's is near Issaquah, just one mile off of Hwy. 18. Take the S.E. 200th exit one mile, turn left on 272 S.E. and look to the left for signs. Farmer Dan's is perfect for kids from preschool age up. Seasonal tours feature every farm animal you can think of, including pumpkin-eating cows! Depending upon the season your kids can plant, tend to or harvest pumpkins, make scarecrows, romp in the hay, take a pony ride ($3) or tractor-driven hay hide ($1). Afterwards a cup of hot cider or cocoa from the snack bar ends a perfect day. You can begin a family tradition at the "cut your own" Christmas tree farm every December and of course there are pumpkins for Halloween! Call for other special seasonal events and hours.

■ FARREL-MCWHIRTER PARK

(425) 556-2300
19545 Redmond Rd.
Redmond, WA 98054

This 68-acre park has a wonderful program of preschool activities with classes like "Breakfast with the Animals"—pigs, rabbits, goats, ponies and chickens and a muffin on the children's farm. What could be more fun? A pony class afterwards! If this makes you wish you were a kid again, take heart—there are plenty of Mommy and Me classes, so get your boots on and your bug scope out! Call ahead for upcoming activities and reservations.

■ FOREST PARK

(425) 259-0300
802 Mukilteo Blvd.
Everett, WA 98203

Hours: Daily   Dawn-dusk
        Animal Farm (April-Sept.):
        Daily   9:00 a.m.-5:00 p.m.

This is a big park with trails, picnic areas, fields, tennis courts, a swimming pool, concessions, and a playground. There's also a sprinkler pool that's open on hot summer days. If you come at the right time (2:00-3:00 p.m.) and the weather and ponies are cooperating, line up for a free pony ride at the Animal Farm. Besides the ponies, the farm area has geese, pigs, sheep, and more.

ACTIVITIES

■ FUN FOREST

(206) 728-1585
Seattle Center
Seattle, WA 98109
Hours: Daily   June 1-Labor Day;
weekends only, remainder of
the year. Call ahead as hours
vary by season; rain closures
not uncommon.

The Fun Forest has lots of rides and carnival temptations for the kids, with special rides for little children on the south side of the park. The new entertainment pavilion ($4) features laser tag, mini golf, video games and a snack bar. Rides are $.95/one to $16/unlimited bracelet.

■ GOLD CREEK TROUT FARM

(425) 483-1415
15844 148th Ave. N.E.
Woodinville, WA 98072

Fishing is the perfect family outdoor sport. Parents spend quality time teaching children patience and the joy of a visual reward. Call ahead because fishing and feeding times vary. The added bonus is the delightful look on a child's face when hundreds of fish are fed. The splashing frenzy leads to loads of giggles every time.

■ KELLY'S RANCH

(425) 392-6979
7212 Renton-Issaquah Rd.
Issaquah, WA 98027

Ages 4 and up may go on a parent-led 30-minute pony ride for $8. Staff does the honors for $10. This is a popular destination so reservations are suggested.

■ KELSEY CREEK COMMUNITY PARK AND FARM

(425) 455-7688
13204 S.E. 8th Pl.
Bellevue, WA 98005

Kelsey Creek Park is a perfect picnic spot, with a wonderful playground, as well as a big barn and lots of farm animals (9:00 a.m.-4:00 p.m.). Day camp is a summer favorite. Call for directions—it can be hard to find the first time!

■ KING COUNTY LIBRARIES

(206) 462-9600 or (800) 462-9600

The best and most inexpensive way to interest your children in reading is to visit the library. Quick information, story times, lectures, books and videos are all available—at absolutely no charge. The library's "Dial a Story" (206-386-4656) is a fun way for a child to learn to listen when they are on the phone.

■ LAKE SAMMAMISH STATE PARK

(425) 455-7010
20606 S.E. 56th St.
Issaquah, WA 98027
Hours: Daily   Dawn to dusk

Fishing, a sandy swimming beach, playground and picnic areas make this a great destination for families. Food concessions are available. Boat launch fee is $4.

■ LAKE SERENE PONY FARM

(425) 743-2112
3915 Serene Way
Lynnwood, WA 98935

Preschoolers may go on a parent-led 15-minute pony ride for $4. Reservations are required.

■ MATTHEW'S BEACH
N.E. 93rd and Sand Point Way N.E.
Seattle, WA 98115
A great playground for kids and a nice swimming area highlight this beach. Matthew's Beach is very popular with families during the summer months.

■ MINI-MOUNTAIN INDOOR SKI SCHOOL
(425) 746-7547
1900 132nd Ave. N.E.
Bellevue, WA 98005

Hours: M-F   9:00 a.m.-9:00 p.m.
        Sat.   9:00 a.m.-6:00 p.m.
        Sun.   Noon-5:00 p.m.
Cost: Five 20-minute lessons $100. Seasonal packages are available such as 10 lessons for $160.

Cash/Check/V/MC
This school specializes in indoor ramp skiing lessons beginning at age 2-1/2. All equipment is provided.

■ MOLBAK'S GREENHOUSE AND NURSERY
(206) 483-5000
13625 N.E. 175th
Woodinville, WA 98072

Hours: Daily   9:00 a.m.-6:00 p.m.
        F   9:00 a.m.-9:00 p.m.
                 Call for expanded spring hours.

Molbak's is a fun place to visit any time of year, with its beautiful flowers and plants inside and out. Kids especially enjoy seeing the birds and waterfalls in the atrium, and parents will marvel at the selection in the garden center and gift shops. Our favorite time to visit is in October, when Molbak's presents free live performances of a fairy tale. Adding to the fun, Molbak's decorates the store with story page scenes from the play.

■ MUSEUM OF FLIGHT
(206) 764-5720
9404 E. Marginal Way S.
Seattle, WA 98108

Hours: Daily   10:00 a.m.-5:00 p.m.
        Th   10:00 a.m.-9:00 p.m.
Cost: $8, $4 for ages 6-15, free for children 5 and under

Cash/Check/MC/V
Located at Boeing Field, this terrific museum is home to a helicopter, monoplane and biplane, and lots of aviation "stuff." You can even climb into the cockpit of a Northrop F/A 18 mock-up and move the joystick, and check out the control panels and radar screens. Family workshops available for children over 5 and their parents. Admission is free from 5:00-9:00 p.m. the first Thursday of each month.

■ NORTHWEST PUPPET CENTER
(206) 523-2579
9123 15th Ave. N.E.
Seattle, WA 98115
Cost: $7.50, $5.50 for children
Cash/Check/MC/V
Seattle's only permanent puppet theater presents several productions between October and May of each year. Several of the shows are geared to younger children, making it a fun experience for toddlers. An American Sign Language (ASL) performance is held on the first Saturday of each new show. Call ahead for show times.

■ NORTHWEST TREK

(360) 832-6117 or (800) 433-TREK
11610 Trek Dr.
Eatonville, WA 98328
Cost: Adults $8.25, ages 5-17 $5.75;
          ages 3-5 $3.75
Cash/Checks/V/MC/Discovery
What animals live in our backyards and
forests? This is the place to find out
firsthand. My favorite happening is the
yearly Slug Festival where you can race a
slug, have a slug face painting, make a
slug puppet or your own pet slug. There
is even a slug parade. The Cheney Discovery Center has hands-on touch and
feel exhibits, summer camp, family camp,
birthday packages and much more.
Northwest Trek is open from March
through September. The park opens daily
at 9:30 a.m.; closing hours vary by season. You'll find Northwest Trek 17 miles
south of Pullyap on State Route 161.

■ PACIFIC SCIENCE CENTER

(206) 443-2001
200 Second Ave. N.
Seattle, WA 98109
Hours: M-F   10:00 a.m.-5:00 p.m.
         Sat., Sun. 10:00 a.m.-6:00 p.m.
Cost: $7.50, $5.50 for ages 6-13,
         $3.50 for ages 2-5
Cash/Check/MC/V
Part of the vast Seattle Center, the Pacific Science Center makes science fun
for kids. There are many permanent
hands-on exhibits that appeal to all ages,
as well as changing exhibits and special
events. Those 48" and under are welcome in the Just For Tots playground.
IMAX movies and laser shows are an
additional $2 charge. The holiday-time
Laser Nutcracker show is especially popular with families. A bat exhibit as well as
virtual games are new in 1998.

■ PIED PIPER PRODUCTIONS

(206) 722-7209
Mt. Baker Community Club
2811 Mt. Rainier Dr. S.
Seattle, WA 98144
Cost: $2 donation
On Saturdays (except during summer-
time) watch for puppet shows, storytell-
ers, dancers and sing-a-longs at Mt. Baker
Community Center. Shows appeal to 2-
to 8-year-olds and their families.

■ POINT DEFIANCE PARK, ZOO AND AQUARIUM

(253) 591-5335
5400 North Pearl St.
Tacoma, WA 98407
Hours: Labor Day-Memorial Day:
         10:00 a.m.-4:00 p.m.
         Memorial Day-Labor Day:
         10:00 a.m.-7:00 p.m.
Cost: $6.50, $4.75 for ages 5-17,
         $2.50 for ages 3-4, free for un-
         der 3. (Park only: no charge)
Point Defiance Zoo and Aquarium is
home to 5,000 animals, including whales,
penguins, polar bears, and many Pacific
Rim-species animals. Other features include: Never Never Land, which is an
additional charge; Fort Nisqually, a restored trading fort complete with black-
smith shop; and Camp 6 Logging Museum, which features steam locomotive
rides during the warmer months.

■ REMLINGER FARMS

(425) 451-8740
32610 N.E. 32nd
Carnation, WA 98014
Open mid-March to mid-December
This working farm is best known for its
pumpkin patch and related activities—
hay maze, covered wagon rides, and
storytelling—but during the other

months you can visit the petting zoo, take farm tours, and harvest everything from strawberries to Christmas trees.

■ ROSALIE WHYEL MUSEUM OF DOLL ART

(425) 455-1116
1116 108th Ave. N.E.
Bellevue, WA 98004

Hours: M-Sat. 10:00 a.m.-5:00 p.m.
        Sun. 1:00 p.m.-5:00 p.m.
Cost: $6, $4 for children 5-17, free for children under 5

Cash/Check/MC/V

Over a thousand dolls from Rosalie Whyel's collection grace this 13,000 square-foot mansion. Preschoolers are welcome; glass cases protect all the dolls. Adults will enjoy everything from antique dolls to Barbie, including two Egyptian tomb dolls.

■ SEATTLE AQUARIUM

(206) 386-4320
Pier 59, Waterfront Park
Seattle, WA 98101

Hours: Labor Day-Memorial Day: 10:00 a.m.-5:00 p.m.
        Memorial Day-Labor Day: 10:00 a.m.-7:00 p.m.
Cost: $7.50, $5.75 seniors, $5 ages ages 6-18, $1.90 for 3-5, under 3 free. Fees slightly lower for King Co. residents

Cash/Check $2/stroller rental

See the only aquarium-based salmon hatchery in the world, walk underwater in the Dome, and explore the tide pool exhibit and Discovery Lab which recreates Washington's rocky outer coast and features a 6,000-gallon wave tank. New overnight programs require advance registration.

■ SEATTLE MIME THEATRE

(206) 324-8788
915 E. Pine
Seattle, WA 98122

You can catch the mimes during one or two performances a year at their Capitol Hill theater; the rest of the year the troupe performs for schools and private groups. Definitely entertaining for kids!

■ SUMMER BEACH PROGRAMS

(206) 684-7185

Seattle's parks and recreation department offers free two-week swimming lesson programs at nine local beaches. Free beginner lessons are 30 minutes a day for two-week sessions from June through August.

■ TRAIN RIDES

Puget Sound and Snoqualmie Valley Railway
(425) 888-0373 or (425) 746-4025
P.O. Box 459
Snoqualmie, WA 98065

Hours: Weekends only, April or May-October.
Cost: Adults $6, age 4+ $4, ages 3 and under free

The Snoqualmie train museum, which houses the ticket booth, is chock-full of "Thomas" hats, books, train engines and other paraphernalia. My husband and I went on opening day and it was a delight to watch all of the kids balancing through the various vintage cars—big kids included!

■ WADING POOL HOTLINE

(206) 684-7796

Seattle has a multitude of free wading pools in its parks that are open from June through August.

■ WASHINGTON ZOOLOGICAL PARK

(425) 392-6278
19525 S.E. 54th St.
Issaquah, WA 98027
Hours: Mar.-Oct.:
        W-Sun. 10:00 a.m.-5:00 p.m.
        Feb. & Nov.:
       . W-Sun. 10:00 a.m.-5:00 p.m.
        Dec. 1-23 (Santa's Reindeer
        Farm) Daily 5 p.m.-8 p.m.
Cost: $2.50-$5.50, under 2 free.
This small, 14-acre zoo features threatened or endangered animals and birds. This is a perfect place for a low-key, up-close look at animals for your young ones.

■ WOODLAND PARK ZOO

(206) 684-4800
5500 Phinney Ave. N.
Seattle, WA 98103
Hours: 9:30 a.m.-various closing times
Cost: $8.00, $5.50 for ages 6-17,
        $3.25 for ages 3-5, free for 2 &
        under. Slightly less for King
        Co. residents. Parking is $3.50.
        Stroller rental $3 at South gate.
Cash/Check/MC/V
This 92-acre zoo features a tropical rain forest exhibit, temperate forest exhibit, northern trails exhibit, African Savannah and Asian elephant exhibits, Nocturnal House and Reptile House, and a family farm. Kid-sized animals' homes are found along the Habitat Discovery Trail.

🍂

EXERCISE CLASSES

■ GYMBOREE

Federal Way: (360) 661-7205
Seattle (Crown Hill): (206) 523-8011
Seattle (Laurelhurst): (206) 522-2045
East Side: (425) 392-8438
Other areas: (800) 520-7529
Cash/Check/MC/V
Gymboree believes that one of the most important parts of a child's day is play time—not only to enhance key early developmental skills, but also to promote positive interactions with others. Gymboree's movement play program is geared to seven developmental stages for newborns through 5-year-olds. With tyke-sized equipment, parachute time, bubbles, songs, and Gymbo the Puppet Clown, every Gymboree class offers fun for parents and children. Children learn socialization, physical and emotional development, and about the world and how to relate to it.

You can register at any time. A 12-week session costs about $99. They also offer a free preview class. Overall, we found Gymboree a fun, diversified program for parents and their children. Good prices and esteem building are just a few of its assets.

■ KID SWIM

(206) 364-7946
14540 Bothell Way N.E.
Lake Forest Park, WA 98155
Cash/Check/MC/V
Kid Swim offers parent-tot classes for infants starting at six months through toddler age. Classes are taught by American Red Cross standards. A series of six half-hour classes cost about $45.

■ KING COUNTY POOLS
(206) 296-4258
This is the number for the public swimming pools in King County. The county offers swim instruction for all ages throughout the year. Prices are reasonable.

■ LITTLE GYM
(425) 885-3866
1800 130th Ave. N.E.
Bellevue, WA 98005

(206) 524-2623
7777 15th Ave. N.E.
Seattle, WA 98115

(425) 481-5889
6728 N.E. 181st #C
Kenmore, WA 98155

(253) 859-8301
10427 S.E. 240th
Kent, WA 98031
Cash/Check/MC/V
This developmentally-based, fun exercise program is designed to offer your child a variety of activities at every age. Programs often begin for infants as early as four months. Activities include stretching, aerobics, songs and games, parachute games and ball play. When we did our research, we found prices reasonable, averaging about $40 per month. Little Gym offers a variety of classes including karate, gymnastics, swimming and summer programs for children through the grade school years. Little Gym offers a unique parents' survival night and birthday parties. The parents' survival night is available for children ages 4-12 at varying times and weekend nights. In Bellevue, for example, it's offered every Saturday night from 6:00 p.m.-10:00 p.m. Kids enjoy an evening filled with games, gymnastics, snacks, and a G-rated movie. If you're looking for an out-of-the-house birthday party, Little Gym does that too! Packages are available for almost any size party and are held on Saturdays and Sundays.

■ SAFE 'N SOUND SWIMMING
(206) 285-9279
2040 Westlake Ave. N.
Seattle, WA 98109
Cash/Check/MC/V
One-on-one swimming lessons, beginning with children at age 13 months, are based on infant swimming research. Children are encouraged to focus on the safety and respect for the water. Classes are offered in 11-week series. They last 15 minutes and cost $12 each. Four sessions per year.

❧

INDOOR PLAYGROUNDS
Indoor playgrounds feature an assortment of giant Habitrail-like tubes, slides, balls to jump in, air bouncing areas, rope-climbing apparatus, and more. They also offer birthday party packages. Except as noted, parents are required to stay with their children while they play. This is especially true for the under 40" play areas. The playgrounds are an excellent workout for parents too, but you'll enjoy it more if you borrow knee pads (which most places have available)—all that scooting through the tubes can be very hard on the knees. There's no extra charge for parents. Kids (and parents) are required to wear socks while

in the play areas. For very small children, some of the places have rocking horses and ride-on toys and/or a mini-version of the big playground for children 40" and under.

Another type of indoor playground is more low-key but offers a great opportunity to interact with other parents and young children. These playgrounds are located at local parks and community recreation centers. You won't find tri-level tubes and slides here, but you'll always find a nice assortment of ride-on toys, balls, mats, bouncing toys, toddler slides, and indoor toys. These play areas are usually open just one or two mornings a week and are just for toddlers and preschool age kids. Parents or caregivers must stay and supervise. Cost is minimal, usually $1-$3 per child with exact change needed at some areas. Yearly passes are often available.

Kids also love the indoor playgrounds under the golden arches. McDonald's has adopted these play areas in recent years and taken our local weather into consideration. Many of the newest play areas are completely enclosed, including the "McBoat" at the McDonald's on Aurora Ave. N. in Shoreline. Burger King is also picking up on this trend. Both chains do birthday parties, too!

■ **PLAYSPACE®**
(425) 644-4500
Crossroads Shopping Center
Bellevue, WA 98008
Hours: M-Th   10:00 a.m.-9:00 p.m.
        F-Sat.   9:30 a.m.-10:30 p.m.
        Sun.   10:00 a.m.-6:00 p.m.
Cost: $5.95 per child for unlimited
        time when parent is on-site
        $7.95 for first hour, $1.49 for
        every 1/4 hour after

Bellevue's Playspace offers child care for children 3 years and potty trained up to 12 years. There's an open play area for toddlers with soft toys and a baby slide. Kids 17 months and under play free when accompanied by a paying sibling and parents are always free! Parents' night out is every Friday and Saturday night. Children receive dinner, a G-rated movie and unlimited play room fun. No reservations are required and kids can be dropped off as early as 5:30 p.m. Cost is $18.50. Parents are loaned a pager but must remain on Crossroads Mall.

■ **COMMUNITY INDOOR PLAYGROUNDS**
Schedules at all centers except Green Lake vary seasonally so it's best to call first to find out the current dates and times that they operate.

Bellevue Indoor Playground
(425) 455-7686
14224 Bellevue-Redmond Rd.
Bellevue, WA 98007
Hours: M,W,F 9:00 a.m.-noon
Cost: $1 per child up to age 4 1/2

Edmonds Playzone
(425) 771-0230
700 Main St.
Edmonds, WA 98020
Hours: Fri.   1:40 p.m.-2:40 p.m.
        Fri.   6:30p.m.-8:30 p.m.
Cost: $2.50 per 1-hour visit
Ages: Potty trained-8 years, under 3
        w/parent
Reservations recommended. Days and hours vary each quarter.

Everett
(425) 259-0300
Everett Community College Gym
13th and Rockefeller
Everett, WA 98203
Hours: T, Th   9:30 a.m.-11:00 a.m.
              Call; hours vary.
Cost: $1 first child, $.50 each additional 90 minute session
Ages: 1-6

Green Lake Community Center
(206) 684-0780
7201 E. Green Lake Dr. N.
Seattle, WA 98103
Hours: M-F   10:00 a.m.-9:00 p.m.
              Sat.   9:00 a.m.-4:00 p.m.
Cost: $1 per child
Ages: Toddler-5
Cash/Check/V/MC. $35/yr pass for up to 4 kids. Reservations recommended.

Kent Indoor Park
(253) 859-3350
Kent Commons
525 4th Ave. N. Kent, 98032
Hours: T, Th   9:30 a.m.-11:00 a.m
Cost: $2/ first child, 50 cents/each additional child; $10 for 10-visit pass
Ages: 10 months-4 1/2 years

Loyal Heights Indoor Playground
(206) 684-4052
Loyal Heights Community Center
2107 N.W. 77th
Seattle, WA 98117
Hours: 3 sessions:
              M-F   8:30 a.m.-10:15 a.m.;
              T-F   10:15- noon;
                            2:30-5:00 p.m.
Cost: Drop in rates $4/session. Package and monthly rates average $3.50/session
Ages: Infants-age 3

Mountlake Terrace
(206) 776-9173
5303 228th St. S.W.
Mountlake Terrace, WA 98043
Hours: T, W   10:30 a.m.-7:15 p.m.
              Th   10:00 a.m.-2:00 p.m.;
              Sat.   10:00 a.m.-noon
Cost: $1.50 child per hour
Ages: Toddler-4
Cash/Check/V/MC

North Kirkland Community Center
(425) 828-1105
12421 103rd Ave. N.E.
Kirkland, WA 98033
Hours: T, Th   11:00 a.m.-2:00 p.m.
Cost: $2 per visit (up to 3 hours)
Ages: 1-5
(Cash, exact change)

Shoreline/King County North End
(206) 546-5041
Shoreline Center Gym
N. 190th and 1st N.E.
Shoreline, WA 98155
Hours: T, F   10:00 a.m.-11:30 p.m.
Cost: $2.00 per visit (90 minutes); each additional child $1
Ages: 1-6
Cash/Check

West Seattle Toddler Mini-Gym
(206) 684-7423
Delridge Community Center
4501 Delridge Way S.W.
Seattle, WA 98106
Hours: T,W,Th 9:30 a.m.- 1:00 p.m.
Cost: W, F: $1/per child, T: free
Ages: 0-5 years

❧

SURVIVAL STRATEGIES

By Allison Blackham

I sat on my deck, nose pressed against the glass of the locked sliding door, watching my 2-year-old, Laura, cavort around the room in her soggy diaper while eight-month-old Kirsten rocked happily back and forth on her bottom, gnawing away at my key ring. Unable to get in, unable to explain to my largely nonverbal toddler how to unlock the door she had so cleverly locked behind me, I sat fuming.

Alternating between a Mister Rogers-like gentle patience and insane shouting, I lured Laura back to the door again and again, coaxing her to open it. I could see both children and knew they were safe. Everything was okay, until the baby lost interest in my keys and crawled away into the unseen reaches of the hall. At that point I broke the bathroom window, struggled through, and rescued my wandering infant.

Later, as I painfully picked broken glass shards from the window frame, baby Kirsten watched, bouncing furiously in her jumper in the bathroom doorway, demanding to be held. Laura, free of mother's watchful eye, stripped all of the sheets from her sisters' beds and got stuck head first in a pillowcase. Quick to reach the scene of this latest household disaster, I watched the wildly screaming bundle of bedding on the floor for a moment. "This is funny," I thought. "This would make a great script for some dumb sitcom. Why am I not laughing?"

Catastrophe and crisis are a regular part of family life. There may be some robotic "wonder parents" out there with luke-warm children who never push the limits, but I have never met them. Every family I know has broken window days, trips to the emergency room, tantrums and general craziness from time to time. I, personally, am the mother of six children. In my early mom-work, I assumed that each crisis was a reflection of my own total inadequacy as a parent. After years of experience and a lot of commiseration with other frazzled moms and dads, I now know we all go through this stuff. Kids and chaos go together like bread and butter. From the non-sleeping newborn stage when we're all walking around like characters from "Night of the Living Dead" to the eerie episodes of hearing our mother's voice come out of our own mouths when we face off with a defiant teenager, these exciting times take their toll. I haven't uncovered any ways of avoiding the

ᴥ

Sibling

arguments,

broken

windows

and lost

lunchboxes

are really

unimportant

things in the

whole scope

of what life

is about.

ᴥ

problems yet, because my husband insists that I live in the same house with the rest of the family, so I've had to deal with them. Here are some ideas that have helped at our house.

Save hysteria for life-and-death situations. Sibling arguments, broken windows and lost lunchboxes are really unimportant things in the whole scope of what life is about. When small things start to bug me, I stop and pull out my mental picture of myself at age 85 (still very peppy and active, by the way). At 85 will I care that my son lost four pairs of shoes in one year? Will it matter that my youngest child ate a worm? (I only found half.) Will my children blame me because we had cold cereal for dinner on Cub Scout night six years running? I hope not. I hope that what is important is that we said "I love you" and made cookies together and played pretend games. What doesn't matter in the long run is not worth getting tense about now.

Avoid out-of-body experiences. We tend to wish ourselves into another time or place when our current moment in life feels nasty. We think, "When the baby sleeps through the night/when the toddler is toilet trained/when my teenager gets through this awful phase, *then* everything will be better." Hey, by the time the kids are all perfect and out of our hair, we'll be dealing with Medicare and nursing home placement. There will always be challenges. No one is excused from the ups and downs of life. Even the Queen of England has to wear silly hats and put up with a lot of deranged relatives. Some day those shiny-eyed kids with their big mouths and

sticky fingers will be grown and gone. We need to live with the awareness that what we have and take for granted now changes and becomes a poignant memory tomorrow.

Seek joy. Life is jammed full of beauty and magic. A warm shower, sun shining on the grass, the smell of chocolate, a baby's smile—all of these things are miracles. Why wait for a trip to Disneyland or a letter of commendation from the President to feel like life is great? One of the best feelings I've ever had is seeing my daughter's face light up when I offer to read her a story, and that happens every day.

Treat yourself. Raising kids takes much more energy than any eight-hour-a-day job. Don't you work hard? Don't you deserve a reward? When was the last time your child kissed your hand and said, "Thank you, dear Mother, for all of your effort on my behalf?" It's not going to happen. Well, maybe at your funeral. We need to take time to reward ourselves. Go for a leisurely walk, eat an unshared candy bar, have lunch with friends, go to the pool and soak up the sunshine. Give to yourself so that you will have something to give away.

Sometimes on a really crazy day, I ask myself why I had children. And, after I answer that question, I ask myself why I had six children. Mostly, it's because I love kids, especially mine. And though I spend most of my days fishing the baby out of the cat food dish, fishing the cat food out of the baby, and pulling small people out of heating ducts and sofa cushions, I know I am actually making an investment, because love lasts, and broken windows can always be replaced.

INDEX

THE
BABY
PAGES

❧ *Consumer information for the greater Seattle area.*

❧ *Coupons are perforated for ease of use.*

❧ *Don't forget to let merchants know you found them through the Seattle Baby Resource Guide.*

Seattle Baby Pages are separate from the editorial portion of this book. I'm Expecting was not paid for its editorial content of the book by participants in the Baby Pages, nor does I'm Expecting endorse any of the merchants in this section.

Decide

to Subscribe!

Making good decisions as a parent isn't easy. You need the right information, and help in gathering it. *Seattle's Child, Eastside Parent* and *Snohomish County Parent* provide feature stories on a wide range of issues affecting families. In addition, your subscription includes:

- **Complete Calendar of Events**
- **Education Directory • Preschool Directory**
- **Summer Learning • Activity Guide**
- **A New Arrival • Winter Times**
- **Family Phone Book • Birthday Guide**
- **Summer in the City**

$15/1 year • $25/2years

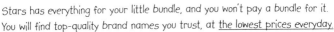

Countryside Montessori School

An Educational, Warm and Nurturing Environment

Infant, Toddlers, Preschool, Kindergarten and First Grade

13630 100th Ave. N.E. Kirkland

823-2211

MERIDIAN
WOMEN'S HEALTH

Dawn Frankwick, MD, F.A.C.O.G
Patricia Rodrigues, MD, F.A.C.O.G
Corry Venema-Weiss, ARNP, Certified Nurse Midwife

Health Care
For Women
By Women

206-368-6644

10330 Meridian Avenue N., Suite 300
Seattle, WA 98133

New!

www.thebabyguide.com

THE WEBSITE CREATED FOR PARENTS-TO-BE!

❧ *For the latest 'Baby' information.*
❧ *For baby product updates and to meet the editors of our guides.*
❧ *To find out where to purchase Baby Guides for other areas.*

THE BABY RESOURCE GUIDE

SEATTLE ❧ PORTLAND ❧ BOSTON ❧ LOS ANGELES ❧ SACRAMENTO

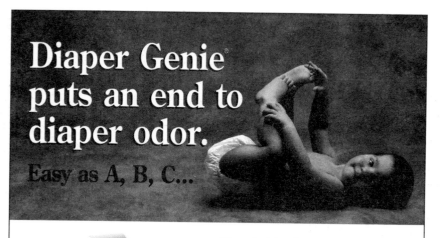

Bellini
(425) 451-0126
Located in Park Row
201 Bellevue Way NE
Bellevue, WA 98004

❧ *Quality, Beautiful*
   Furniture
❧ *Personal Service*
❧ *Unique Items*
Hours:
   M-Sat.   10-6
   Thurs.   10-8
   Closed Sunday

Designer Maternity
Factory and Kids Rack
(425) 451-1945
11010 N.E. 8th St.
Bellevue, WA 98004

Voted Best Maternity Store
by Eastside Parent
Newsmagazine

Baby Diaper Service
(206) 634-2229
Seattle
(253) 383-2229
Tacoma
(800) 562-2229
400 N. 36th St.
Seattle, WA 98103

Nothing Less Than the
Best...For Your Baby's
Comfort Quality & Service

Just Bearly
(206) 546-8581
17818 Aurora Ave. N.
Shoreline, WA 98133
(east side on little brick road)

Hours: Mon.-Sat. 10 - 5

Many name-brands of children's clothing and toys. Gift certificates available. Come in and save a fortune!

Safety for Toddlers
(425) 487-3460 or
800-775-3460
12865 N.E. 85th St.
Ste. 296
Kirkland, WA 98033

Safety for Toddlers is well known in Seattle for custom installation, in-home consultations & safety products.

Birth and Beyond
(206) 324-4831
2610 E. Madison St.
Seattle, WA 98112

(425) 402-9366
14450 Woodinville/
Redmond Road
Woodinville, WA 98072
A unique store specializing in Pregnancy and Childbirth and beyond. Complete with books, breastfeeding supplies, baby carriers, personal care products, jewelry and much more.

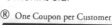

USA Baby
(206) 575-1016
17720 Southcenter Parkway
Tukwila, WA 98188

*America's leading chain
of Juvenile Furniture
Stores*

Kid's Club
(425) 643-5437
Crossroads Center
15600 N.E. 8th
Bellevue, WA 98008

(206) 524-2553
University Village
2676 N.E. University Way
Seattle, WA 98105

*See the stores review to
learn more about
Kid's Club.*

The Take Care Store

Northgate
(206) 527-7878

Seattle
(206) 326-3496

Redmond
(425) 883-5052

Olympia
(360) 923-7678

Mail Order
800-447-2839

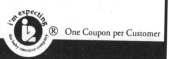

New England Cord Blood Bank, Inc.
888-700-CORD (2673)
or (617) 262-5612
665 Beacon Street
Suite 302
Boston, MA 02215-3202
Hours:
    M-F 8 a.m.-5 p.m.

See the section on Umbilical Cord Blood Banking to find out more about New England Cord Blood Bank, Inc.

McGregor's Garden
206-634-2969
2108 N. 55th St.
Seattle, WA 98103

We carry skin care by Mustela®—A European Tradition since 1950.

A children's hair salon that makes it fun!

Grandmother's House
(425) 771-4640
7331 196th S.W.
Lynnwood, WA 98036

We have it all!
In business since 1975

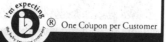

**NW Medical Supply
Breast Pump
Rental Station
(206) 368-1196**
1530 N. 115th, Suite 108
Seattle, WA 98133

**Rising Stars
(206) 781-0138**
7404 Greenwood Ave. N.
Seattle, WA 98103
*(just one mile north of
Woodland Park Zoo)*

Hours:
Tues.-Fri. 10-5:30
Sat.   10-5
Sun.   12-5

**Mary Kay
(206) 367-4288**

ADVANCED SKIN CARE
Skin supplements from
Mary Kay help defend
your skin against the
environment, stress and
the signs of aging.
Call Michelle Aucott,
Independent Mary Kay
Beauty Consultant

VIACORD
(800) 998-4226
551 Boylston Street
Suite 40
Boston, MA 02116

VIACORD—The Leader
in Cord Blood Banking
Service ™

Yuen Lui Studio
Seattle
(206) 622-0338
N. Seattle
(206) 523-5707
Lynnwood
(425) 771-3423
Everett
(425) 353-5151

Yuen Lui has been
photographing children
in the Northwest for over
fifty years.

For information about
one of our software titles
call 1-800-225-1635 or
check out our website at:
www.daxtech.com

Software titles available at
baby stores nationwide!